Get organ-ised for Biology with CGP...

There's a lot to learn in GCSE Biology, that's for sure. Luckily, this CGP book explains the facts, theory and practical skills you'll need — with practice questions on each page to test you on what you've learned.

How to access your free Online Edition

This book includes a free Online Edition to read on your PC, Mac or tablet. To access it, just go to **cgpbooks.co.uk/extras** and enter this code...

2162 3205 2086 9498

By the way, this code only works for one person. If somebody else has used this book before you, they might have already claimed the Online Edition.

CGP — still the best! ☺

Our sole aim here at CGP is to produce the highest quality books — carefully written, immaculately presented and dangerously close to being funny.

Then we work our socks off to get them out to you — at the cheapest possible prices.

Contents

Working Scientifically

The Scientific Method 1

Communication & Issues Created by Science 2

Risk 3

Designing Investigations 4

Collecting Data 5

Processing and Presenting Data 6

Units and Equations 8

Drawing Conclusions 9

Uncertainties and Evaluations 10

Topic 1 — Cell Biology

Cells 11

Microscopy 12

More on Microscopy 13

Cell Differentiation and Specialisation 14

Chromosomes and Mitosis 15

Binary Fission 16

Culturing Microorganisms 17

Stem Cells 19

Diffusion 20

Osmosis 21

Active Transport 22

Exchange Surfaces 23

Exchanging Substances 24

More on Exchanging Substances 25

Revision Questions for Topic 1 26

Topic 2 — Organisation

Cell Organisation 27

Enzymes 28

Investigating Enzymatic Reactions 29

Enzymes and Digestion 30

More on Enzymes and Digestion 31

Food Tests 32

The Lungs 33

Circulatory System — The Heart 34

Circulatory System — Blood Vessels 35

Circulatory System — Blood 36

Cardiovascular Disease 37

More on Cardiovascular Disease 38

Health and Disease 39

Risk Factors for Non-Communicable Diseases 40

Cancer 41

Plant Cell Organisation 42

Transpiration and Translocation 43

Transpiration and Stomata 44

Revision Questions for Topic 2 45

Topic 3 — Infection and Response

Communicable Disease 46

Viral, Fungal and Protist Diseases 47

Bacterial Diseases and Preventing Disease 48

Fighting Disease 49

Fighting Disease — Vaccination 50

Fighting Disease — Drugs 51

Developing Drugs 52

Monoclonal Antibodies 53

More on Monoclonal Antibodies 54

Plant Diseases and Defences 55

Revision Questions for Topic 3 56

Topic 4 — Bioenergetics

Photosynthesis and Limiting Factors 57

The Rate of Photosynthesis 58

Respiration and Metabolism 61

Aerobic and Anaerobic Respiration 62

Exercise 63

Revision Questions for Topic 4 64

Topic 5 — Homeostasis and Response

Homeostasis 65

The Nervous System 66

Synapses and Reflexes 67

Investigating Reaction Time 68

The Brain 69

The Eye 70

Correcting Vision Defects 71

Controlling Body Temperature 72

The Endocrine System 73

Controlling Blood Glucose 74

The Kidneys 75

Kidney Failure 76

Puberty and the Menstrual Cycle 77

Controlling Fertility 78

More on Controlling Fertility 79

Adrenaline and Thyroxine 80

Plant Hormones 81

Commercial Uses of Plant Hormones 82

Revision Questions for Topic 5 83

Topic 6 — Inheritance, Variation and Evolution

DNA 84

The Structure of DNA and Protein Synthesis 85

Mutations 86

Reproduction 87

Meiosis 88

More on Reproduction 89

X and Y Chromosomes 90

Genetic Diagrams 91

More Genetic Diagrams 92

Inherited Disorders 93

The Work of Mendel 94

Variation 95

Evolution 96

More About Evolution 97

Selective Breeding 98

Genetic Engineering 99

Cloning 100

Fossils 101

Speciation 102

Antibiotic-Resistant Bacteria 103

Classification 104

Revision Questions for Topic 6 105

Topic 7 — Ecology

Competition 106

Abiotic and Biotic Factors 107

Adaptations 108

Food Chains 109

Using Quadrats 110

Using Transects 111

Environmental Change & The Water Cycle 112

The Carbon Cycle 113

Decay 114

Investigating Decay 115

Biodiversity and Waste Management 116

Global Warming 117

Deforestation and Land Use 118

Maintaining Ecosystems and Biodiversity 119

Trophic Levels 120

Pyramids of Biomass 121

Biomass Transfer 122

Food Security and Farming 123

Biotechnology 124

Revision Questions for Topic 7 125

Practical Skills

Measuring Substances 126

Heating, Safety and Ethics 127

Potometers and Microscopes 128

Sampling 129

Comparing Results 130

Answers 131

Index 134

Published by CGP

From original material by Richard Parsons

Editors: Charlotte Burrows, Katherine Faudemer, Chris McGarry and Sarah Pattison

Contributor: Paddy Gannon

With thanks to Hayley Thompson and Sophie Anderson for the proofreading.

Printed by Elanders Ltd, Newcastle upon Tyne.
Clipart from Corel®

The Scientific Method

This section <u>isn't</u> about how to 'do' science — but it does show you the way <u>most scientists</u> work.

Scientists Come Up With Hypotheses — Then Test Them

1) Scientists try to <u>explain</u> things. They start by <u>observing</u> something they don't understand.

2) They then come up with a <u>hypothesis</u> — a possible <u>explanation</u> for what they've observed.

3) The next step is to <u>test</u> whether the hypothesis might be <u>right or not</u>. This involves making a <u>prediction</u> based on the hypothesis and testing it by <u>gathering evidence</u> (i.e. <u>data</u>) from <u>investigations</u>. If <u>evidence</u> from <u>experiments</u> backs up a prediction, you're a step closer to figuring out if the hypothesis is true.

Hundreds of years ago, we thought demons caused illness.

Several Scientists Will Test a Hypothesis

1) Normally, scientists <u>share</u> their <u>findings</u> in <u>peer-reviewed journals</u>, or at <u>conferences</u>.

2) <u>Peer-review</u> is where <u>other scientists</u> check results and scientific explanations to make sure they're 'scientific' (e.g. that experiments have been done in a sensible way) <u>before</u> they're published. It helps to <u>detect false claims</u>, but it doesn't mean that findings are <u>correct</u> — just that they're not wrong in any <u>obvious</u> way.

3) Once other scientists have found out about a hypothesis, they'll start basing their <u>own predictions</u> on it and carry out their <u>own experiments</u>. They'll also try to <u>reproduce</u> the original experiments to <u>check the results</u> — and if all the experiments in the world <u>back up</u> the <u>hypothesis</u>, then scientists start to think the hypothesis is <u>true</u>.

4) However, if a scientist does an experiment that <u>doesn't fit</u> with the hypothesis (and other scientists can reproduce the results) then the hypothesis may need to be <u>modified</u> or <u>scrapped</u> altogether.

Then we thought it was caused by 'bad blood' (and treated it with leeches).

If All the Evidence Supports a Hypothesis, It's Accepted — For Now

1) <u>Accepted hypotheses</u> are often referred to as <u>theories</u>. Our <u>currently accepted</u> theories are the ones that have survived this 'trial by evidence' — they've been <u>tested many times</u> over the years and <u>survived</u>.

2) However, theories <u>never</u> become totally indisputable <u>fact</u>. If <u>new evidence</u> comes along that <u>can't be explained</u> using the existing theory, then the hypothesising and testing is likely to <u>start all over again</u>.

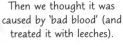

Now we've collected more evidence, we know that illnesses that can be spread between people are due to microorganisms.

Theories Can Involve Different Types of Models

1) A <u>representational model</u> is a <u>simplified description</u> or <u>picture</u> of what's going on in real life. Like all models, it can be used to <u>explain observations</u> and <u>make predictions</u>. E.g. the <u>lock and key model</u> of enzyme action is a simplified way of showing how <u>enzymes</u> work (see p.28). It can be used to explain why enzymes only catalyse particular reactions.

Scientists test models by carrying out experiments to check that the predictions made by the model happen as expected.

2) <u>Computational models</u> use computers to make <u>simulations</u> of complex real-life processes, such as climate change. They're used when there are a <u>lot</u> of different <u>variables</u> (factors that change) to consider, and because you can easily <u>change their design</u> to take into account <u>new data</u>.

3) All models have <u>limitations</u> on what they can <u>explain</u> or <u>predict</u>. Climate change models have several limitations — for example, it's hard to take into account all the biological and chemical processes that influence climate. It can also be difficult to include regional variations in climate.

I'm off to the zoo to test my hippo-thesis...

The scientific method has been developed over time, and many people have helped to develop it. From Aristotle to modern day scientists, lots of people have contributed. And many more are likely to contribute in the future.

Communication & Issues Created by Science

Scientific developments can be great, but they can sometimes <u>raise more questions</u> than they answer...

It's Important to Communicate Scientific Discoveries to the General Public

Some scientific discoveries show that people should <u>change their habits</u>, or they might provide ideas that could be <u>developed</u> into new <u>technology</u>. So scientists need to <u>tell the world</u> about their discoveries.

<u>Gene technologies</u> are used in <u>genetic engineering</u> to produce <u>genetically modified crops</u>. Information about these crops needs to be communicated to <u>farmers</u> who might <u>benefit</u> from growing them and to the <u>general public</u>, so they can make <u>informed decisions</u> about the food they buy and eat.

Scientific Evidence can be Presented in a Biased Way

1) Reports about scientific discoveries in the <u>media</u> (e.g. newspapers or television) <u>aren't</u> peer-reviewed.

2) This means that, even though news stories are often <u>based</u> on data that has been peer-reviewed, the data might be <u>presented</u> in a way that is <u>over-simplified</u> or <u>inaccurate</u>, making it open to <u>misinterpretation</u>.

3) People who want to make a point can sometimes <u>present data</u> in a <u>biased way</u>. (Sometimes <u>without knowing</u> they're doing it.) For example, a scientist might overemphasise a relationship in the data, or a newspaper article might describe details of data <u>supporting</u> an idea without giving any evidence <u>against</u> it.

Scientific Developments are Great, but they can Raise Issues

Scientific <u>knowledge is increased</u> by doing experiments. And this knowledge leads to <u>scientific developments</u>, e.g. new technologies or new advice. These developments can create <u>issues</u> though. For example:

<u>Economic issues:</u> Society <u>can't</u> always <u>afford</u> to do things scientists recommend (e.g. investing in alternative energy sources) without <u>cutting back elsewhere</u>.

<u>Social issues:</u> Decisions based on scientific evidence affect <u>people</u> — e.g. should alcohol be banned (to prevent health problems)? Would the <u>effect on</u> <u>people's lifestyles</u> be <u>acceptable...?</u>

<u>Personal issues:</u> Some decisions will affect <u>individuals</u>. For example, someone might support <u>alternative energy</u>, but object if a <u>wind farm</u> is built next to their house.

<u>Environmental issues:</u> <u>Human activity</u> often affects the <u>natural environment</u> — e.g. <u>genetically modified crops</u> may help us to produce <u>more food</u> — but some people think they could cause <u>environmental problems</u> (see p.99).

Science Can't Answer Every Question — Especially Ethical Ones

1) We don't <u>understand everything</u>. We're always finding out <u>more</u>, but we'll never know <u>all</u> the answers.

2) In order to answer scientific questions, scientists need <u>data</u> to provide <u>evidence</u> for their hypotheses.

3) Some questions can't be answered <u>yet</u> because the data <u>can't</u> currently be <u>collected</u>, or because there's <u>not enough</u> data to <u>support</u> a theory.

4) <u>Eventually</u>, as we get <u>more evidence</u>, we'll answer some of the questions that <u>currently</u> can't be answered, e.g. what the impact of global warming on sea levels will be. But there will always be the "<u>Should we be doing this at all?</u>"-type questions that experiments <u>can't</u> help us to answer...

Think about <u>new drugs which can be taken to boost your 'brain power'</u>.

- Some people think they're <u>good</u> as they could improve concentration or memory. New drugs could let people think in ways beyond the powers of normal brains.

- Other people say they're <u>bad</u> — they could give you an <u>unfair advantage</u> in exams. And people might be <u>pressured</u> into taking them so that they could work more <u>effectively</u>, and for <u>longer hours</u>.

THE GAZETTE
BRAIN-BOOSTING DRUGS MAKE A MOCKERY OF EXAMS

THE POST
GENIUS PILLS TO BECOME THE NEW COFFEE

Tea to milk or milk to tea? — Totally unanswerable by science...

Science can't tell you whether or not you should do something. That's for you and society to decide. But there are tons of questions science might be able to answer, like where life came from and where my superhero socks are.

Risk

By reading this page you are agreeing to the risk of a paper cut or severe drowsiness...

Nothing is Completely Risk-Free

1) A hazard is something that could potentially cause harm.

2) All hazards have a risk attached to them — this is the chance that the hazard will cause harm.

3) The risks of some things seem pretty obvious, or we've known about them for a while, like the risk of causing acid rain by polluting the atmosphere, or of having a car accident when you're travelling in a car.

4) New technology arising from scientific advances can bring new risks, e.g. scientists are unsure whether nanoparticles that are being used in cosmetics and suncream might be harming the cells in our bodies. These risks need to be considered alongside the benefits of the technology, e.g. improved sun protection.

5) You can estimate the size of a risk based on how many times something happens in a big sample (e.g. 100 000 people) over a given period (e.g. a year). For example, you could assess the risk of a driver crashing by recording how many people in a group of 100 000 drivers crashed their cars over a year.

6) To make decisions about activities that involve hazards, we need to take into account the chance of the hazard causing harm, and how serious the consequences would be if it did. If an activity involves a hazard that's very likely to cause harm, with serious consequences if it does, it's considered high risk.

People Make Their Own Decisions About Risk

1) Not all risks have the same consequences, e.g. if you chop veg with a sharp knife you risk cutting your finger, but if you go scuba-diving you risk death. You're much more likely to cut your finger during half an hour of chopping than to die during half an hour of scuba-diving. But most people are happier to accept a higher probability of an accident if the consequences are short-lived and fairly minor.

2) People tend to be more willing to accept a risk if they choose to do something (e.g. go scuba diving), compared to having the risk imposed on them (e.g. having a nuclear power station built next door).

3) People's perception of risk (how risky they think something is) isn't always accurate. They tend to view familiar activities as low-risk and unfamiliar activities as high-risk — even if that's not the case. For example, cycling on roads is often high-risk, but many people are happy to do it because it's a familiar activity. Air travel is actually pretty safe, but a lot of people perceive it as high-risk.

4) People may over-estimate the risk of things with long-term or invisible effects, e.g. ionising radiation.

Investigations Can be Hazardous

1) Hazards from science experiments might include:

- Microorganisms, e.g. some bacteria can make you ill.
- Chemicals, e.g. sulfuric acid can burn your skin and alcohols catch fire easily.
- Fire, e.g. an unattended Bunsen burner is a fire hazard.
- Electricity, e.g. faulty electrical equipment could give you a shock.

Hmm... Where did my bacteria sample go?

2) Part of planning an investigation is making sure that it's safe.

3) You should always make sure that you identify all the hazards that you might encounter. Then you should think of ways of reducing the risks from the hazards you've identified. For example:

- If you're working with sulfuric acid, always wear gloves and safety goggles. This will reduce the risk of the acid coming into contact with your skin and eyes.
- If you're using a Bunsen burner, stand it on a heat proof mat. This will reduce the risk of starting a fire.

You can find out about potential hazards by looking in textbooks, doing some internet research, or asking your teacher.

Not revising — an unacceptable exam hazard...

The world's a dangerous place, but if you can recognise hazards, decide how to reduce their risks, and be happy to accept some risks, you can still have fun. Just maybe don't go skydiving with a great white shark on Friday 13th.

Designing Investigations

Dig out your lab coat and dust down your badly-scratched safety goggles... it's <u>investigation time</u>.

Investigations Produce Evidence to Support or Disprove a Hypothesis

1) Scientists <u>observe</u> things and come up with <u>hypotheses</u> to explain them (see p.1).
You need to be able to do the same. For example:

> <u>Observation:</u> People have big feet and spots. <u>Hypothesis:</u> Having big feet causes spots.

2) To <u>determine</u> whether or not a hypothesis is <u>right</u>, you need to do an <u>investigation</u> to gather evidence. To do this, you need to use your hypothesis to make a <u>prediction</u> — something you think <u>will happen</u> that you can test. E.g. people who have bigger feet will have more spots.

3) Investigations are used to see if there are <u>patterns</u> or <u>relationships</u> between <u>two variables</u>, e.g. to see if there's a pattern or relationship between the variables 'number of spots' and 'size of feet'.

Evidence Needs to be Repeatable, Reproducible and Valid

1) <u>Repeatable</u> means that if the <u>same person</u> does an experiment again using the <u>same methods</u> and equipment, they'll get <u>similar results</u>.

Investigations include experiments and studies.

2) <u>Reproducible</u> means that if <u>someone else</u> does the experiment, or a <u>different</u> method or piece of equipment is used, the results will still be <u>similar</u>.

3) If data is <u>repeatable</u> and <u>reproducible</u>, it's <u>reliable</u> and scientists are more likely to <u>have confidence</u> in it.

4) <u>Valid results</u> are both repeatable and reproducible AND they <u>answer the original question</u>. They come from experiments that were designed to be a FAIR TEST...

To Make an Investigation a Fair Test You Have to Control the Variables

1) In a lab experiment you usually <u>change one variable</u> and <u>measure</u> how it affects <u>another variable</u>.

2) To make it a fair test, <u>everything else</u> that could affect the results should <u>stay the same</u> — otherwise you can't tell if the thing you're changing is causing the results or not.

3) The variable you CHANGE is called the INDEPENDENT variable.

4) The variable you MEASURE when you change the independent variable is the DEPENDENT variable.

5) The variables that you KEEP THE SAME are called CONTROL variables.

> You could find how <u>temperature</u> affects the rate of an <u>enzyme-controlled reaction</u>. The <u>independent variable</u> is the <u>temperature</u>. The <u>dependent variable</u> is the <u>rate of reaction</u>. <u>Control variables</u> include the <u>concentration</u> and <u>amounts</u> of reactants, <u>pH</u>, the <u>time period</u> you measure, etc.

6) Because you can't always control all the variables, you often need to use a <u>control experiment</u>. This is an experiment that's kept under the <u>same conditions</u> as the rest of the investigation, but <u>doesn't</u> have anything <u>done</u> to it. This is so that you can see what happens when you don't change anything at all.

The Bigger the Sample Size the Better

1) Data based on <u>small samples</u> isn't as good as data based on large samples. A sample should <u>represent</u> the <u>whole population</u> (i.e. it should share as many of the characteristics in the population as possible) — a small sample can't do that as well. It's also harder to spot <u>anomalies</u> if your sample size is too small.

2) The <u>bigger</u> the sample size the <u>better</u>, but scientists have to be <u>realistic</u> when choosing how big. For example, if you were studying how lifestyle affects people's weight it'd be great to study everyone in the UK (a huge sample), but it'd take ages and cost a bomb. It's more realistic to study a thousand people, with a mixture of ages, gender and race.

This is no high street survey — it's a designer investigation...

Not only do you need to be able to plan your own investigations, you should also be able to look at someone else's plan and decide whether or not it needs improving. Those examiners aren't half demanding.

Collecting Data

You've designed the perfect investigation — now it's time to get your hands mucky and collect some data.

Your Data Should be Repeatable, Reproducible, Accurate and Precise

1) To check repeatability you need to repeat the readings and check that the results are similar. You need to repeat each reading at least three times.

2) To make sure your results are reproducible you can cross check them by taking a second set of readings with another instrument (or a different observer).

3) Your data also needs to be ACCURATE. Really accurate results are those that are really close to the true answer. The accuracy of your results usually depends on your method — you need to make sure you're measuring the right thing and that you don't miss anything that should be included in the measurements. E.g. estimating the amount of gas released from a reaction by counting the bubbles isn't very accurate because you might miss some of the bubbles and they might have different volumes. It's more accurate to measure the volume of gas released using a gas syringe.

4) Your data also needs to be PRECISE. Precise results are ones where the data is all really close to the mean (average) of your repeated results (i.e. not spread out).

Brian's result was a curate.

Repeat	Data set 1	Data set 2
1	12	11
2	14	17
3	13	14
Mean	13	14

Data set 1 is more precise than data set 2.

Your Equipment has to be Right for the Job

1) The measuring equipment you use has to be sensitive enough to measure the changes you're looking for. For example, if you need to measure changes of 1 cm³ you need to use a measuring cylinder that can measure in 1 cm³ steps — it'd be no good trying with one that only measures in 10 cm³ steps.

2) The smallest change a measuring instrument can detect is called its RESOLUTION. E.g. some mass balances have a resolution of 1 g, some have a resolution of 0.1 g, and some are even more sensitive.

3) Also, equipment needs to be calibrated by measuring a known value. If there's a difference between the measured and known value, you can use this to correct the inaccuracy of the equipment.

You Need to Look out for Errors and Anomalous Results

1) The results of your experiment will always vary a bit because of RANDOM ERRORS — unpredictable differences caused by things like human errors in measuring. E.g. the errors you make when reading from a measuring cylinder are random. You have to estimate or round the level when it's between two marks — so sometimes your figure will be a bit above the real one, and sometimes it will be a bit below.

2) You can reduce the effect of random errors by taking repeat readings and finding the mean. This will make your results more precise.

If there's no systematic error, then doing repeats and calculating a mean can make your results more accurate.

3) If a measurement is wrong by the same amount every time, it's called a SYSTEMATIC ERROR. For example, if you measured from the very end of your ruler instead of from the 0 cm mark every time, all your measurements would be a bit small. Repeating the experiment in the exact same way and calculating a mean won't correct a systematic error.

4) Just to make things more complicated, if a systematic error is caused by using equipment that isn't zeroed properly, it's called a ZERO ERROR. For example, if a mass balance always reads 1 gram before you put anything on it, all your measurements will be 1 gram too heavy.

5) You can compensate for some systematic errors if you know about them though, e.g. if your mass balance always reads 1 gram before you put anything on it you can subtract 1 gram from all your results.

6) Sometimes you get a result that doesn't fit in with the rest at all. This is called an ANOMALOUS RESULT. You should investigate it and try to work out what happened. If you can work out what happened (e.g. you measured something totally wrong) you can ignore it when processing your results.

Watch what you say to that mass balance — it's very sensitive...

Weirdly, data can be really precise but not very accurate. For example, a fancy piece of lab equipment might give results that are really precise, but if it's not been calibrated properly those results won't be accurate.

Processing and Presenting Data

Processing your data means doing some <u>calculations</u> with it to make it <u>more useful</u>. Once you've done that, you can present your results in a nice <u>chart</u> or <u>graph</u> to help you <u>spot any patterns</u> in your data.

Data Needs to be Organised

Tables are dead useful for <u>organising data</u>. When you draw a table <u>use a ruler</u> and make sure <u>each column</u> has a <u>heading</u> (including the <u>units</u>).

You Might Have to Process Your Data

1) When you've done repeats of an experiment you should always calculate the <u>mean</u> (a type of average). To do this <u>add together</u> all the data values and <u>divide</u> by the total number of values in the sample.

2) You might also need to calculate the <u>range</u> (how spread out the data is). To do this find the <u>largest</u> number and <u>subtract</u> the <u>smallest</u> number from it.

Ignore anomalous results when calculating these.

EXAMPLE: The results of an experiment to find the volume of gas produced in an enzyme-controlled reaction are shown below. Calculate the mean volume and the range.

Repeat 1 (cm³)	Repeat 2 (cm³)	Repeat 3 (cm³)	Mean (cm³)	Range (cm³)
28	37	32	(28 + 37 + 32) ÷ 3 = 32	37 − 28 = 9

3) You might also need to calculate the <u>median</u> or <u>mode</u> (two more types of average). To calculate the <u>median</u>, put all your data in <u>numerical order</u> — the median is the <u>middle value</u>. The number that appears <u>most often</u> in a data set is the <u>mode</u>.

E.g. If you have the data set: 1 2 1 1 3 4 2
The <u>median</u> is: 1 1 1 <u>2</u> 2 3 4. The <u>mode</u> is <u>1</u> because 1 appears most often.

If you have an even number of values, the median is halfway between the middle two values.

Round to the Lowest Number of Significant Figures

The <u>first significant figure</u> of a number is the first digit that's <u>not zero</u>. The second and third significant figures come <u>straight after</u> (even if they're zeros). You should be aware of significant figures in calculations.

1) In <u>any</u> calculation, you should round the answer to the <u>lowest number of significant figures</u> (s.f.) given.

2) Remember to write down <u>how many</u> significant figures you've rounded to after your answer.

3) If your calculation has multiple steps, <u>only</u> round the <u>final</u> answer, or it won't be as accurate.

EXAMPLE: A plant produces 10.2 cm³ of oxygen in 6.5 minutes whilst photosynthesising. Calculate the rate of photosynthesis.

rate = 10.2 cm³ ÷ 6.5 min = 1.5692... = 1.6 cm³/min (2 s.f.) — Final answer should be rounded to 2 s.f.

3 s.f.   2 s.f.

If Your Data Comes in Categories, Present It in a Bar Chart

1) If the independent variable is <u>categoric</u> (comes in distinct categories, e.g. flower colour, blood group) you should use a <u>bar chart</u> to display the data.

2) You also use them if the independent variable is <u>discrete</u> (the data can be counted in chunks, where there's no in-between value, e.g. number of bacteria is discrete because you can't have half a bacterium).

3) There are some <u>golden rules</u> you need to follow for <u>drawing</u> bar charts:

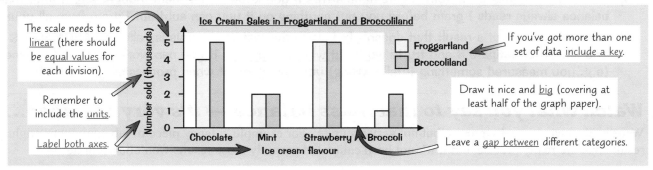

The scale needs to be <u>linear</u> (there should be <u>equal values</u> for each division).

Remember to include the <u>units</u>.

Label both axes.

Ice Cream Sales in Froggartland and Broccoliland

Number sold (thousands)

Ice cream flavour

Chocolate   Mint   Strawberry   Broccoli

□ Froggartland
□ Broccoliland

If you've got more than one set of data <u>include a key</u>.

Draw it nice and <u>big</u> (covering at least half of the graph paper).

Leave a <u>gap between</u> different categories.

If Your Data is Continuous, Plot a Graph

If both variables are <u>continuous</u> (numerical data that can have any value within a range, e.g. length, volume, temperature) you should use a <u>graph</u> to display the data.

Here are the rules for plotting points on a graph:

Use the biggest data values you've got to draw a <u>sensible scale</u> on your axes. Here, the highest rate of reaction is <u>22 cm³/s</u>, so it makes sense to label the y-axis up to <u>25 cm³/s</u>.

The <u>dependent</u> variable goes on the <u>y-axis</u> (the <u>vertical</u> one).

The <u>independent</u> variable goes on the <u>x-axis</u> (the <u>horizontal</u> one).

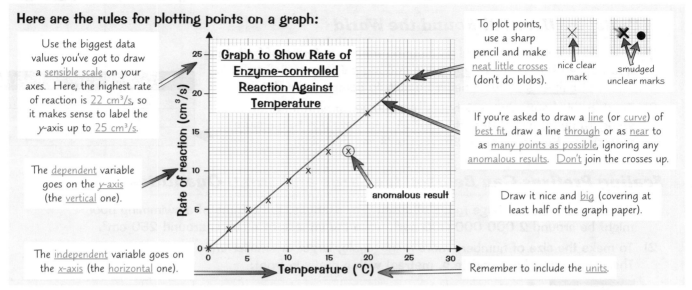

To plot points, use a sharp pencil and make <u>neat little crosses</u> (don't do blobs). nice clear mark / smudged unclear marks

If you're asked to draw a <u>line</u> (or <u>curve</u>) of <u>best fit</u>, draw a line <u>through</u> or as <u>near</u> to as <u>many points as possible</u>, ignoring any <u>anomalous results</u>. <u>Don't</u> join the crosses up.

Draw it nice and <u>big</u> (covering at least half of the graph paper).

Remember to include the <u>units</u>.

Graphs Can Give You a Lot of Information About Your Data

1) The <u>gradient</u> (slope) of a graph tells you how quickly the <u>dependent variable</u> changes if you change the <u>independent variable</u>.

$$\text{gradient} = \frac{\text{change in } y}{\text{change in } x}$$

You can use this method to calculate any rates from a graph, not just the rate of a reaction. Just remember that a rate is how much something changes over time, so x needs to be the time.

This <u>graph</u> shows the <u>volume of gas</u> produced in a reaction against <u>time</u>. The graph is <u>linear</u> (it's a straight line graph), so you can simply calculate the <u>gradient</u> of the line to find out the <u>rate of reaction</u>.

1) To calculate the gradient, pick <u>two points</u> on the line that are easy to read and a <u>good distance</u> apart.
2) <u>Draw a line down</u> from one of the points and a <u>line across</u> from the other to make a <u>triangle</u>. The line drawn down the side of the triangle is the <u>change in y</u> and the line across the bottom is the <u>change in x</u>.

Change in y = 6.8 – 2.0 = 4.8 cm³   Change in x = 5.2 – 1.6 = 3.6 s

$$\text{Rate} = \text{gradient} = \frac{\text{change in } y}{\text{change in } x} = \frac{4.8 \text{ cm}^3}{3.6 \text{ s}} = \underline{1.3 \text{ cm}^3/\text{s}} \text{ or } \underline{1.3 \text{ cm}^3\text{s}^{-1}}$$

The units of the gradient are (units of y)/(units of x). cm³/s can also be written as cm³s⁻¹.

If you've got a curved graph, you can find the rate at any point by drawing a tangent — a straight line that touches a single point on a curve. You can then find the gradient of the tangent in the usual way, to give you the rate at that point.

2) The <u>intercept</u> of a graph is where the line of best fit crosses one of the <u>axes</u>. The <u>x-intercept</u> is where the line of best fit crosses the x-axis and the <u>y-intercept</u> is where it crosses the <u>y-axis</u>.

Graphs Show the Relationship Between Two Variables

1) You can get <u>three</u> types of <u>correlation</u> (relationship) between variables:
2) Just because there's correlation, it doesn't mean the change in one variable is <u>causing</u> the change in the other — there might be <u>other factors</u> involved (see page 9).

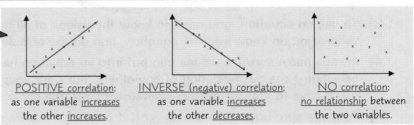

<u>POSITIVE</u> correlation: as one variable <u>increases</u> the other <u>increases</u>.

<u>INVERSE</u> (negative) correlation: as one variable <u>increases</u> the other <u>decreases</u>.

<u>NO</u> correlation: <u>no relationship</u> between the two variables.

I love eating apples — I call it core elation...

Science is all about finding relationships between things. And I don't mean that chemists gather together in corners to discuss whether or not Devini and Sebastian might be a couple... though they probably do that too.

Units and Equations

Graphs and maths skills are all very well, but the numbers don't mean much if you can't get the <u>units</u> right.

SI Units Are Used All Round the World

1) It wouldn't be all that useful if I defined volume in terms of <u>bath tubs</u>, you defined it in terms of <u>egg-cups</u> and my pal Sarwat defined it in terms of <u>balloons</u> — we'd never be able to compare our data.

2) To stop this happening, scientists have come up with a set of <u>standard units</u>, called SI units, that all scientists use to measure their data. Here are some SI units you'll see in Biology:

Quantity	SI Base Unit
mass	kilogram, kg
length	metre, m
time	second, s

Scaling Prefixes Can Be Used for Large and Small Quantities

1) Quantities come in a huge <u>range</u> of sizes. For example, the volume of a swimming pool might be around 2 000 000 000 cm³, while the volume of a cup is around 250 cm³.

2) To make the size of numbers more <u>manageable</u>, larger or smaller units are used. These are the <u>SI base unit</u> (e.g. metres) with a <u>prefix</u> in front:

prefix	tera (T)	giga (G)	mega (M)	kilo (k)	deci (d)	centi (c)	milli (m)	micro (µ)	nano (n)
multiple of unit	10^{12}	10^9	1 000 000 (10^6)	1000	0.1	0.01	0.001	0.000001 (10^{-6})	10^{-9}

3) These <u>prefixes</u> tell you <u>how much bigger</u> or <u>smaller</u> a unit is than the base unit. So one <u>kilometre</u> is <u>one thousand</u> metres.

The conversion factor is the number of times the smaller unit goes into the larger unit.

4) To <u>swap</u> from one unit to another, all you need to know is what number you have to divide or multiply by to get from the original unit to the new unit — this is called the <u>conversion factor</u>.

- To go from a <u>bigger unit</u> (like m) to a <u>smaller unit</u> (like cm), you <u>multiply</u> by the conversion factor.
- To go from a <u>smaller unit</u> (like g) to a <u>bigger unit</u> (like kg), you <u>divide</u> by the conversion factor.

5) Here are some conversions that'll be useful for GCSE biology:

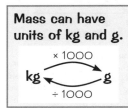

Mass can have units of kg and g.

kg ⇄ g (× 1000, ÷ 1000)

Length can have lots of units, including mm, µm and nm.

mm ⇄ µm ⇄ nm (× 1000, ÷ 1000)

Time can have units of min and s.

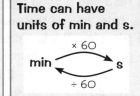

min ⇄ s (× 60, ÷ 60)

Volume can have units of m³, dm³ and cm³.

m³ ⇄ dm³ ⇄ cm³ (× 1000, ÷ 1000)

Always Check The Values Used in Equations Have the Right Units

1) Equations (sometimes called formulas) show <u>relationships</u> between <u>variables</u>.

2) To <u>rearrange</u> an equation, make sure that whatever you do to <u>one side</u> of the equation you also do to the <u>other side</u>.

You can find the <u>magnification</u> of something using the equation: magnification = image size ÷ real size (see p.12). You can <u>rearrange</u> this equation to find the <u>image size</u> by <u>multiplying each side</u> by the real size: image size = magnification × real size.

3) To use an equation, you need to know the values of <u>all but one</u> of the variables. <u>Substitute</u> the values you do know into the equation, and do the calculation to work out the final variable.

4) Always make sure the values you put into an equation have the <u>right units</u>. For example, if you're calculating the magnification of something, but your image size is in mm and the real size is in µm, you'll have to <u>convert</u> both measurements into the same unit (either mm or µm) before you start.

5) To make sure your units are <u>correct</u>, it can help to write down the <u>units</u> on each line of your <u>calculation</u>.

I wasn't sure I liked units, but now I'm converted...

It's easy to get in a muddle when converting between units, but there's a handy way to check you've done it right. If you're moving from a smaller unit to a larger unit (e.g. g to kg) the number should get smaller, and vice versa.

Drawing Conclusions

Congratulations — you're nearly at the end of a gruelling investigation, time to draw conclusions.

You Can Only Conclude What the Data Shows and NO MORE

1) Drawing conclusions might seem pretty straightforward — you just look at your data and say what pattern or relationship you see between the dependent and independent variables.

The table on the right shows the heights of pea plant seedlings grown for three weeks with different fertilisers.

Fertiliser	Mean growth / mm
A	13.5
B	19.5
No fertiliser	5.5

CONCLUSION:
Fertiliser B makes pea plant seedlings grow taller over a three week period than fertiliser A.

2) But you've got to be really careful that your conclusion matches the data you've got and doesn't go any further.

You can't conclude that fertiliser B makes any other type of plant grow taller than fertiliser A — the results could be totally different.

3) You also need to be able to use your results to justify your conclusion (i.e. back up your conclusion with some specific data).

Over the three week period, fertiliser B made the pea plants grow 6 mm more on average than fertiliser A.

4) When writing a conclusion you need to refer back to the original hypothesis and say whether the data supports it or not:

The hypothesis for this experiment might have been that adding fertiliser would increase the growth of plants and that different types of fertiliser would affect growth by different amounts. If so, the data supports the hypothesis.

Correlation DOES NOT Mean Cause

If two things are correlated (i.e. there's a relationship between them) it doesn't necessarily mean a change in one variable is causing the change in the other — this is REALLY IMPORTANT — DON'T FORGET IT. There are three possible reasons for a correlation:

1) CHANCE: It might seem strange, but two things can show a correlation purely due to chance.

For example, one study might find a correlation between people's hair colour and how good they are at frisbee. But other scientists don't get a correlation when they investigate it — the results of the first study are just a fluke.

2) LINKED BY A 3RD VARIABLE: A lot of the time it may look as if a change in one variable is causing a change in the other, but it isn't — a third variable links the two things.

For example, there's a correlation between water temperature and shark attacks. This isn't because warmer water makes sharks crazy. Instead, they're linked by a third variable — the number of people swimming (more people swim when the water's hotter, and with more people in the water you get more shark attacks).

3) CAUSE: Sometimes a change in one variable does cause a change in the other. You can only conclude that a correlation is due to cause when you've controlled all the variables that could, just could, be affecting the result.

For example, there's a correlation between smoking and lung cancer. This is because chemicals in tobacco smoke cause lung cancer. This conclusion was only made once other variables (such as age and exposure to other things that cause cancer) had been controlled and shown not to affect people's risk of getting lung cancer.

I conclude that this page is a bit dull...

...although, just because I find it dull doesn't mean that I can conclude it's dull (you might think it's the most interesting thing since that kid got his head stuck in the railings near school). In the exams you could be given a conclusion and asked whether some data supports it — so make sure you understand how far conclusions can go.

Uncertainties and Evaluations

Hurrah! The end of another investigation. Well, now you have to work out all the things you did <u>wrong</u>.

Uncertainty is the Amount of Error Your Measurements Might Have

1) When you <u>repeat</u> a measurement, you often get a <u>slightly different</u> figure each time you do it due to <u>random error</u>. This means that <u>each result</u> has some <u>uncertainty</u> to it.

2) The measurements you make will also have some uncertainty in them due to <u>limits</u> in the <u>resolution</u> of the equipment you use (see page 5).

3) This all means that the <u>mean</u> of a set of results will also have some uncertainty to it. You can calculate the uncertainty of a <u>mean result</u> using the equation:

4) The <u>larger</u> the range, the <u>less precise</u> your results are and the <u>more uncertainty</u> there will be in your results. Uncertainties are shown using the '±' symbol.

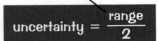

The range is the largest value minus the smallest value (p.6).

$$\text{uncertainty} = \frac{\text{range}}{2}$$

EXAMPLE: The table below shows the results of a respiration experiment to determine the volume of carbon dioxide produced. Calculate the uncertainty of the mean.

Repeat	1	2	3	mean
Volume of CO_2 produced (cm³)	20.1	19.8	20.0	20.0

1) First work out the range:
Range = 20.1 − 19.8
= 0.300 cm³

2) Use the range to find the uncertainty:
Uncertainty = range ÷ 2 = 0.300 ÷ 2 = 0.150 cm³. So the uncertainty of the mean = 20.0 ± 0.150 cm³

5) Measuring a <u>greater amount</u> of something helps to <u>reduce uncertainty</u>. For example, in a rate of reaction experiment, measuring the amount of product formed over a <u>longer period</u> compared to a shorter period will <u>reduce</u> the <u>percentage uncertainty</u> in your results.

Evaluations — Describe How it Could be Improved

An evaluation is a <u>critical analysis</u> of the whole investigation.

I'd value this E somewhere in the region of 250-300k

1) You should comment on the <u>method</u> — was it <u>valid</u>? Did you control all the other variables to make it a <u>fair test</u>?

2) Comment on the <u>quality</u> of the <u>results</u> — was there <u>enough evidence</u> to reach a valid <u>conclusion</u>? Were the results <u>repeatable</u>, <u>reproducible</u>, <u>accurate</u> and <u>precise</u>?

3) Were there any <u>anomalous</u> results? If there were <u>none</u> then <u>say so</u>. If there were any, try to <u>explain</u> them — were they caused by <u>errors</u> in measurement? Were there any other <u>variables</u> that could have <u>affected</u> the results? You should comment on the level of <u>uncertainty</u> in your results too.

4) All this analysis will allow you to say how <u>confident</u> you are that your conclusion is <u>right</u>.

5) Then you can suggest any <u>changes</u> to the <u>method</u> that would <u>improve</u> the quality of the results, so that you could have <u>more confidence</u> in your conclusion. For example, you might suggest <u>changing</u> the way you controlled a variable, or <u>increasing</u> the number of <u>measurements</u> you took. Taking more measurements at <u>narrower intervals</u> could give you a <u>more accurate result</u>. For example:

> <u>Enzymes</u> have an <u>optimum temperature</u> (a temperature at which they <u>work best</u>). Say you do an experiment to find an enzyme's optimum temperature and take measurements at 10 °C, 20 °C, 30 °C, 40 °C and 50 °C. The results of this experiment tell you the optimum is <u>40 °C</u>. You could then <u>repeat</u> the experiment, taking <u>more measurements around 40 °C</u> to a get a <u>more accurate</u> value for the optimum.

6) You could also make more <u>predictions</u> based on your conclusion, then <u>further experiments</u> could be carried out to test them.

When suggesting improvements to the investigation, always make sure that you say why you think this would make the results better.

Evaluation — next time, I'll make sure I don't burn the lab down...

So there you have it — Working Scientifically. Make sure you know this stuff like the back of your hand. It's not just in the lab that you'll need to know how to work scientifically. You can be asked about it in the exams as well.

Cells

When someone first peered down a microscope at a slice of cork and drew the <u>boxes</u> they saw, little did they know that they'd seen the <u>building blocks</u> of <u>every organism on the planet</u>...

Organisms can be Prokaryotes or Eukaryotes

1) <u>All living things</u> are made of <u>cells</u>.
2) Cells can be either <u>prokaryotic</u> or <u>eukaryotic</u>. Eukaryotic cells are <u>complex</u> and include all <u>animal</u> and <u>plant</u> cells. Prokaryotic cells are <u>smaller</u> and <u>simpler</u>, e.g. bacteria (see below).
3) <u>Eukaryotes</u> are organisms that are made up of <u>eukaryotic cells</u>.
4) A <u>prokaryote</u> is a <u>prokaryotic cell</u> (it's a single-celled organism).

Plant and Animal Cells have Similarities and Differences

The different parts of a cell are called <u>subcellular structures</u>.
Most <u>animal</u> cells have the following subcellular structures — make sure you know them all:

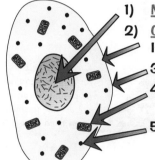

1) <u>Nucleus</u> — contains <u>genetic material</u> that controls the activities of the cell.
2) <u>Cytoplasm</u> — gel-like substance where most of the <u>chemical reactions</u> happen. It contains <u>enzymes</u> (see page 28) that control these chemical reactions.
3) <u>Cell membrane</u> — holds the cell together and controls what goes <u>in</u> and <u>out</u>.
4) <u>Mitochondria</u> — these are where most of the reactions for <u>aerobic respiration</u> take place (see page 62). Respiration transfers <u>energy</u> that the cell needs to work.
5) <u>Ribosomes</u> — these are where <u>proteins</u> are made in the cell.

Plant cells usually have <u>all the bits</u> that <u>animal</u> cells have, plus a few <u>extra</u> things that animal cells <u>don't</u> have:

1) Rigid <u>cell wall</u> — made of <u>cellulose</u>. It <u>supports</u> the cell and strengthens it.
2) <u>Permanent vacuole</u> — contains <u>cell sap</u>, a weak solution of sugar and salts.
3) <u>Chloroplasts</u> — these are where <u>photosynthesis</u> occurs, which makes food for the plant (see page 57). They contain a <u>green</u> substance called <u>chlorophyll</u>, which absorbs the <u>light</u> needed for photosynthesis.

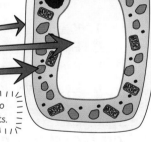

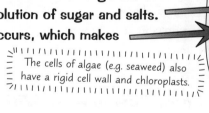

The cells of algae (e.g. seaweed) also have a rigid cell wall and chloroplasts.

Bacterial Cells Are Much Smaller

You might see the sizes of cells written in standard form (see the next page).

Bacteria are <u>prokaryotes</u>. Here's what a bacterial cell might look like:

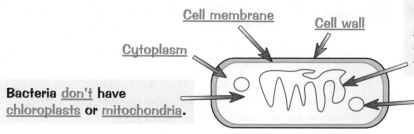

Cell membrane

Cell wall

Cytoplasm

Bacteria <u>don't</u> have <u>chloroplasts</u> or <u>mitochondria</u>.

Bacterial cells <u>don't</u> have a 'true' <u>nucleus</u> — instead they have a <u>single circular strand</u> of <u>DNA</u> that floats <u>freely</u> in the cytoplasm.

They may also contain one or more small rings of DNA called <u>plasmids</u>.

Cell structures — become an estate agent...

You could get asked to estimate the area of a subcellular structure in your exam. If you do, treat it as a regular shape. For example, if it's close to a rectangle, use the area formula 'area = length × width'.

Q1   Give two differences in structure between prokaryotic and eukaryotic cells.   [2 marks]

Microscopy

Microscopes are pretty important for biology. So here's a couple of pages all about them...

Cells are Studied Using Microscopes

1) <u>Microscopes</u> let us see things that we <u>can't see</u> with the <u>naked eye</u>. The <u>microscopy techniques</u> we can use have <u>developed</u> over the years as technology and knowledge have improved.

2) <u>Light microscopes</u> use <u>light</u> and <u>lenses</u> to form an image of a specimen and <u>magnify</u> it (make it look bigger). They let us see <u>individual cells</u> and <u>large subcellular structures</u>, like <u>nuclei</u>.

3) <u>Electron microscopes</u> use <u>electrons</u> instead of light to form an image. They have a much <u>higher magnification</u> than light microscopes.

4) They also have a <u>higher resolution</u>. (Resolution is the ability to <u>distinguish</u> between <u>two points</u>, so a higher resolution gives a <u>sharper image</u>.)

5) Electron microscopes let us see much <u>smaller things</u> in <u>more detail</u>, like the <u>internal structure</u> of <u>mitochondria</u> and <u>chloroplasts</u>. They even let us see <u>tinier</u> things like <u>ribosomes</u> and <u>plasmids</u>.

See the next page for how to use a light microscope.

You Need to be Able to Use the Formula for Magnification

You can calculate the magnification of an image using this formula:

$$\text{magnification} = \frac{\text{image size}}{\text{real size}}$$

Image size and real size should have the same units. If they don't, you'll need to convert them first (see page 8).

If you want to work out the <u>image size</u> or the <u>real size</u> of the object, you can rearrange the equation using this <u>formula triangle</u>:

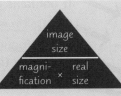

Cover up the thing you're trying to find. The parts you can still see are the formula you need to use.

EXAMPLE: A specimen is 50 μm wide. Calculate the width of the image of the specimen under a magnification of × 100. Give your answer in mm.

1) <u>Rearrange</u> the formula.
2) Fill in the <u>values</u> you know.
3) Remember the <u>units</u> in your answer.
4) <u>Convert</u> the units.

image size = magnification × real size
image size = 100 × 50
= 5000 μm
= 5 mm

Remember, to convert from micrometres (μm) to millimetres (mm), you need to divide by 1000 (see p.8). E.g. 5000 μm ÷ 1000 = 5 mm

You Need to Know How to Work With Numbers in Standard Form

1) Because microscopes can see such <u>tiny objects</u>, sometimes it's useful to write numbers in <u>standard form</u>.

2) This is where you change <u>very big</u> or <u>small</u> numbers with <u>lots of zeros</u> into something more manageable, e.g. 0.017 can be written 1.7×10^{-2}.

3) To do this you just need to <u>move</u> the <u>decimal point</u> left or right.

4) **The number of places the decimal point moves is then represented by a <u>power of 10</u> — this is <u>positive</u> if the decimal point's moved to the <u>left</u>, and <u>negative</u> if it's moved to the <u>right</u>.**

EXAMPLE: A mitochondrion is approximately 0.0025 mm long. Write this figure in standard form.

1) The first number needs to be <u>between 1 and 10</u> so the decimal point needs to move after the '2'.

2) <u>Count</u> how many places the decimal point has <u>moved</u> — this is the power of 10. Don't forget the <u>minus</u> sign because the decimal point has moved <u>right</u>.

0.0025

2.5×10^{-3}

Your resolution to revise should be increasing right now...

Keep an eye on the units for that equation — if they're not the same, it just won't work.

Q1   An onion cell is viewed under a microscope with × 100 magnification. The image of the cell is 7.5 mm wide. What is the real width of the onion cell? Give your answer in μm.   [2 marks]

More on Microscopy

It's all very well knowing what microscopes <u>do</u> — you also have to know how to actually <u>use</u> one.

You Need to Prepare Your Slide

If you want to look at a specimen (e.g. plant or animal cells) under a light microscope, you need to put it on a <u>microscope slide</u> first. A slide is a strip of clear <u>glass</u> or <u>plastic</u> onto which the specimen is <u>mounted</u>. Here's how to prepare a slide to view onion cells:

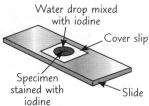

1) Add a <u>drop of water</u> to the middle of a clean slide.
2) Cut up an onion and separate it out into <u>layers</u>. Use <u>tweezers</u> to peel off some <u>epidermal tissue</u> from the bottom of one of the layers.
3) Using the tweezers, place the epidermal tissue into the <u>water</u> on the slide.
4) Add a drop of <u>iodine solution</u>. Iodine solution is a <u>stain</u>. Stains are used to highlight objects in a cell by adding <u>colour</u> to them.
5) Place a <u>cover slip</u> (a square of thin, transparent plastic or glass) on top. To do this, stand the cover slip <u>upright</u> on the slide, <u>next to</u> the water droplet. Then carefully <u>tilt</u> and <u>lower</u> it so it covers the specimen. Try <u>not</u> to get any <u>air bubbles</u> under there — they'll <u>obstruct</u> your view of the specimen.

Use a Light Microscope to Look at Your Slide

To look at your prepared slides, you need to know how to use a light microscope:

1) Clip the <u>slide</u> you've prepared onto the <u>stage</u>.
2) Select the <u>lowest-powered objective lens</u> (i.e. the one that produces the lowest magnification).
3) Use the <u>coarse adjustment knob</u> to move the stage up to just below the objective lens.
4) Look down the <u>eyepiece</u>. Use the coarse adjustment knob to move the stage downwards until the image is <u>roughly in focus</u>.
5) Adjust the <u>focus</u> with the <u>fine adjustment knob</u>, until you get a <u>clear image</u> of what's on the slide.
6) If you need to see the slide with <u>greater magnification</u>, swap to a <u>higher-powered objective lens</u> and refocus.

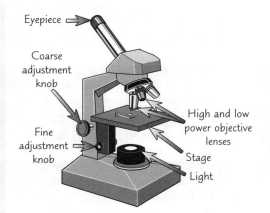

Draw Your Observations Neatly with a Pencil

1) Draw what you see under the microscope using a <u>pencil</u> with a <u>sharp point</u>.
2) Make sure your drawing takes up <u>at least half</u> of the space available and that it is drawn with <u>clear, unbroken lines</u>.
3) Your drawing should not include any <u>colouring</u> or <u>shading</u>.
4) If you are drawing <u>cells</u>, the <u>subcellular structures</u> should be drawn in <u>proportion</u>.
5) Remember to include a <u>title</u> of what you were observing and write down the <u>magnification</u> that it was observed under.
6) <u>Label</u> the <u>important features</u> of your drawing (e.g. nucleus, chloroplasts), using <u>straight, uncrossed lines</u>.

You can work out the real size of a cell by counting the number of cells in 1 mm of the sample (see p.128). You can work out the magnification of your drawing using this formula: magnification = length of drawing of cell ÷ real length of cell. So here, magnification = 33 mm ÷ 0.3 mm = × 110.

A light microscope is better than a heavy one...

If you can use a microscope, you're halfway to ruling the world. That's what I like to think, anyway.

Q1   Why might you add stain to the sample on a microscope slide?   [1 mark]

Cell Differentiation and Specialisation

Cells <u>don't</u> all look the <u>same</u>. They have <u>different structures</u> to suit their <u>different functions</u>.

Cells Differentiate to Become Specialised

1) <u>Differentiation</u> is the process by which a cell <u>changes</u> to become <u>specialised</u> for its job.

2) As cells change, they develop <u>different subcellular structures</u> and turn into <u>different types of cells</u>. This allows them to carry out <u>specific functions</u>.

3) Most differentiation occurs as an organism <u>develops</u>. In most <u>animal</u> cells, the ability to differentiate is then <u>lost</u> at an early stage, after they become specialised. However, lots of <u>plant</u> cells <u>don't</u> ever lose this ability.

4) The cells that differentiate in <u>mature animals</u> are mainly used for <u>repairing</u> and <u>replacing cells</u>, such as skin or blood cells.

5) Some cells are undifferentiated cells — they're called <u>stem cells</u>. There's more about them on page 19.

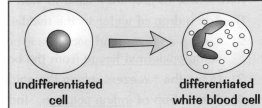

undifferentiated cell → differentiated white blood cell

You Need To Know These Examples of Specialised Cells

SPERM CELLS are specialised for REPRODUCTION

The function of a <u>sperm</u> is basically to get the <u>male DNA</u> to the <u>female DNA</u>. It has a <u>long tail</u> and a <u>streamlined head</u> to help it <u>swim</u> to the egg. There are a lot of <u>mitochondria</u> in the cell to provide the <u>energy</u> needed. It also carries <u>enzymes</u> in its head to digest through the egg cell membrane.

NERVE CELLS are specialised for RAPID SIGNALLING

The function of <u>nerve cells</u> is to <u>carry electrical signals</u> from one part of the body to another. These cells are <u>long</u> (to cover more distance) and have <u>branched connections</u> at their ends to <u>connect</u> to other nerve cells and form a <u>network</u> throughout the body.

MUSCLE CELLS are specialised for CONTRACTION

The function of a <u>muscle cell</u> is to contract quickly. These cells are <u>long</u> (so that they have space to <u>contract</u>) and contain <u>lots of mitochondria</u> to generate the <u>energy</u> needed for contraction.

ROOT HAIR CELLS are specialised for absorbing WATER and MINERALS

Root hair cells are cells on the surface of plant roots, which grow into long "<u>hairs</u>" that stick out into the soil. This gives the plant a <u>big surface area</u> for absorbing <u>water</u> and <u>mineral ions</u> from the soil.

PHLOEM and XYLEM CELLS are specialised for TRANSPORTING SUBSTANCES

<u>Phloem</u> and <u>xylem cells</u> form phloem and xylem <u>tubes</u>, which <u>transport</u> substances such as <u>food</u> and <u>water</u> around plants. To form the tubes, the cells are long and joined <u>end to end</u>. Xylem cells are <u>hollow</u> in the centre and phloem cells have <u>very few subcellular structures</u>, so that stuff can <u>flow through</u> them.

phloem   xylem

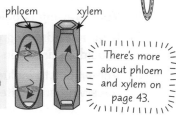

There's more about phloem and xylem on page 43.

Tadpoles and tent pegs — cells are masters of disguise...

You need to know how the structure of each of the cells on this page relates to its function. Lucky you.

Q1   Plants transport food substances from the leaves to growing parts of the plant through phloem tubes. Give one feature of a phloem cell that makes it specialised for its function.   [1 mark]

Q2   Describe how a root hair cell is specialised for its function.   [2 marks]

Chromosomes and Mitosis

In order to survive and grow, our cells have got to be able to <u>divide</u>. And that means our DNA as well...

Chromosomes Contain Genetic Information

1) Most cells in your body have a <u>nucleus</u>. The nucleus contains your <u>genetic material</u> in the form of <u>chromosomes</u>.

2) Chromosomes are <u>coiled up</u> lengths of <u>DNA molecules</u>.

3) Each chromosome carries a <u>large number</u> of genes. Different genes <u>control</u> the development of different <u>characteristics</u>, e.g. hair colour.

4) <u>Body cells</u> normally have <u>two copies</u> of each <u>chromosome</u> — one from the organism's 'mother', and one from its 'father'. So, humans have two copies of chromosome 1, two copies of chromosome 2, etc.

5) The diagram shows the <u>23 pairs of chromosomes</u> from a human cell.

The Cell Cycle Makes New Cells for Growth, Development and Repair

1) <u>Body cells</u> in <u>multicellular</u> organisms <u>divide</u> to produce new cells as part of a series of stages called the <u>cell cycle</u>.

2) The stage of the cell cycle when the cell divides is called <u>mitosis</u>.

3) Multicellular organisms use <u>mitosis</u> to <u>grow</u> or <u>replace cells</u> that have been <u>damaged</u>.

4) The end of the cell cycle results in two new cells <u>identical</u> to the <u>original</u> cell, with the <u>same number</u> of chromosomes.

5) You need to know about these two main stages of the <u>cell cycle</u>:

growth and DNA replication

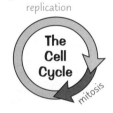

The Cell Cycle

mitosis

Growth & DNA Replication

1) In a cell that's not dividing, the DNA is all spread out in <u>long strings</u>.

2) Before it divides, the cell has to <u>grow</u> and <u>increase</u> the amount of <u>subcellular structures</u> such as <u>mitochondria</u> and <u>ribosomes</u>.

3) It then <u>duplicates</u> its DNA — so there's one copy for each new cell. The DNA is copied and forms <u>X-shaped</u> chromosomes. Each 'arm' of the chromosome is an <u>exact duplicate</u> of the other.

The left arm has the same DNA as the right arm of the chromosome.

Mitosis

Once its contents and DNA have been copied, the cell is ready for <u>mitosis</u>...

4) The chromosomes <u>line up</u> at the centre of the cell and <u>cell fibres</u> pull them apart. The <u>two arms</u> of each chromosome go to <u>opposite ends</u> of the cell.

5) <u>Membranes</u> form around each of the sets of chromosomes. These become the <u>nuclei</u> of the two new cells — the <u>nucleus</u> has <u>divided</u>.

6) Lastly, the <u>cytoplasm</u> and <u>cell membrane</u> divide.

The cell has now produced <u>two new daughter cells</u>. The daughter cells contain exactly the <u>same DNA</u> — they're <u>identical</u>. Their DNA is also <u>identical</u> to the <u>parent cell</u>.

A cell's favourite computer game — divide and conquer...

Mitosis can seem tricky at first. But don't worry — just go through it slowly, one step at a time. This type of division produces identical cells, but there's another type which doesn't... (see page 88).

Q1   Describe the events of the cell cycle that need to occur before mitosis can begin.   **[2 marks]**

Binary Fission

Prokaryotic cells can reproduce using a type of simple cell division called binary fission.

Prokaryotic Cells Replicate by Binary Fission

In binary fission, the cell... splits into two. There's a bit more to it than that though:

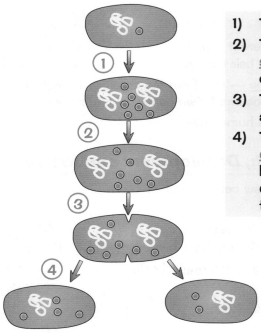

1) The circular DNA and plasmid(s) replicate.
2) The cell gets bigger and the circular DNA strands move to opposite 'poles' (ends) of the cell.
3) The cytoplasm begins to divide and new cell walls begin to form.
4) The cytoplasm divides and two daughter cells are produced. Each daughter cell has one copy of the circular DNA, but can have a variable number of copies of the plasmid(s).

Bacteria can divide very quickly if given the right conditions (e.g. a warm environment and lots of nutrients). Some bacteria, such as *E. coli*, can take as little as 20 minutes to replicate in the right environment. However, if conditions become unfavourable, the cells will stop dividing and eventually begin to die.

Use the Mean Division Time to Find the Number of Bacteria in a Population

The mean division time is just the average amount of time it takes for one bacterial cell to divide into two. If you know the mean division time of a cell, you can work out how many times it has divided in a certain amount of time, and so the number of cells it has produced in that time.

 **EXAMPLE:** A bacterial cell has a mean division time of 30 minutes. How many cells will it have produced after 2.5 hours?

1) Make sure both times are in the same units.   2.5 hours × 60 = 150 minutes.

2) Divide the total time that the bacteria are producing cells by the mean division time. This gives you the number of divisions.   150 minutes ÷ 30 minutes = 5 divisions

3) Multiply 2 by itself for the number of divisions to find the number of cells. $2^5 = 2 \times 2 \times 2 \times 2 \times 2 = 32$ cells

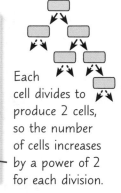

Each cell divides to produce 2 cells, so the number of cells increases by a power of 2 for each division.

Fission is division, there's no splitting hairs there...

Binary fission is the sort of subject where standard form could show up. Head back to page 12 if you're unsure.

Q1   Give two things that help to maximise the rate of binary fission.   [2 marks]

Q2   A bacterial cell has a mean division time of 30 minutes.
How many cells will it have produced in 3 hours?   [2 marks]

Culturing Microorganisms

And now for some hands-on stuff. You can grow your own microorganisms and test how effective different antibiotics, antiseptics or disinfectants are at killing them — just watch out for those bacterial rights activists...

You Can Grow Bacteria in the Lab

1) Bacteria (and some other microorganisms) are grown (cultured) in a "culture medium", which contains the carbohydrates, minerals, proteins and vitamins they need to grow.

2) The culture medium used can be a nutrient broth solution or solid agar jelly.

3) Bacteria grown on agar 'plates' will form visible colonies on the surface of the jelly, or will spread out to give an even covering of bacteria.

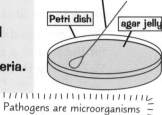

- To make an agar plate, hot agar jelly is poured into shallow round plastic dishes called Petri dishes.
- When the jelly's cooled and set, inoculating loops (wire loops) can be used to transfer microorganisms to the culture medium. Alternatively, a sterile dropping pipette and spreader can be used to get an even covering of bacteria.
- The microorganisms then multiply.

4) In the lab at school, cultures of microorganisms are not kept above 25 °C, because harmful pathogens are more likely to grow above this temperature.

Pathogens are microorganisms that cause disease (see p.46).

5) In industrial conditions, cultures are incubated at higher temperatures so that they can grow a lot faster.

You Can Investigate the Effect of Antibiotics on Bacterial Growth

You can test the action of antibiotics (or antiseptics) on cultures of bacteria:

1) Place paper discs soaked in different types (or different concentrations) of antibiotics on an agar plate that has an even covering of bacteria. Leave some space between the discs.

2) The antibiotic should diffuse (soak) into the agar jelly. Antibiotic-resistant bacteria (i.e. bacteria that aren't affected by the antibiotic — see p.51) will continue to grow on the agar around the paper discs, but non-resistant strains will die. A clear area will be left where the bacteria have died — this is called an inhibition zone.

3) Make sure you use a control. This is a paper disc that has not been soaked in an antibiotic. Instead, soak it in sterile water. You can then be sure that any difference between the growth of the bacteria around the control disc and around one of the antibiotic discs is due to the effect of the antibiotic alone (and not something weird in the paper, for example).

no bacteria growing (inhibition zone)

bacteria growing

paper disc — control

paper disc — with antibiotic

4) Leave the plate for 48 hours at 25 °C.

5) The more effective the antibiotic is against the bacteria, the larger the inhibition zone will be — see next page.

You Need to Use Uncontaminated Cultures

Contamination by unwanted microorganisms will affect your results and can potentially result in the growth of pathogens. To avoid this:

1) The Petri dishes and culture medium must be sterilised before use (e.g. by heating to a high temperature), to kill any unwanted microorganisms that may be lurking on them.

2) If an inoculating loop is used to transfer the bacteria to the culture medium, it should be sterilised first by passing it through a hot flame.

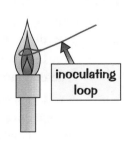

inoculating loop

3) After transferring the bacteria, the lid of the Petri dish should be lightly taped on — to stop microorganisms from the air getting in.

4) The Petri dish should be stored upside down — to stop drops of condensation falling onto the agar surface.

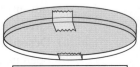

storing a Petri dish

PRACTICAL Culturing Microorganisms

Calculate the Sizes of the Inhibition Zones to Compare Results

You can <u>compare</u> the <u>effectiveness</u> of different antibiotics (or antiseptics) on bacteria by looking at the <u>relative sizes</u> of the <u>inhibition zones</u>. The <u>larger</u> the inhibition zone around a disc, the <u>more effective</u> the antibiotic is against the bacteria.

You can do this <u>by eye</u> if there are large differences in size. But to get more accurate results it's a good idea to calculate the <u>area</u> of the inhibition zones using their <u>diameter</u> (the distance <u>across</u>).

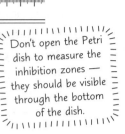

\\\\|||||||||||||||||//
Don't open the Petri
dish to measure the
inhibition zones —
they should be visible
through the bottom
of the dish.
//||||||||||||||\\\\

To calculate the area of an inhibition zone, you need to use <u>this equation</u>:

This is the equation for the area of a circle. You're likely to use the units cm² or mm².

$$\text{Area} = \pi r^2$$

r is the radius of the inhibition zone — it's equal to half the diameter.

π is just a number. You should have a button for it on your calculator. If not, just use the value 3.14.

EXAMPLE:

The diagram below shows the inhibition zones produced by antibiotics A and B. Use the areas of the inhibition zones to compare the effectiveness of the antibiotics.

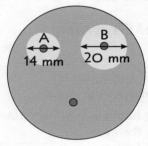

1) Divide the diameter of zone A by <u>two</u> to find the <u>radius</u>.

2) Stick the radius value into the <u>equation</u> area = πr^2.

3) <u>Repeat</u> steps 1 and 2 for zone B.

4) <u>Compare</u> the <u>sizes</u> of the <u>areas</u>. 314 mm² is just over twice 154 mm², so you could say that:

Radius of A = 14 ÷ 2 = 7 mm

Area of A = π × 7² = 154 mm²

Radius of B = 20 ÷ 2 = 10 mm

Area of B = π × 10² = 314 mm²

The inhibition zone of antibiotic B is roughly twice the size of the inhibition zone of antibiotic A.

You Can Also Find the Area of a Colony

The equation above can also be used to calculate the <u>area</u> of a bacterial <u>colony</u>. You just need to measure the <u>diameter</u> of the colony you are interested in first.

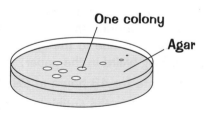

One colony

Agar

Agar — my favourite jelly flavour after raspberry...

Microorganisms might be the perfect pets. You don't have to walk them, they won't get lonely and they hardly cost anything to feed. But whatever you do, do not feed them after midnight.

Q1 A researcher was investigating the effect of four different antiseptics on the growth of bacteria. The diagram on the right shows the results.

a) Which antiseptic was most effective against the bacteria? [1 mark]

b) Calculate the size of the inhibition zone for Antiseptic C. Give your answer in mm². [2 marks]

c) Describe a control that could have been used for this investigation. [1 mark]

d) Explain why a control should be used. [1 mark]

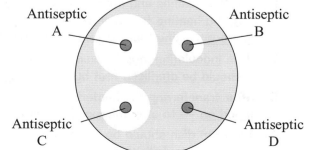

Antiseptic A
Antiseptic B
Antiseptic C
Antiseptic D

Stem Cells

Stem cell research has exciting possibilities, but it's also pretty controversial.

Embryonic Stem Cells Can Turn into ANY Type of Cell

1) Differentiation is the process by which a cell changes to become specialised for its job — see p.14.
2) Undifferentiated cells, called stem cells, can divide to produce lots more undifferentiated cells. They can differentiate into different types of cell, depending on what instructions they're given.
3) Stem cells are found in early human embryos. They're exciting to doctors and medical researchers because they have the potential to turn into any kind of cell at all. This makes sense if you think about it — all the different types of cell found in a human being have to come from those few cells in the early embryo.
4) Adults also have stem cells, but they're only found in certain places, like bone marrow. Unlike embryonic stem cells, they can't turn into any cell type at all, only certain ones, such as blood cells.
5) Stem cells from embryos and bone marrow can be grown in a lab to produce clones (genetically identical cells) and made to differentiate into specialised cells to use in medicine or research.

Stem Cells May Be Able to Cure Many Diseases

1) Medicine already uses adult stem cells to cure disease. For example, stem cells transferred from the bone marrow of a healthy person can replace faulty blood cells in the patient who receives them.
2) Embryonic stem cells could also be used to replace faulty cells in sick people — you could make insulin-producing cells for people with diabetes, nerve cells for people paralysed by spinal injuries, and so on.
3) In a type of cloning, called therapeutic cloning, an embryo could be made to have the same genetic information as the patient. This means that the stem cells produced from it would also contain the same genes and so wouldn't be rejected by the patient's body if used to replace faulty cells.
4) However, there are risks involved in using stem cells in medicine. For example, stem cells grown in the lab may become contaminated with a virus which could be passed on to the patient and so make them sicker.

Some People Are Against Stem Cell Research

1) Some people are against stem cell research because they feel that human embryos shouldn't be used for experiments since each one is a potential human life.
2) Others think that curing existing patients who are suffering is more important than the rights of embryos.
3) One fairly convincing argument in favour of this point of view is that the embryos used in the research are usually unwanted ones from fertility clinics which, if they weren't used for research, would probably just be destroyed. But of course, campaigners for the rights of embryos usually want this banned too.
4) These campaigners feel that scientists should concentrate more on finding and developing other sources of stem cells, so people could be helped without having to use embryos.
5) In some countries stem cell research is banned. It's allowed in the UK as long as it follows strict guidelines.

Stem Cells Can Produce Identical Plants

1) In plants, stem cells are found in the meristems (parts of the plant where growth occurs — see p.42).
2) Throughout the plant's entire life, cells in the meristem tissues can differentiate into any type of plant cell.
3) These stem cells can be used to produce clones (identical copies) of whole plants quickly and cheaply.
4) They can be used to grow more plants of rare species (to prevent them being wiped out).
5) Stem cells can also be used to grow crops of identical plants that have desired features for farmers, for example, disease resistance.

But florists cell stems, and nobody complains about that...

Whatever your opinion is, make sure know the uses of stem cells and the arguments for and against using them.

Q1 How can stem cells be used to preserve rare plant species? [2 marks]

Topic 1 — Cell Biology

Diffusion

Particles <u>move about randomly</u>, and after a bit they end up <u>evenly spaced</u>. It's not rocket science, is it...

Don't Be Put Off by the Fancy Word

1) "<u>Diffusion</u>" is simple. It's just the <u>gradual movement</u> of particles from places where there are <u>lots</u> of them to places where there are <u>fewer</u> of them — it's just the <u>natural tendency</u> for stuff to <u>spread out</u>.

2) Unfortunately you also have to learn the fancy way of saying the same thing, which is this:

> <u>DIFFUSION</u> is the <u>SPREADING OUT</u> of <u>particles</u> from an area of <u>HIGHER CONCENTRATION</u> to an area of <u>LOWER CONCENTRATION</u>.

3) Diffusion happens in both <u>solutions</u> and <u>gases</u> — that's because the particles in these substances are free to <u>move about</u> randomly.

4) The <u>simplest type</u> is when different <u>gases</u> diffuse through each other. This is what's happening when the smell of perfume diffuses through the air in a room:

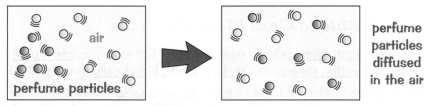

perfume particles diffused in the air

5) The <u>bigger</u> the <u>concentration gradient</u> (the <u>difference</u> in concentration), the <u>faster</u> the diffusion rate.

6) A <u>higher temperature</u> will also give a <u>faster</u> diffusion rate because the particles have more energy, so move around faster.

Cell Membranes Are Kind of Clever...

1) They're clever because they <u>hold</u> the cell together <u>BUT</u> they let stuff <u>in and out</u> as well.

2) Dissolved substances can move in and out of cells by <u>diffusion</u>.

3) Only very <u>small</u> molecules can <u>diffuse</u> through cell membranes though — things like <u>oxygen</u> (needed for respiration — see page 62), <u>glucose</u>, <u>amino acids</u> and <u>water</u>.

4) <u>Big</u> molecules like <u>starch</u> and <u>proteins</u> can't fit through the membrane:

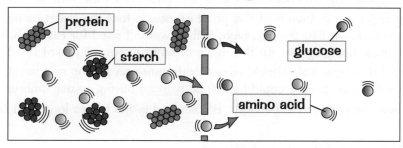

5) Just like with diffusion in air, particles flow through the cell membrane from where there's a <u>higher concentration</u> (a lot of them) to where there's a <u>lower concentration</u> (not such a lot of them).

6) They're only moving about <u>randomly</u> of course, so they go <u>both</u> ways — but if there are a lot <u>more</u> particles on one side of the membrane, there's a <u>net</u> (overall) movement <u>from</u> that side.

7) The <u>larger</u> the <u>surface area</u> of the membrane, the <u>faster</u> the diffusion rate, because more particles can pass through at once — see page 23.

Revision by diffusion — you wish...

Wouldn't it be great if all the ideas in this book would just gradually drift across into your mind...

Q1 A student adds a drop of ink to a glass of cold water.
  a) What will the student observe to happen to the drop of ink. Explain your answer. [2 marks]
  b) How might the observation differ if the ink was added to a glass of warm water? [1 mark]

Osmosis

If you've got your head round <u>diffusion</u>, osmosis will be a <u>breeze</u>. If not, have another read of the previous page.

Osmosis is a Special Case of Diffusion, That's All

> <u>OSMOSIS</u> is the <u>movement of water molecules</u> across a <u>partially permeable membrane</u> from a region of <u>higher water concentration</u> to a region of <u>lower water concentration</u>.

1) A <u>partially permeable</u> membrane is just one with very small holes in it. So small, in fact, only tiny <u>molecules</u> (like water) can pass through them, and bigger molecules (e.g. <u>sucrose</u>) can't.

2) The water molecules actually pass <u>both ways</u> through the membrane during osmosis. This happens because water molecules <u>move about randomly</u> all the time.

3) But because there are <u>more</u> water molecules on one side than on the other, there's a steady <u>net flow</u> of water into the region with <u>fewer</u> water molecules, i.e. into the <u>stronger</u> sugar solution.

4) This means the <u>strong sugar</u> solution gets more <u>dilute</u>. The water acts like it's trying to "<u>even up</u>" the concentration either side of the membrane.

5) Osmosis is a type of <u>diffusion</u> — passive movement of <u>water particles</u> from an area of <u>higher water concentration</u> to an area of <u>lower water concentration</u>.

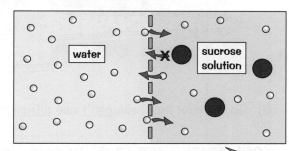

water | sucrose solution

Net movement of water molecules

You can Observe the Effect of Sugar Solutions on Plant Tissue

<u>PRACTICAL</u>

There's a fairly dull <u>experiment</u> you can do to show osmosis at work.

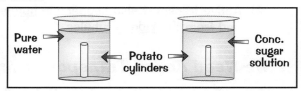

Pure water — Potato cylinders — Conc. sugar solution

1) You cut up an innocent <u>potato</u> into identical cylinders, and get some beakers with <u>different sugar solutions</u> in them. One should be <u>pure water</u> and another should be a <u>very concentrated sugar solution</u> (e.g. 1 mol/dm³). Then you can have a few others with concentrations <u>in between</u> (e.g. 0.2 mol/dm³, 0.4 mol/dm³, 0.6 mol/dm³, etc.)

2) You measure the <u>mass</u> of the cylinders, then leave one cylinder in each beaker for twenty four hours or so.

3) Then you take them out, <u>dry</u> them with a paper towel and measure their masses <u>again</u>.

4) If the cylinders have drawn in water by osmosis, they'll have <u>increased in mass</u>. If water has been drawn out, they'll have <u>decreased in mass</u>. You can calculate the <u>percentage change in mass</u>, then plot a few <u>graphs</u> and things.

> By calculating the percentage change (see p.130), you can compare the effect of sugar concentration on cylinders that didn't have the same initial mass. An increase in mass will give a positive percentage change and a decrease will give a negative percentage change.

5) The <u>dependent variable</u> is the <u>chip mass</u> and the <u>independent variable</u> is the <u>concentration</u> of the sugar solution. All <u>other</u> variables (volume of solution, temperature, time, type of sugar used, etc. etc.) must be kept the <u>same</u> in each case or the experiment won't be a <u>fair test</u>.

6) Like any experiment, you need to be aware of how <u>errors</u> (see p.5) may arise. Sometimes they may occur when <u>carrying out the method</u>, e.g. if some potato cylinders were not <u>fully dried</u>, the excess water would give a <u>higher mass</u>, or if water <u>evaporated</u> from the beakers, the <u>concentrations</u> of the sugar solutions would change. You can <u>reduce the effect</u> of these errors by <u>repeating</u> the experiment and calculating a <u>mean percentage change</u> at each concentration.

> You could also carry out this experiment using different salt solutions and see what effect they have on potato chip mass.

And to all you cold-hearted potato murderers...

Just remember, osmosis is really just a fancy word for the diffusion of water molecules. It's simple really.

Q1   Explain what will happen to the mass of a piece of potato added to a concentrated salt solution.   [2 marks]

Active Transport

Sometimes substances need to be absorbed against a concentration gradient, i.e. from a lower to a higher concentration. This process is lovingly referred to as <u>ACTIVE TRANSPORT</u>.

Root Hairs Take In Minerals and Water

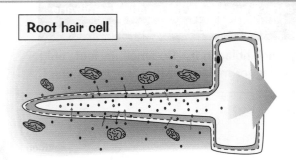

Root hair cell

1) As you saw on page 14, the cells on plant roots grow into "<u>hairs</u>" which stick out into the soil.
2) Each branch of a root will be covered in <u>millions</u> of these microscopic hairs.
3) This gives the plant a <u>large surface area</u> for absorbing <u>water</u> and <u>mineral ions</u> from the soil.
4) Plants <u>need</u> these mineral ions for <u>healthy growth</u>.
5) The concentration of minerals is usually <u>higher</u> in the <u>root hair</u> cells than in the <u>soil</u> around them.
6) So the root hair cells <u>can't</u> use <u>diffusion</u> to take up minerals from the soil.

Water is taken into root hair cells by osmosis (see page 21).

Root Hairs Take in Minerals Using Active Transport

1) Minerals should move <u>out</u> of the root hairs if they followed the rules of diffusion. The cells must use another method to draw them in.
2) That method is, in fact, a conveniently mysterious process called "<u>active transport</u>".
3) Active transport allows the plant to absorb minerals from a very <u>dilute</u> solution, <u>against</u> a concentration gradient. This is essential for its growth. But active transport needs <u>ENERGY</u> from <u>respiration</u> to make it work.
4) Active transport also happens in <u>humans</u>, for example in taking <u>glucose</u> from the <u>gut</u> (see below), and from the <u>kidney tubules</u>.

We Need Active Transport to Stop Us Starving

<u>Active transport</u> is used in the gut when there is a <u>lower concentration</u> of nutrients in the <u>gut</u>, but a <u>higher concentration</u> of nutrients in the <u>blood</u>.

1) When there's <u>a higher concentration</u> of glucose and amino acids in the gut they <u>diffuse naturally</u> into the blood.
2) <u>BUT</u> — sometimes there's a <u>lower concentration</u> of nutrients in the gut than there is in the blood.
3) This means that the <u>concentration gradient</u> is the wrong way.
4) The same process used in plant roots is used here...
    ..."<u>Active transport</u>".

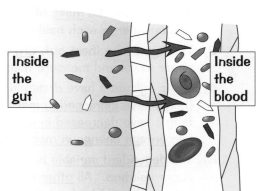

Inside the gut

Inside the blood

5) Active transport allows nutrients to be taken into the blood, despite the fact that the <u>concentration gradient</u> is the wrong way.
6) This means that <u>glucose</u> can be taken into the bloodstream when its concentration in the blood is already <u>higher</u> than in the gut. It can then be transported to cells, where it's used for <u>respiration</u> (see p.61).

Active transport — get on yer bike...

An important difference between active transport and diffusion is that active transport uses energy. Imagine a pen of sheep in a field. If you open the pen, the sheep will happily diffuse from the area of higher sheep concentration into the field, which has a lower sheep concentration — you won't have to do a thing. To get them back in the pen though, you'll have to put in quite a bit of energy.

Q1   What is the purpose of active transport in the gut?   [1 mark]

Topic 1 — Cell Biology

Exchange Surfaces

How easily stuff <u>moves</u> between an <u>organism</u> and its <u>environment</u> depends on its <u>surface area to volume ratio</u>.

Organisms Exchange Substances with their Environment

1) Cells can use <u>diffusion</u> to <u>take in</u> substances they <u>need</u> and <u>get rid</u> of <u>waste products</u>. For example:
   - <u>Oxygen</u> and <u>carbon dioxide</u> are transferred between <u>cells</u> and the <u>environment</u> during <u>gas exchange</u>.
   - In humans, <u>urea</u> (a waste product produced from the breakdown of proteins, see p.75) diffuses from <u>cells</u> into the <u>blood plasma</u> for removal from the body by the kidneys.

2) How <u>easy</u> it is for an organism to exchange substances with its environment depends on the organism's <u>surface area to volume ratio</u> (<u>SA : V</u>).

You Can Compare Surface Area to Volume Ratios

A ratio shows <u>how big</u> one value is <u>compared</u> to another. The <u>larger</u> an organism is, the <u>smaller</u> its surface area is compared to its volume. You can show this by calculating <u>surface area to volume ratios</u>:

A hippo can be represented by a 2 cm × 4 cm × 4 cm block.

The area of a surface is found by the equation: LENGTH × WIDTH
So the hippo's total <u>surface area</u> is:
    (4 × 4) × 2 (top and bottom surfaces of block)
    + (4 × 2) × 4 (four sides of the block)
    = 64 cm².

The volume of a block is found by the equation: LENGTH × WIDTH × HEIGHT
So the hippo's <u>volume</u> is 4 × 4 × 2 = 32 cm³.

The surface area to volume ratio of the hippo can be written as <u>64 : 32</u>.
To <u>simplify</u> the ratio, <u>divide both sides</u> of the ratio by the <u>volume</u>.
So the surface area to volume ratio of the hippo is <u>2 : 1</u>.

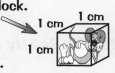

A mouse can be represented by a 1 cm × 1 cm × 1 cm block.
Its <u>surface area</u> is (1 × 1) × 6 = 6 cm².
Its <u>volume</u> is 1 × 1 × 1 = 1 cm³.
So the surface area to volume ratio of the mouse is <u>6 : 1</u>.

The cube mouse's surface area is <u>six</u> times its volume, but the cube hippo's surface area is only <u>twice</u> its volume. So the <u>mouse</u> has a <u>larger</u> surface area compared to its volume.

Multicellular Organisms Need Exchange Surfaces

1) In <u>single-celled organisms</u>, gases and dissolved substances can diffuse <u>directly into</u> (or out of) the cell across the cell membrane. It's because they have a <u>large surface area</u> compared to their <u>volume</u>, so <u>enough substances</u> can be exchanged across the membrane to supply the volume of the cell.

2) <u>Multicellular organisms</u> have a <u>smaller surface area</u> compared to their <u>volume</u> — <u>not enough</u> substances can diffuse from their outside surface to supply their entire volume. This means they need some sort of <u>exchange surface</u> for efficient diffusion (see pages 24-25 for some examples). The exchange surface structures have to allow <u>enough</u> of the necessary substances to pass through.

3) Exchange surfaces are <u>ADAPTED</u> to maximise effectiveness:
   - They have a <u>thin membrane</u>, so substances only have a <u>short distance</u> to <u>diffuse</u>.
   - They have a <u>large surface area</u> so <u>lots</u> of a substance can <u>diffuse</u> at once.
   - Exchange surfaces in <u>animals</u> have <u>lots of blood vessels</u>, to get stuff into and out of the blood quickly.
   - <u>Gas exchange surfaces</u> in animals (e.g. alveoli) are often <u>ventilated</u> too — air moves in and out.

Not that I'm endorsing putting animals in boxes...

A large surface area is a key way that organisms' exchange surfaces are made more effective.

Q1 A bacterial cell can be represented by a 2 μm × 2 μm × 1 μm block.
    Calculate the cell's surface area to volume ratio.
                                                                    [3 marks]

Exchanging Substances

This page is about how two different parts of the human body are <u>adapted</u> so that substances can diffuse through them <u>most effectively</u>. The first bit is about how <u>gases</u> in the lungs get <u>into and out of the blood</u>. The second is about how <u>digested food</u> gets from the <u>gut to the blood</u>.

Gas Exchange Happens in the Lungs

1) The job of the lungs is to transfer <u>oxygen</u> to the <u>blood</u> and to remove <u>waste carbon dioxide</u> from it.

2) To do this the lungs contain millions of little air sacs called <u>alveoli</u> where <u>gas exchange</u> takes place.

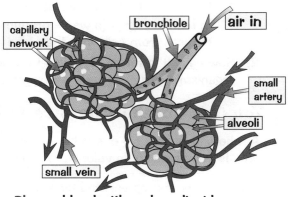

Blue = blood with carbon dioxide.
Red = blood with oxygen.

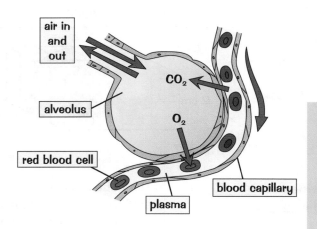

3) The alveoli are specialised to maximise the <u>diffusion</u> of O_2 and CO_2. They have:
- An <u>enormous</u> surface area (about 75 m² in humans).
- A <u>moist lining</u> for dissolving gases.
- Very <u>thin walls</u>.
- A <u>good blood supply</u>.

The Villi Provide a Really Really Big Surface Area

1) The inside of the <u>small intestine</u> is covered in millions and millions of these tiny little projections called <u>villi</u>.

2) They increase the surface area in a big way so that digested food is <u>absorbed</u> much more quickly into the <u>blood</u>.

3) Notice they have:
- a <u>single</u> layer of surface cells,
- a very good <u>blood supply</u> to assist <u>quick absorption</u>.

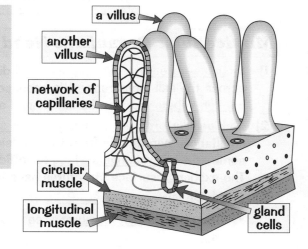

The digested food moves into the blood by diffusion and by active transport (see page 22).

Al Veoli — the Italian gas man...

Thankfully, our bodies are well adapted for efficient diffusion of substances. But the array of life's snazzy exchange surfaces doesn't stop here, oh no — just take a look at what's coming up on the next page...

Q1   Give one way in which alveoli are adapted for gas exchange.   [1 mark]

Q2   Describe how the surface area of the small intestine is maximised for absorption.   [1 mark]

More on Exchanging Substances

More stuff on adaptations for diffusion now — only this time, it's _plants_ and _fish_. Whoopee...

The Structure of Leaves Lets Gases Diffuse In and Out of Cells

1) Carbon dioxide <u>diffuses into the air spaces</u> within the leaf, then it <u>diffuses into the cells</u> where photosynthesis happens. The leaf's structure is <u>adapted</u> so that this can happen easily.

2) The underneath of the leaf is an <u>exchange surface</u>. It's covered in biddy little holes called <u>stomata</u> which the carbon dioxide diffuses in through.

3) <u>Oxygen</u> (produced in photosynthesis) and <u>water vapour</u> also diffuse <u>out</u> through the stomata. (Water vapour is actually lost from all over the leaf surface, but most of it is lost through the stomata.)

4) The size of the stomata are controlled by <u>guard cells</u> — see page 44. These <u>close</u> the stomata if the plant is losing water faster than it is being replaced by the roots. Without these guard cells the plant would soon <u>wilt</u>.

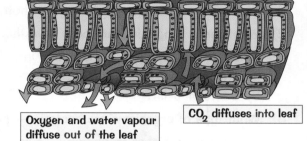

Oxygen and water vapour diffuse out of the leaf

CO_2 diffuses into leaf

5) The <u>flattened shape</u> of the leaf increases the <u>area</u> of this exchange surface so that it's more effective.

6) The <u>walls of the cells</u> inside the leaf form another exchange surface. The <u>air spaces</u> inside the leaf increase the <u>area</u> of this surface so there's more chance for carbon dioxide to get into the cells.

> The water vapour <u>evaporates</u> from the cells inside the leaf. Then it escapes by <u>diffusion</u> because there's a lot of it <u>inside</u> the leaf and less of it in the <u>air outside</u>.

Gills Have a Large Surface Area for Gas Exchange

1) The <u>gills</u> are the gas exchange surface in <u>fish</u>.

2) Water (containing <u>oxygen</u>) enters the fish through its <u>mouth</u> and passes out through the <u>gills</u>. As this happens, <u>oxygen</u> diffuses from the water into the blood in the gills and <u>carbon dioxide</u> diffuses from the blood into the water.

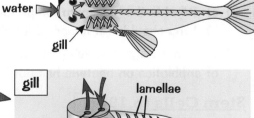

mouth

water

gill

3) Each gill is made of lots of thin plates called <u>gill filaments</u>, which give a <u>big surface area</u> for <u>exchange</u> of <u>gases</u>.

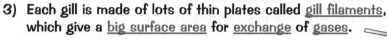

4) The gill filaments are covered in lots of tiny structures called <u>lamellae</u>, which <u>increase</u> the <u>surface area</u> even more.

5) The lamellae have <u>lots of blood capillaries</u> to <u>speed up diffusion</u>.

6) They also have a <u>thin surface layer</u> of cells to <u>minimise</u> the <u>distance</u> that the gases have to diffuse.

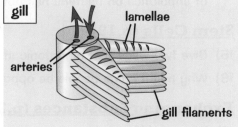

gill

lamellae

arteries

gill filaments

7) <u>Blood</u> flows through the lamellae in one direction and <u>water</u> flows over in the opposite direction. This maintains a <u>large concentration gradient</u> between the water and the blood.

8) The <u>concentration of oxygen</u> in the <u>water</u> is always <u>higher</u> than that in the <u>blood</u>, so as much oxygen as possible diffuses from the water into the blood.

In, out, in, out, shake that oxygen about...

There's a theme here — multicellular organisms are really well adapted for getting the substances they need to their cells. It makes sense — if they couldn't do this well, they'd die out. If you're asked in an exam how something's adapted for exchange, think about whether surface area is important — cos it often is.

Q1 Give two ways in which the structure of a gill is adapted for effective gas exchange. [2 marks]

Revision Questions for Topic 1

Well, that's <u>Topic 1</u> done and dusted. Now there's only one way to find out whether you've learnt anything from it. And you know what that is, I'll bet. It's obvious... I mean, there's a whole load of questions staring you in the face — chances are, it's got to involve those in some way. And sure enough, it does.

•   Try these questions and <u>tick off each one</u> when you <u>get it right</u>.

•   When you've done <u>all the questions</u> under a heading and are <u>completely happy</u> with it, tick it off.

Cells and Microscopy (p.11-13) ☑

1)   Name five subcellular structures that both plant and animal cells have.   ☑

2)   What three things do plant cells have that animal cells don't?   ☑

3)   Where is the genetic material found in:
    a) animal cells,
    b) bacterial cells?   ☑

4)   What type of organisms are bacteria — prokaryotes or eukaryotes?   ☑

5)   Which gives a higher resolution — a light microscope or an electron microscope?   ☑

Differentiation and Division (p.14-16) ☑

6)   What is cell differentiation?   ☑

7)   Give three ways that a sperm cell is adapted for swimming to an egg cell.   ☑

8)   Draw a diagram of a nerve cell. Why is it this shape?   ☑

9)   What are chromosomes?   ☑

10) What is the cell cycle?   ☑

11) What is mitosis used for by multicellular organisms?   ☑

12) What is the name of the process by which bacteria divide?   ☑

Culturing Microorganisms (p.17-18) ☑

13) a) What is the maximum temperature that microorganisms should be grown at in a school lab?
    b) Why shouldn't a temperature above this be used?   ☐

14) There are ways in which you can make sure an experiment testing the effect
     of antibiotics on bacteria has not been contaminated. Give three of these ways.   ☐

Stem Cells (p.19) ☑

15) Give two ways that embryonic stem cells could be used to cure diseases.   ☑

16) Why might some people be opposed to the use of human embryos in stem cell research?   ☑

Exchanging Substances (p.20-25) ☑

17) What is diffusion?   ☑

18) Name three substances that can diffuse through cell membranes, and two that can't.   ☑

19) What type of molecules move by osmosis?   ☑

20) Give the two main differences between active transport and diffusion.   ☑

21) Give three adaptations of exchange surfaces that increase the efficiency of diffusion.   ☑

22) Give two ways that the villi in the small intestine are adapted for absorbing digested food.   ☑

23) Explain how leaves are adapted to maximise the amount of carbon dioxide that gets to their cells.   ☑

Cell Organisation

Some organisms contain loads of <u>cells</u>, but how, you might wonder, do all these cells end up making a working human or squirrel... the answer's <u>organisation</u>. Without it, they'd just make a meaty splodge.

Large Multicellular Organisms are Made Up of Organ Systems

1) <u>Cells</u> are the <u>basic building blocks</u> that make up <u>all living organisms</u>.
2) As you know from page 14, <u>specialised cells</u> carry out a <u>particular function</u>.
3) The <u>process</u> by which cells become specialised for a particular job is called <u>differentiation</u>. Differentiation occurs during the <u>development</u> of a multicellular organism.
4) These specialised cells form <u>tissues</u>, which form <u>organs</u>, which form <u>organ systems</u> (see below).
5) <u>Large multicellular organisms</u> (e.g. squirrels) have different <u>systems</u> inside them for <u>exchanging</u> and <u>transporting</u> materials.

Epithelial cell

less than 0.1 mm

Similar Cells are Organised into Tissues

A <u>tissue</u> is a <u>group</u> of <u>similar cells</u> that work together to carry out a particular <u>function</u>. It can include <u>more than one type</u> of cell.

Epithelial tissue

In <u>mammals</u> (like humans), examples of tissues include:
1) <u>Muscular tissue</u>, which <u>contracts</u> (shortens) to <u>move</u> whatever it's attached to.
2) <u>Glandular tissue</u>, which <u>makes</u> and <u>secretes</u> chemicals like <u>enzymes</u> and <u>hormones</u>.
3) <u>Epithelial tissue</u>, which <u>covers</u> some parts of the body, e.g. the <u>inside</u> of the <u>gut</u>.

Tissues are Organised into Organs

An <u>organ</u> is a group of <u>different tissues</u> that work together to perform a certain <u>function</u>.

Stomach

For example, the <u>stomach</u> is an organ made of these tissues:
1) <u>Muscular tissue</u>, which moves the stomach wall to <u>churn up the food</u>.
2) <u>Glandular tissue</u>, which makes <u>digestive juices</u> to digest food.
3) <u>Epithelial tissue</u>, which covers the <u>outside</u> and <u>inside</u> of the stomach.

about 10 cm (over 1000 times longer than an epithelial cell)

Organs are Organised into Organ Systems

An <u>organ system</u> is a <u>group of organs</u> working together to perform a particular <u>function</u>.

Salivary glands

Liver

For example, the <u>digestive system</u> (found in humans and other mammals) <u>breaks down</u> and <u>absorbs</u> food. It's made up of these organs:
1) <u>Glands</u> (e.g. the <u>pancreas</u> and <u>salivary glands</u>), which produce <u>digestive juices</u>.
2) The <u>stomach</u> and <u>small intestine</u>, which <u>digest</u> food.
3) The <u>liver</u>, which produces <u>bile</u>.
4) The <u>small intestine</u>, which <u>absorbs</u> soluble <u>food</u> molecules.
5) The <u>large intestine</u>, which <u>absorbs water</u> from undigested food, leaving <u>faeces</u>.

<u>Digestive system</u>
- Stomach
- Pancreas
- Small intestine
- Large intestine

Organ systems work together to make entire <u>organisms</u>.

You need to know where these organs are on a diagram — see page 31 too.

Soft and quilted — the best kind of tissues...

So in summary, an organism consists of organ systems, which are groups of organs, which are made of tissues, which are groups of cells working together. Now just for the thrill of it, here's a practice question.

Q1   The bladder is an organ. Explain what this means.   [2 marks]

Enzymes

Chemical reactions are what make you work. And enzymes are what make them work.

Enzymes Are Catalysts Produced by Living Things

1) Living things have thousands of different chemical reactions going on inside them all the time. These reactions need to be carefully controlled — to get the right amounts of substances.

2) You can usually make a reaction happen more quickly by raising the temperature. This would speed up the useful reactions but also the unwanted ones too... not good. There's also a limit to how far you can raise the temperature inside a living creature before its cells start getting damaged.

3) So... living things produce enzymes that act as biological catalysts. Enzymes reduce the need for high temperatures and we only have enzymes to speed up the useful chemical reactions in the body.

> A CATALYST is a substance which INCREASES the speed of a reaction, without being CHANGED or USED UP in the reaction.

4) Enzymes are all large proteins and all proteins are made up of chains of amino acids. These chains are folded into unique shapes, which enzymes need to do their jobs (see below).

Enzymes Have Special Shapes So They Can Catalyse Reactions

1) Chemical reactions usually involve things either being split apart or joined together.

2) Every enzyme has an active site with a unique shape that fits onto the substance involved in a reaction.

3) Enzymes are really picky — they usually only catalyse one specific reaction.

The substance that an enzyme acts on is called the substrate.

4) This is because, for the enzyme to work, the substrate has to fit into its active site. If the substrate doesn't match the enzyme's active site, then the reaction won't be catalysed.

5) This diagram shows the 'lock and key' model of enzyme action. This is simpler than how enzymes actually work. In reality, the active site changes shape a little as the substrate binds to it to get a tighter fit. This is called the 'induced fit' model of enzyme action.

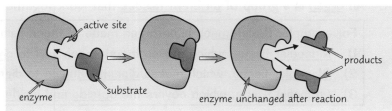

active site · enzyme · substrate · enzyme unchanged after reaction · products

Enzymes Need the Right Temperature and pH

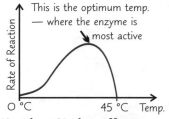

This is the optimum temp. — where the enzyme is most active

1) Changing the temperature changes the rate of an enzyme-catalysed reaction.

2) Like with any reaction, a higher temperature increases the rate at first. But if it gets too hot, some of the bonds holding the enzyme together break. This changes the shape of the enzyme's active site, so the substrate won't fit any more. The enzyme is said to be denatured.

3) All enzymes have an optimum temperature that they work best at.

4) The pH also affects enzymes. If it's too high or too low, the pH interferes with the bonds holding the enzyme together. This changes the shape of the active site and denatures the enzyme.

5) All enzymes have an optimum pH that they work best at. It's often neutral pH 7, but not always — e.g. pepsin is an enzyme used to break down proteins in the stomach. It works best at pH 2, which means it's well-suited to the acidic conditions there.

Rate of reaction · Optimum pH · pH

If only enzymes could speed up revision...

Make sure you use the special terms like 'active site' and 'denatured' — the examiners will love it.

Q1   Explain why enzymes have an optimum pH.   [2 marks]

Investigating Enzymatic Reactions

You'll soon know how to investigate the effect of <u>pH</u> on the rate of <u>enzyme activity</u>... I bet you're thrilled.

You Can Investigate the Effect of pH on Enzyme Activity | PRACTICAL

The enzyme <u>amylase</u> catalyses the breakdown of <u>starch</u> to <u>maltose</u>. It's easy to <u>detect starch</u> using <u>iodine solution</u> — if starch is present, the iodine solution will change from <u>browny-orange</u> to <u>blue-black</u>. This is how you can <u>investigate</u> how pH affects <u>amylase activity</u>:

1) Put a <u>drop</u> of iodine solution into every well of a <u>spotting tile</u>.

2) Place a <u>Bunsen burner</u> on a <u>heat-proof mat</u>, and a <u>tripod</u> and <u>gauze</u> over the Bunsen burner. Put a beaker of <u>water</u> on top of the tripod and <u>heat</u> the water until it is <u>35 °C</u> (use a <u>thermometer</u> to measure the temperature). Try to keep the temperature of the water <u>constant</u> throughout the experiment.

You could use an electric water bath, instead of a Bunsen and a beaker of water, to control the temperature.

3) Use a <u>syringe</u> to add 1 cm³ of <u>amylase solution</u> and 1 cm³ of a <u>buffer solution</u> with a pH of 5 to a boiling tube. Using <u>test tube holders</u>, put the tube into the beaker of water and wait for five minutes.

4) Next, use a <u>different syringe</u> to add 5 cm³ of a <u>starch solution</u> to the boiling tube.

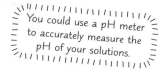
amylase, starch and buffer solution — mixture sampled every 30 seconds — dropping pipette — drop of iodine solution — spotting tile

5) Immediately <u>mix the contents</u> of the boiling tube and start a <u>stop clock</u>.

6) Use <u>continuous sampling</u> to record <u>how long</u> it takes for the amylase to break down all of the starch. To do this, use a dropping pipette to take a <u>fresh sample</u> from the boiling tube <u>every 30 seconds</u> and put a <u>drop</u> into a <u>well</u>. When the iodine solution <u>remains browny-orange</u>, starch is no longer present.

7) <u>Repeat</u> the whole experiment with buffer solutions of different <u>pH values</u> to see how pH <u>affects</u> the time taken for the starch to be broken down.

You could use a pH meter to accurately measure the pH of your solutions.

8) Remember to <u>control any variables</u> each time (e.g. concentration and volume of amylase solution) to make it a <u>fair test</u>.

Here's How to Calculate the Rate of Reaction

1) It's often useful to calculate the <u>rate of reaction</u> after an experiment. Rate is a measure of how much something changes over time.

2) For the <u>experiment above</u>, you can calculate the rate of reaction using <u>this formula:</u>

$$\text{Rate} = \frac{1000}{\text{time}}$$

E.g.

> At <u>pH 6</u>, the <u>time taken</u> for amylase to break down all of the starch in a solution was <u>90 seconds</u>. So the <u>rate</u> of the reaction = <u>1000 ÷ 90</u> = <u>11 s⁻¹</u> **(2 s.f.)**

The units are in s^{-1} since rate is given per unit time.

3) If an experiment measures <u>how much something changes</u> over time, you calculate the rate of reaction by <u>dividing</u> the <u>amount</u> that it has <u>changed</u> by the <u>time taken</u>.

EXAMPLE: The enzyme catalase catalyses the breakdown of hydrogen peroxide into water and oxygen. During an investigation into the activity of catalase, 24 cm³ of oxygen was released in 50 seconds (s). Calculate the rate of the reaction. Write your answer in cm³/s.

Amount of product formed = change = 24 cm³

Rate of reaction = change ÷ time = 24 cm³ ÷ 50 s = 0.48 cm³/s

Mad scientists — they're experi-mental...

You could easily adapt this experiment to investigate how factors other than pH affect the rate of amylase activity. For example, you could use a water bath set to different temperatures to investigate the effect of temperature.

Q1 An enzyme-controlled reaction was carried out at pH 4. After 60 seconds, 33 cm³ of product had been released. Calculate the rate of reaction in cm³/s. **[1 mark]**

Enzymes and Digestion

The <u>enzymes</u> used in <u>digestion</u> are produced by <u>cells</u> and then released into the <u>gut</u> to mix with food.

Digestive Enzymes Break Down Big Molecules

1) <u>Starch</u>, <u>proteins</u> and <u>fats</u> are BIG molecules. They're too big to pass through the walls of the digestive system, so <u>digestive enzymes</u> break these BIG molecules down into smaller ones like <u>sugars</u> (e.g. glucose and maltose), <u>amino acids</u>, <u>glycerol</u> and <u>fatty acids</u>. These smaller, <u>soluble</u> molecules can <u>pass easily</u> through the walls of the digestive system, allowing them to be <u>absorbed</u> into the <u>bloodstream</u>.

Carbohydrases Convert Carbohydrates into Simple Sugars

<u>Amylase</u> is an example of a <u>carbohydrase</u>. It breaks down <u>starch</u>.

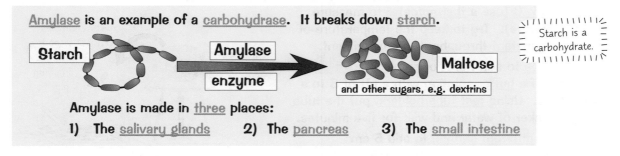

Starch is a carbohydrate.

Starch → **Amylase enzyme** → **Maltose** and other sugars, e.g. dextrins

Amylase is made in <u>three</u> places:
1) The <u>salivary glands</u>   2) The <u>pancreas</u>   3) The <u>small intestine</u>

Proteases Convert Proteins into Amino Acids

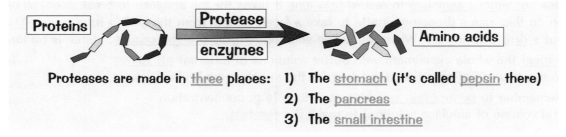

Proteins → **Protease enzymes** → **Amino acids**

Proteases are made in <u>three</u> places:
1) The <u>stomach</u> (it's called <u>pepsin</u> there)
2) The <u>pancreas</u>
3) The <u>small intestine</u>

Lipases Convert Lipids into Glycerol and Fatty Acids

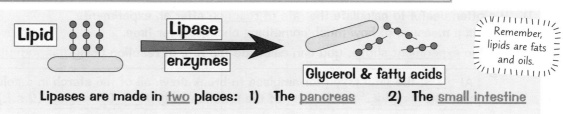

Remember, lipids are fats and oils.

Lipid → **Lipase enzymes** → **Glycerol & fatty acids**

Lipases are made in <u>two</u> places: 1) The <u>pancreas</u>   2) The <u>small intestine</u>

2) The body makes good use of the <u>products</u> of digestion. They can be used to make <u>new carbohydrates</u>, <u>proteins</u> and <u>lipids</u>. Some of the <u>glucose</u> (a carbohydrate) that's made is used in <u>respiration</u> (see p.61).

Bile Neutralises the Stomach Acid and Emulsifies Fats

1) Bile is <u>produced</u> in the <u>liver</u>. It's <u>stored</u> in the <u>gall bladder</u> before it's released into the <u>small intestine</u>.
2) The <u>hydrochloric acid</u> in the stomach makes the pH <u>too acidic</u> for enzymes in the small intestine to work properly. Bile is <u>alkaline</u> — it <u>neutralises</u> the acid and makes conditions <u>alkaline</u>. The enzymes in the small intestine <u>work best</u> in these alkaline conditions.
3) It <u>emulsifies</u> fats. In other words it breaks the fat into <u>tiny droplets</u>. This gives a much <u>bigger surface area</u> of fat for the enzyme lipase to work on — which makes its digestion <u>faster</u>.

What do you call an acid that's eaten all the pies...

Make sure you know the examples of amylase, protease and lipase, and the reactions that they catalyse.

Q1   Bile is a product of the liver. Describe and explain its role in digestion.   [4 marks]

More on Enzymes and Digestion

So now you know what the enzymes do, here's a nice big picture of the whole of the digestive system.

The Breakdown of Food is Catalysed by Enzymes

1) Enzymes used in the digestive system are produced by specialised cells in glands and in the gut lining.
2) Different enzymes catalyse the breakdown of different food molecules.

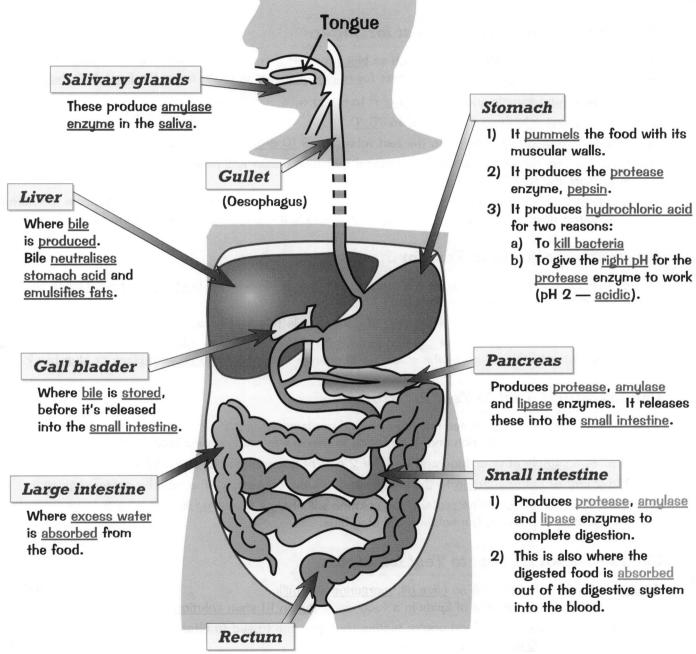

Tongue

Salivary glands
These produce amylase enzyme in the saliva.

Gullet
(Oesophagus)

Liver
Where bile is produced. Bile neutralises stomach acid and emulsifies fats.

Gall bladder
Where bile is stored, before it's released into the small intestine.

Large intestine
Where excess water is absorbed from the food.

Rectum
Where the faeces (made up mainly of indigestible food) are stored before they bid you a fond farewell through the anus.

Stomach
1) It pummels the food with its muscular walls.
2) It produces the protease enzyme, pepsin.
3) It produces hydrochloric acid for two reasons:
   a) To kill bacteria
   b) To give the right pH for the protease enzyme to work (pH 2 — acidic).

Pancreas
Produces protease, amylase and lipase enzymes. It releases these into the small intestine.

Small intestine
1) Produces protease, amylase and lipase enzymes to complete digestion.
2) This is also where the digested food is absorbed out of the digestive system into the blood.

Mmmm — so who's for a chocolate digestive...

Did you know that the whole of your digestive system is actually a hole that goes right through your body. Think about it. It just gets loads of food, digestive juices and enzymes piled into it. Most of it's then absorbed into the body and the rest is politely stored for removal.

Q1   Name the three parts of the digestive system that produce protease enzymes.   [3 marks]

Food Tests

There are some clever ways to <u>identify</u> what type of <u>food molecule</u> a sample contains. For each of the tests, you need to prepare a <u>food sample</u>. It's the same each time though — here's what you'd do:

1) Get a piece of food and <u>break it up</u> using a <u>pestle and mortar</u>.
2) Transfer the ground up food to a <u>beaker</u> and add some <u>distilled water</u>.
3) Give the mixture a good <u>stir</u> with a glass rod to <u>dissolve</u> some of the food.
4) <u>Filter</u> the solution using a funnel lined with filter paper to <u>get rid</u> of the <u>solid</u> bits of food.

Use the Benedict's Test to Test for Sugars

Sugars are found in all sorts of foods such as <u>biscuits</u>, <u>cereal</u> and <u>bread</u>. There are two types of sugars — <u>non-reducing</u> and <u>reducing</u>. You can test for <u>reducing sugars</u> in foods using the <u>Benedict's test</u>:

1) Prepare a <u>food sample</u> and transfer <u>5 cm³</u> to a test tube.
2) Prepare a <u>water bath</u> so that it's set to <u>75 °C</u>.
3) Add some <u>Benedict's solution</u> to the test tube (about <u>10 drops</u>) using a pipette.
4) Place the test tube in the water bath using a test tube holder and leave it in there for <u>5 minutes</u>. Make sure the tube is <u>pointing away</u> from you.
5) If the food sample contains a reducing sugar, the solution in the test tube will change from the normal <u>blue</u> colour to <u>green</u>, <u>yellow</u> or <u>brick-red</u> — it depends on <u>how much</u> sugar is in the food.

Use Iodine Solution to Test for Starch

You can also check food samples for the presence of <u>starch</u>. Foods like <u>pasta</u>, <u>rice</u> and <u>potatoes</u> contain a lot of starch. Here's how to do the test:

1) Make a <u>food sample</u> and transfer <u>5 cm³</u> of your sample to a test tube.
2) Then add a few drops of <u>iodine solution</u> and <u>gently shake</u> the tube to mix the contents. If the sample contains starch, the colour of the solution will change from <u>browny-orange</u> to <u>black</u> or <u>blue-black</u>.

Use the Biuret Test to Test for Proteins

You can use the <u>biuret test</u> to see if a type of food contains <u>protein</u>. <u>Meat</u> and <u>cheese</u> are protein rich and good foods to use in this test. Here's how it's done:

1) Prepare a <u>sample</u> of your food and transfer <u>2 cm³</u> of your sample to a test tube.
2) Add 2 cm³ of <u>biuret solution</u> to the sample and mix the contents of the tube by <u>gently shaking</u> it.
3) If the food sample contains protein, the solution will change from <u>blue</u> to <u>purple</u>. If no protein is present, the solution will stay blue.

Use the Sudan III Test to Test for Lipids

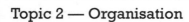

<u>Lipids</u> are found in foods such as <u>olive oil</u>, <u>margarine</u> and <u>milk</u>. You can test for the presence of lipids in a food using <u>Sudan III stain solution</u>.

1) Prepare a <u>sample</u> of the food you're testing (but you don't need to filter it). Transfer about <u>5 cm³</u> into a test tube.
2) Use a pipette to add <u>3 drops</u> of <u>Sudan III stain solution</u> to the test tube and <u>gently shake</u> the tube.
3) Sudan III stain solution <u>stains</u> lipids. If the sample contains lipids, the mixture will separate out into <u>two layers</u>. The top layer will be <u>bright red</u>. If no lipids are present, no separate red layer will form at the top of the liquid.

All this talk of food is making me hungry...

Make sure you do a risk assessment before starting these tests — there are a lot of chemicals to use here.

Q1   Name the chemical that you would use to test a sample for the presence of starch.   [1 mark]

The Lungs

You need to get oxygen into your bloodstream to supply your cells for respiration. You also need to get rid of carbon dioxide from your blood. This all happens in your lungs when you breathe air in and out.

The Lungs Are in the Thorax

1) The thorax is the top part of your body.
2) It's separated from the lower part of the body by the diaphragm.
3) The lungs are like big pink sponges and are protected by the ribcage. They're surrounded by the pleural membranes.
4) The air that you breathe in goes through the trachea. This splits into two tubes called bronchi (each one is a bronchus), one going to each lung.
5) The bronchi split into progressively smaller tubes called bronchioles.
6) The bronchioles finally end at small bags called alveoli where the gas exchange takes place (see below).

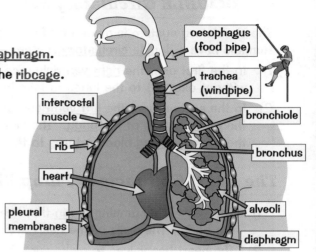

Alveoli Carry Out Gas Exchange in the Body

1) The lungs contain millions and millions of little air sacs called alveoli, surrounded by a network of blood capillaries. This is where gas exchange happens.
2) The blood passing next to the alveoli has just returned to the lungs from the rest of the body, so it contains lots of carbon dioxide and very little oxygen. Oxygen diffuses out of the alveolus (high concentration) into the blood (low concentration). Carbon dioxide diffuses out of the blood (high concentration) into the alveolus (low concentration) to be breathed out.

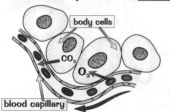

3) When the blood reaches body cells oxygen is released from the red blood cells (where there's a high concentration) and diffuses into the body cells (where the concentration is low).
4) At the same time, carbon dioxide diffuses out of the body cells (where there's a high concentration) into the blood (where there's a low concentration). It's then carried back to the lungs.

You Can Calculate the Breathing Rate in Breaths Per Minute

Rate calculations pop up all the time in biology, and you're expected to know how to do them — thankfully they're pretty easy. Breathing rate is the sort of thing that you could get asked to work out in your exam.

> **EXAMPLE:**
>
> Bob takes 91 breaths in 7 minutes. Calculate his average breathing rate in breaths per minute.
>
> breaths per minute = number of breaths ÷ number of minutes
>
> = 91 ÷ 7
>
> = 13 breaths per minute

Stop huffing and puffing and just learn it...

Alveoli are really well adapted for carrying out gas exchange. It could be a wise move to learn all about exactly how they're adapted. You met them back on page 24, so head back there if you need a reminder.

Q1 During a 12 minute run, Aaqib took 495 breaths.
Calculate his average breathing rate in breaths per minute. [1 mark]

Circulatory System — The Heart

The circulatory system carries <u>food</u> and <u>oxygen</u> to every cell in the body. As well as being a delivery service, it's also a waste collection service — it carries <u>waste products</u> to where they can be removed from the body.

The DOUBLE Circulatory System, Actually

The circulatory system is made up of the <u>heart</u>, <u>blood vessels</u> and <u>blood</u>.
Humans have a <u>double circulatory system</u> — <u>two circuits</u> joined together:

1) In the first one, the <u>right ventricle</u> (see below) pumps <u>deoxygenated</u> blood (blood without oxygen) to the <u>lungs</u> to take in <u>oxygen</u>. The blood then <u>returns</u> to the heart.

2) In the second one, the <u>left ventricle</u> (see below) pumps <u>oxygenated</u> blood around all the <u>other organs</u> of the <u>body</u>. The blood <u>gives up</u> its oxygen at the body cells and the <u>deoxygenated</u> blood <u>returns</u> to the heart to be pumped out to the <u>lungs</u> again.

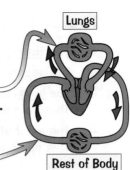

The Heart Contracts to Pump Blood Around The Body

1) The <u>heart</u> is a pumping <u>organ</u> that keeps the blood flowing around the body. The walls of the heart are mostly made of <u>muscle tissue</u>.

2) The heart has <u>valves</u> to make sure that blood flows in the right direction — they prevent it flowing <u>backwards</u>.

3) This is how the <u>heart</u> uses its <u>four chambers</u> (right atrium, right ventricle, left atrium and left ventricle) to pump blood around:

1) <u>Blood flows into</u> the two <u>atria</u> from the <u>vena cava</u> and the <u>pulmonary vein</u>.

2) The <u>atria contract</u>, pushing the blood into the <u>ventricles</u>.

3) The <u>ventricles contract</u>, forcing the blood into the <u>pulmonary artery</u> and the <u>aorta</u>, and <u>out</u> of the <u>heart</u>.

4) The blood then flows to the <u>organs</u> through <u>arteries</u>, and <u>returns</u> through <u>veins</u> (see next page).

5) The atria fill again and the whole cycle <u>starts over</u>.

The heart also needs its <u>own</u> supply of <u>oxygenated</u> blood. Arteries called <u>coronary arteries</u> branch off the aorta and surround the heart, making sure that it gets all the <u>oxygenated</u> blood it needs.

Atrium is when there is just one. Atria is plural.

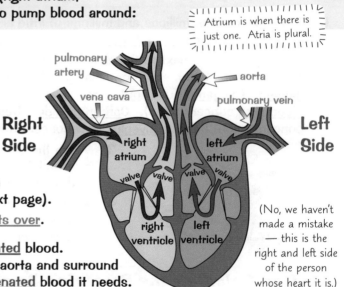

(No, we haven't made a mistake — this is the right and left side of the person whose heart it is.)

The Heart Has a Pacemaker

1) Your resting heart rate is <u>controlled</u> by a group of cells in the right atrium wall that act as a <u>pacemaker</u>.

2) These cells produce a small <u>electric impulse</u> which spreads to the surrounding muscle cells, causing them to <u>contract</u>.

3) An <u>artificial pacemaker</u> is often used to control heartbeat if the natural pacemaker cells don't work properly (e.g. if the patient has an <u>irregular heartbeat</u>). It's a little device that's implanted under the skin and has a wire going to the heart. It produces an <u>electric current</u> to keep the heart <u>beating regularly</u>.

Okay — let's get to the heart of the matter...

Interesting fact — when doctors use a stethoscope to listen to your heart, it's the valves closing that they hear.

Q1 Which chamber of the heart pumps deoxygenated blood to the lungs? [1 mark]

Q2 What is the function of the coronary arteries? [1 mark]

Circulatory System — Blood Vessels

Want to know more about the circulatory system... Good. Because here's a whole extra page.

Blood Vessels are Designed for Their Function

There are three different types of blood vessel:
1) ARTERIES — these carry the blood away from the heart.
2) CAPILLARIES — these are involved in the exchange of materials at the tissues.
3) VEINS — these carry the blood to the heart.

Arteries Carry Blood Under Pressure

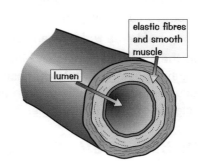

1) The heart pumps the blood out at high pressure so the artery walls are strong and elastic.
2) The walls are thick compared to the size of the hole down the middle (the "lumen" — silly name!).
3) They contain thick layers of muscle to make them strong, and elastic fibres to allow them to stretch and spring back.

Capillaries are Really Small

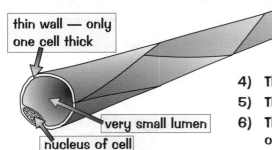

thin wall — only one cell thick

very small lumen

nucleus of cell

1) Arteries branch into capillaries.
2) Capillaries are really tiny — too small to see.
3) They carry the blood really close to every cell in the body to exchange substances with them.
4) They have permeable walls, so substances can diffuse in and out.
5) They supply food and oxygen, and take away waste like CO_2.
6) Their walls are usually only one cell thick. This increases the rate of diffusion by decreasing the distance over which it occurs.

Veins Take Blood Back to the Heart

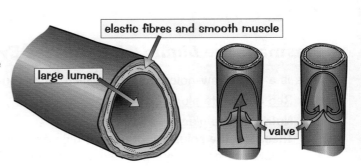

elastic fibres and smooth muscle

large lumen

valve

1) Capillaries eventually join up to form veins. The blood is at lower pressure in the veins so the walls don't need to be as thick as artery walls.
2) They have a bigger lumen than arteries to help the blood flow despite the lower pressure.
3) They also have valves to help keep the blood flowing in the right direction.

You Can Calculate the Rate of Blood Flow

You might get asked to calculate the rate of blood flow in your exam. Thankfully, it's not too tricky. Take a look at this example:

EXAMPLE: 1464 ml of blood passed through an artery in 4.5 minutes. Calculate the rate of blood flow through the artery in ml/min.

rate of blood flow = volume of blood ÷ number of minutes
= 1464 ÷ 4.5 = 325 ml/min

Learn this page — don't struggle in vein...

Here's an interesting fact for you — your body contains about 60 000 miles of blood vessels.

Q1 Describe how veins are adapted to carry blood back to the heart. [2 marks]

Circulatory System — Blood

Blood is a tissue. One of its jobs is to act as a huge transport system. There are four main things in blood...

Red Blood Cells Carry Oxygen

1) The job of red blood cells is to carry oxygen from the lungs to all the cells in the body.

2) Their shape is a biconcave disc (like a doughnut) — this gives a large surface area for absorbing oxygen.

3) They don't have a nucleus — this allows more room to carry oxygen.

4) They contain a red pigment called haemoglobin.

5) In the lungs, haemoglobin binds to oxygen to become oxyhaemoglobin. In body tissues, the reverse happens — oxyhaemoglobin splits up into haemoglobin and oxygen, to release oxygen to the cells.

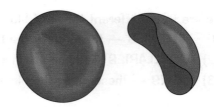

The more red blood cells you've got, the more oxygen can get to your cells. At high altitudes there's less oxygen in the air — so people who live there produce more red blood cells to compensate.

White Blood Cells Defend Against Infection

1) Some can change shape to gobble up unwelcome microorganisms, in a process called phagocytosis.

2) Others produce antibodies to fight microorganisms, as well as antitoxins to neutralise any toxins produced by the microorganisms.

3) Unlike red blood cells, they do have a nucleus.

Platelets Help Blood Clot

1) These are small fragments of cells. They have no nucleus.

2) They help the blood to clot at a wound — to stop all your blood pouring out and to stop microorganisms getting in. (So basically platelets just float about waiting for accidents to happen.)

3) Lack of platelets can cause excessive bleeding and bruising.

Plasma is the Liquid That Carries Everything in Blood

This is a pale straw-coloured liquid which carries just about everything:

1) Red and white blood cells and platelets.

2) Nutrients like glucose and amino acids. These are the soluble products of digestion which are absorbed from the gut and taken to the cells of the body.

3) Carbon dioxide from the organs to the lungs.

4) Urea from the liver to the kidneys.

5) Hormones.

6) Proteins.

7) Antibodies and antitoxins produced by the white blood cells.

Platelets — ideal for small dinners...

When you're ill the doctor often takes a blood sample for analysis. Blood tests can be used to diagnose loads of things — not just disorders of the blood. This is because the blood transports so many chemicals produced by so many organs... and it's easier to take blood than, say, a piece of muscle.

Q1   Describe the purpose of platelets in blood.   [1 mark]

Q2   Outline three ways in which red blood cells are adapted to carry oxygen.   [3 marks]

Cardiovascular Disease

Cardiovascular disease is a term used to describe diseases of the heart or blood vessels, for example coronary heart disease. This page tells you all about how stents and statins are used to combat coronary heart disease.

Stents Keep Arteries Open

1) Coronary heart disease is when the coronary arteries that supply the blood to the muscle of the heart get blocked by layers of fatty material building up. This causes the arteries to become narrow, so blood flow is restricted and there's a lack of oxygen to the heart muscle — this can result in a heart attack.

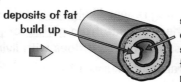

outside of heart

coronary artery

2) Stents are tubes that are inserted inside arteries. They keep them open, making sure blood can pass through to the heart muscles. This keeps the person's heart beating (and the person alive).

normal artery

deposits of fat build up

space in centre of artery shrinks, so it's harder for blood to pass through

stent pushes artery wall out, squashing fatty deposit

more space in the centre of the artery

3) Stents are a way of lowering the risk of a heart attack in people with coronary heart disease. They are effective for a long time and the recovery time from the surgery is relatively quick.

4) On the down side, there is a risk of complications during the operation (e.g. heart attack) and a risk of infection from surgery. There is also the risk of patients developing a blood clot near the stent — this is called thrombosis.

Statins Reduce Cholesterol in the Blood

1) Cholesterol is an essential lipid that your body produces and needs to function properly. However, too much of a certain type of cholesterol (known as 'bad' or LDL cholesterol) can cause health problems.

2) Having too much of this 'bad' cholesterol in the bloodstream can cause fatty deposits to form inside arteries, which can lead to coronary heart disease.

3) Statins are drugs that can reduce the amount of 'bad' cholesterol present in the bloodstream. This slows down the rate of fatty deposits forming.

Statins Have Advantages and Disadvantages

Advantages

1) By reducing the amount of 'bad' cholesterol in the blood, statins can reduce the risk of strokes, coronary heart disease and heart attacks.

2) As well as reducing the amount of 'bad' cholesterol, statins can increase the amount of a beneficial type of cholesterol (known as 'good' or HDL cholesterol) in your bloodstream. This type can remove 'bad' cholesterol from the blood.

3) Some studies suggest that statins may also help prevent some other diseases.

Disadvantages

1) Statins are a long-term drug that must be taken regularly. There's the risk that someone could forget to take them.

2) Statins can sometimes cause negative side effects, e.g. headaches. Some of these side effects can be serious, e.g. kidney failure, liver damage and memory loss.

3) The effect of statins isn't instant. It takes time for their effect to kick in.

Unlike stents and statins, using CGP books only has advantages...

Stents and statins might be good treatments for coronary heart disease, but they're not perfect. Make sure you're aware of the drawbacks as well as the advantages of each. That way, you'll be covered if they come up in the exam.

Q1   a)   How can stents be used to reduce the risk of heart attacks in people with coronary heart disease?   [2 marks]

      b)   Suggest two disadvantages of treating patients using stents.   [2 marks]

More on Cardiovascular Disease

With more fakery than a 'Rollecks' watch, this page is about artificial hearts, artificial blood and replacing heart valves. All a bit gruesome, I'll admit — but it's life-saving stuff.

An Artificial Heart Can Pump Blood Around the Body

1) If a patient has heart failure, doctors may perform a heart transplant (or heart and lungs transplant if the lungs are also diseased) using donor organs from people who have recently died. However, if donor organs aren't available right away or they're not the best option, doctors may fit an artificial heart.

2) Artificial hearts are mechanical devices that pump blood for a person whose own heart has failed. They're usually only used as a temporary fix, to keep a person alive until a donor heart can be found or to help a person recover by allowing the heart to rest and heal. In some cases though they're used as a permanent fix, which reduces the need for a donor heart.

3) The main advantage of artificial hearts is that they're less likely to be rejected by the body's immune system than a donor heart. This is because they're made from metals or plastics, so the body doesn't recognise them as 'foreign' and attack in the same way as it does with living tissue.

4) But surgery to fit an artificial heart (as with transplant surgery) can lead to bleeding and infection. Also, artificial hearts don't work as well as healthy natural ones — parts of the heart could wear out or the electrical motor could fail. Blood doesn't flow through artificial hearts as smoothly, which can cause blood clots and lead to strokes. The patient has to take drugs to thin their blood and make sure this doesn't happen, which can cause problems with bleeding if they're hurt in an accident.

Faulty Heart Valves Can Be Replaced With Biological or Mechanical Valves

1) The valves in the heart can be damaged or weakened by heart attacks, infection or old age.

2) The damage may cause the valve tissue to stiffen, so it won't open properly. Or a valve may become leaky, allowing blood to flow in both directions rather than just forward. This means that blood doesn't circulate as effectively as normal.

3) Severe valve damage can be treated by replacing the valve. Replacement valves can be ones taken from humans or other mammals (e.g. cows or pigs) — these are biological valves. Or they can be man-made — these are mechanical valves.

4) Replacing a valve is a much less drastic procedure than a whole heart transplant. But fitting artificial valves is still major surgery and there can still be problems with blood clots.

Artificial Blood Can Keep You Alive In An Emergency

1) When someone loses a lot of blood, e.g. in an accident, their heart can still pump the remaining red blood cells around (to get oxygen to their organs), as long as the volume of their blood can be topped up.

2) Artificial blood is a blood substitute, e.g. a salt solution ("saline"), which is used to replace the lost volume of blood. It's safe (if no air bubbles get into the blood) and can keep people alive even if they lose 2/3 of their red blood cells. This may give the patient enough time to produce new blood cells. If not, the patient will need a blood transfusion.

3) Ideally, an artificial blood product would replace the function of the lost red blood cells, so that there's no need for a blood transfusion. Scientists are currently working on products that can do this.

Pity they can't fit me an artificial brain before the exam...

Make sure you know about the consequences of faulty heart valves or heart failure, as well as the advantages and disadvantages of the treatments on this page. Obviously if someone is really ill, it's unlikely that they'd turn down an artificial heart, artificial blood or a valve replacement — but these treatments aren't perfect.

Q1 a) Describe how faulty heart valves can lead to poor blood circulation. [2 marks]
    b) Suggest how severe damage to a heart valve can be treated. [1 mark]

Q2 Suggest one disadvantage of treating coronary heart disease with an artificial heart. [1 mark]

Health and Disease

There's not a great deal about diseases and health problems that you can laugh about, so excuse me if this page is a bit dull. It's important stuff to know about though, so you'd best get cracking.

Diseases are a Major Cause of Ill Health

Health is the state of physical and mental wellbeing. Diseases are often responsible for causing ill health.

Diseases Can be Communicable or Non-Communicable

1) Communicable diseases are those that can spread from person to person or between animals and people. They can be caused by things like bacteria, viruses, parasites and fungi. They're sometimes described as contagious or infectious diseases. Measles and malaria are examples of communicable diseases. There's more about them on pages 46-48.

2) Non-communicable diseases are those that cannot spread between people or between animals and people. They generally last for a long time and get worse slowly. Asthma, cancer and coronary heart disease (see page 37) are examples of non-communicable diseases.

Different Types of Disease Sometimes Interact

Sometimes diseases can interact and cause other physical and mental health issues that don't immediately seem related. Here are a few examples:

Pathogen is just the fancy term for a microorganism that can cause a disease when it infects its host.

1) People who have problems with their immune system (the system that your body uses to help fight off infection — see p.49) have an increased chance of suffering from communicable diseases such as influenza (flu), because their body is less likely to be able to defend itself against the pathogen that causes the disease.

2) Some types of cancer can be triggered by infection by certain viruses. For example, infection with some types of hepatitis virus can cause long-term infections in the liver, where the virus lives in the cells. This can lead to an increased chance of developing liver cancer. Another example is infection with HPV (human papilloma virus), which can cause cervical cancer in women.

3) Immune system reactions in the body caused by infection by a pathogen can sometimes trigger allergic reactions such as skin rashes or worsen the symptoms of asthma for asthma sufferers.

4) Mental health issues such as depression can be triggered when someone is suffering from severe physical health problems, particularly if they have an impact on the person's ability to carry out everyday activities or if they affect the person's life expectancy.

Other Factors Can Also Affect Your Health

There are plenty of factors other than diseases that can also affect your health. For example:

1) Whether or not you have a good, balanced diet that provides your body with everything it needs, and in the right amounts. A poor diet can affect your physical and mental health.

2) The stress you are under — being constantly under lots of stress can lead to health issues.

3) Your life situation — for example, whether you have easy access to medicines to treat illness, or whether you have access to things that can prevent you from getting ill in the first place, e.g. being able to buy healthy food or access condoms to prevent the transmission of some sexually transmitted diseases.

If stress can affect your health, why do we have exams...

You really need to get the terms communicable and non-communicable disease into your head.
They could come up in the exam and you'd be really sad if you didn't understand the question.

Q1   What is meant by 'health'?   [1 mark]

Q2   Why is influenza classed as a communicable disease?   [1 mark]

Risk Factors for Non-Communicable Diseases

You've probably heard the term 'risk factor' before. This page has all the info you need to know about them.

Risk Factors Increase Your Chance of Getting a Disease

1) Risk factors are things that are linked to an increase in the likelihood that a person will develop a certain disease during their lifetime. They don't guarantee that someone will get the disease.

2) Risk factors are often aspects of a person's lifestyle (e.g. how much exercise they do). They can also be the presence of certain substances in the environment (e.g. air pollution) or substances in your body (e.g. asbestos fibres — asbestos was a material used in buildings until it was realised that the fibres could build up in your airways and cause diseases such as cancer later in life).

3) Many non-communicable diseases are caused by several different risk factors interacting with each other rather than one factor alone.

4) Lifestyle factors can have different impacts locally, nationally and globally. E.g. in developed countries, non-communicable diseases are more common as people generally have a higher income and can buy high-fat food. Nationally, people from deprived areas are more likely to smoke, have a poor diet and not exercise. This means the incidence of cardiovascular disease, obesity and Type 2 diabetes is higher in those areas. Your individual choices affect the local incidence of disease.

Some Risk Factors Can Cause a Disease Directly

1) Some risk factors are able to directly cause a disease. For example:

> 1) Smoking has been proven to directly cause cardiovascular disease, lung disease and lung cancer. It damages the walls of arteries and the cells in the lining of the lungs.
>
> 2) It's thought that obesity can directly cause Type 2 diabetes by making the body less sensitive or resistant to insulin, meaning that it struggles to control the concentration of glucose in the blood.
>
> 3) Drinking too much alcohol has been shown to cause liver disease. Too much alcohol can affect brain function too. It can damage the nerve cells in the brain, causing the brain to lose volume.
>
> 4) Smoking when pregnant can cause lots of health problems for the unborn baby. Drinking alcohol has similar effects.
>
> 5) Cancer can be directly caused by exposure to certain substances or radiation. Things that cause cancer are known as carcinogens. Ionising radiation (e.g. from X-rays) is an example of a carcinogen.

2) However, risk factors are identified by scientists looking for correlations in data, and correlation doesn't always equal cause (see p.9). Some risk factors aren't capable of directly causing a disease. For example, a lack of exercise and a high fat diet are heavily linked to an increased chance of cardiovascular disease, but they can't cause the disease directly. It's the resulting high blood pressure and high 'bad' cholesterol levels (see p.37) that can actually cause it.

Non-Communicable Diseases Can Be Costly

1) The HUMAN cost of non-communicable diseases is obvious. Tens of millions of people around the world die from non-communicable diseases per year. People with these diseases may have a lower quality of life or a shorter lifespan. This not only affects the sufferers themselves, but their loved ones too.

2) It's also important to think about the FINANCIAL cost. The cost to the NHS of researching and treating these diseases is huge — and it's the same for other health services and organisations around the world. Families may have to move or adapt their home to help a family member with a disease, which can be costly. Also, if the family member with the disease has to give up work or dies, the family's income will be reduced. A reduction in the number of people able to work can also affect a country's economy.

Best put down that cake and go for a run...

You might be asked to interpret data about risk factors. See p.9 for a few tips on what you can and can't say.

Q1   Give an example of a type of risk factor other than an aspect of a person's lifestyle.   [1 mark]

Cancer

Cancer's <u>not</u> a pleasant topic, but the more we understand about it, the better our chances of <u>avoiding</u> and <u>beating</u> it (and getting <u>good marks</u> in the exam). You're a good way through the topic, so keep going.

Cancer is Caused by Uncontrolled Cell Growth and Division

This <u>uncontrolled</u> growth and division is a result of <u>changes</u> that occur to the <u>cells</u> and results in the formation of a <u>tumour</u> (a mass of cells). Not all tumours are cancerous. They can be <u>benign</u> or <u>malignant</u>:

1) <u>Benign</u> — This is where the tumour grows until there's no more room. The tumour <u>stays</u> in one place (usually within a membrane) rather than invading other tissues in the body. This type <u>isn't</u> normally dangerous, and the tumour <u>isn't</u> cancerous.

2) <u>Malignant</u> — This is where the tumour grows and <u>spreads</u> to neighbouring healthy tissues. Cells can <u>break off</u> and spread to other parts of the body by travelling in the <u>bloodstream</u>. The malignant cells then <u>invade</u> healthy tissues elsewhere in the body and form <u>secondary tumours</u>. Malignant tumours are <u>dangerous</u> and can be fatal — <u>they are cancers</u>.

Risk Factors Can Increase the Chance of Some Cancers

<u>Anyone</u> can develop cancer. Having risk factors <u>doesn't</u> mean that you'll definitely get cancer. It just means that you're at an <u>increased risk</u> of developing the disease. Cancer <u>survival rates</u> have <u>increased</u> due to medical advances such as <u>improved treatment</u>, being able to <u>diagnose</u> cancer <u>earlier</u> and <u>increased screening</u> for the disease.

Risk Factors Can Be Associated With Lifestyle

Scientists have identified <u>lots</u> of lifestyle risk factors for various types of cancer. For example:

1) <u>Smoking</u> — It's a well known fact that smoking is linked to <u>lung cancer</u>, but research has also linked it to <u>other types</u> of cancer too, including mouth, bowel, stomach and cervical cancer.

2) <u>Obesity</u> — Obesity has been linked to <u>many different cancers</u>, including bowel, liver and kidney cancer. It's the <u>second biggest</u> preventable cause of cancer after smoking.

3) <u>UV exposure</u> — People who are often exposed to <u>UV radiation</u> from the Sun have an increased chance of developing <u>skin cancer</u>. People who live in <u>sunny climates</u> and people who spend a lot of time <u>outside</u> are at <u>higher risk</u> of the disease. People who frequently use <u>sun beds</u> are also putting themselves at higher risk of developing skin cancer.

4) <u>Viral infection</u> — Infection with some viruses has been shown to <u>increase</u> the chances of developing <u>certain types</u> of cancer. For example, infection with <u>hepatitis B</u> and <u>hepatitis C</u> viruses can increase the risk of developing <u>liver cancer</u>. The likelihood of becoming infected with these viruses sometimes depends on lifestyle — e.g. they can be spread between people through <u>unprotected sex</u> or <u>sharing needles</u>.

Risk Factors Can Also Be Associated With Genetics

1) Sometimes you can <u>inherit faulty genes</u> that make you <u>more susceptible</u> to cancer.

2) For example, mutations (changes) in the <u>BRCA</u> genes have been linked to an <u>increased likelihood</u> of developing <u>breast</u> and <u>ovarian cancer</u>.

At least our rubbish summers reduce our UV exposure...

Joking aside, UV radiation can still reach us through the clouds, and like many other lifestyle risk factors, we can take steps to reduce the risk, e.g. by keeping covered up outside and wearing sun block.

Q1   What are tumours the result of?   [1 mark]

Q2   List three lifestyle factors that can increase the risk of developing cancer.   [3 marks]

Plant Cell Organisation

You saw on page 27 how animals keep their specialised cells neat and tidy — plants are in on the act too.

Plant Cells Are Organised Into Tissues And Organs

Plants are made of organs like stems, roots and leaves. Plant organs work together to make organ systems. These can perform the various tasks that a plant needs to carry out to survive and grow — for example, transporting substances around the plant. Plant organs are made of tissues. Examples of plant tissues are:

1) Epidermal tissue — this covers the whole plant.

2) Palisade mesophyll tissue — this is the part of the leaf where most photosynthesis happens.

3) Spongy mesophyll tissue — this is also in the leaf, and contains big air spaces to allow gases to diffuse in and out of cells.

4) Xylem and phloem — they transport things like water, mineral ions and food around the plant (through the roots, stems and leaves — see next page for more).

5) Meristem tissue — this is found at the growing tips of shoots and roots and is able to differentiate (change) into lots of different types of plant cell, allowing the plant to grow.

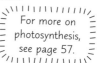
For more on photosynthesis, see page 57.

A merry stem.

The Leaf is an Organ Made Up of Several Types of Tissue

Leaves contain epidermal, mesophyll, xylem and phloem tissues.

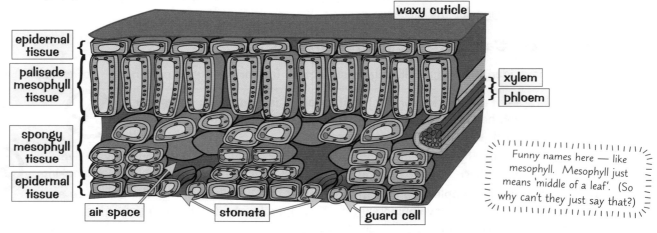

waxy cuticle

epidermal tissue

palisade mesophyll tissue

spongy mesophyll tissue

epidermal tissue

xylem

phloem

air space   stomata   guard cell

Funny names here — like mesophyll. Mesophyll just means 'middle of a leaf'. (So why can't they just say that?)

You need to know how the structures of the tissues that make up the leaf are related to their function:

1) The epidermal tissues are covered with a waxy cuticle, which helps to reduce water loss by evaporation.

2) The upper epidermis is transparent so that light can pass through it to the palisade layer.

3) The palisade layer has lots of chloroplasts (the little structures where photosynthesis takes place). This means that they're near the top of the leaf where they can get the most light.

4) The xylem and phloem form a network of vascular bundles, which deliver water and other nutrients to the entire leaf and take away the glucose produced by photosynthesis. They also help support the structure.

5) The tissues of leaves are also adapted for efficient gas exchange (see page 25). E.g. the lower epidermis is full of little holes called stomata, which let CO_2 diffuse directly into the leaf. The opening and closing of stomata is controlled by guard cells in response to environmental conditions. The air spaces in the spongy mesophyll tissue increase the rate of diffusion of gases.

Plant cell organisation — millions of members worldwide...

There are a lot of weird names here, so make sure you spend plenty of time on this page. Maybe you could draw your own leaf diagram and label it with descriptions of the different tissue types. It would make an excellent Christmas present for someone, or an art collector might even want it.

Q1   Describe the characteristics of meristem tissue.   [2 marks]

Transpiration and Translocation

You might be surprised to learn that there aren't tiny trucks that transport substances around plants. Then again, you might not be — either way, you need to learn the stuff on this page...

Phloem Tubes Transport Food:

1) Made of columns of <u>elongated</u> living cells with small <u>pores in the end walls</u> to allow <u>cell sap</u> to flow through.

2) They transport <u>food substances</u> (mainly dissolved <u>sugars</u>) made in the leaves to the rest of the plant for <u>immediate use</u> (e.g. in growing regions) or for <u>storage</u>.

3) The transport goes in <u>both directions</u>.

4) This process is called <u>translocation</u>.

Cell sap is a liquid that's made up of the substances being transported and water.

Food (mainly dissolved sugars)

Xylem Tubes Take Water Up:

1) Made of <u>dead cells</u> joined end to end with <u>no</u> end walls between them and a hole down the middle. They're strengthened with a material called <u>lignin</u>.

2) They carry <u>water</u> and <u>mineral</u> ions from the <u>roots</u> to the <u>stem</u> and <u>leaves</u>.

3) The movement of water <u>from</u> the <u>roots</u>, <u>through</u> the <u>xylem</u> and <u>out</u> of the <u>leaves</u> is called the <u>transpiration stream</u> (see below).

Water and minerals

Transpiration is the Loss of Water from the Plant

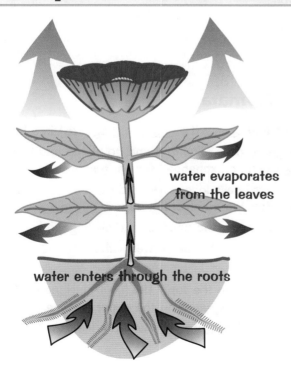

water evaporates from the leaves

water enters through the roots

1) Transpiration is caused by the <u>evaporation</u> and <u>diffusion</u> (see page 20) of water from a plant's surface. Most transpiration happens at the <u>leaves</u>.

2) This evaporation creates a slight <u>shortage</u> of water in the leaf, and so more water is drawn up from the rest of the plant through the <u>xylem vessels</u> to replace it.

3) This in turn means more water is drawn up from the <u>roots</u>, and so there's a constant <u>transpiration stream</u> of water through the plant.

Head back to page 22 to see how root hair cells are adapted for taking up water.

Transpiration is just a <u>side-effect</u> of the way leaves are adapted for <u>photosynthesis</u>. They have to have <u>stomata</u> in them so that gases can be exchanged easily (see page 25). Because there's more water <u>inside</u> the plant than in the <u>air outside</u>, the water escapes from the leaves through the stomata by diffusion.

Don't let revision stress you out — just go with the phloem...

Phl<u>oe</u>m transports substances in b<u>o</u>th directions, but xylem only transports things upwards — x<u>y</u> to the sky.

Q1   Describe the structure of xylem.   [3 marks]

Transpiration and Stomata

Sorry, more on <u>transpiration</u>. But then it's a quick dash through <u>stomata</u> and out of the other end of the topic.

Transpiration Rate is Affected by Four Main Things

1) <u>LIGHT INTENSITY</u> — the <u>brighter</u> the light, the <u>greater</u> the transpiration rate.

   <u>Stomata</u> begin to <u>close</u> as it gets darker. Photosynthesis can't happen in the dark, so they don't need to be open to let CO_2 in. When the stomata are closed, very little water can escape.

2) <u>TEMPERATURE</u> — the <u>warmer</u> it is, the <u>faster</u> transpiration happens.

   When it's warm the water particles have <u>more energy</u> to evaporate and diffuse out of the stomata.

3) <u>AIR FLOW</u> — the <u>better</u> the air flow around a leaf (e.g. stronger wind), the <u>greater</u> the transpiration rate.

   If air flow around a leaf is <u>poor</u>, the water vapour just <u>surrounds the leaf</u> and doesn't move away. This means there's a <u>high concentration</u> of water particles outside the leaf as well as inside it, so <u>diffusion</u> doesn't happen as quickly. If there's <u>good</u> air flow, the water vapour is <u>swept away</u>, maintaining a <u>low concentration</u> of water in the air outside the leaf. Diffusion then happens quickly, from an area of higher concentration to an area of lower concentration.

4) <u>HUMIDITY</u> — the <u>drier</u> the air around a leaf, the <u>faster</u> transpiration happens.

   This is like what happens with air flow. If the air is <u>humid</u> there's a lot of water in it already, so there's not much of a <u>difference</u> between the inside and the outside of the leaf. Diffusion happens <u>fastest</u> if there's a <u>really high concentration</u> in one place, and a <u>really low concentration</u> in the other.

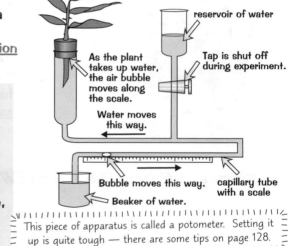

As the plant takes up water, the air bubble moves along the scale.

Water moves this way.

reservoir of water

Tap is shut off during experiment.

Bubble moves this way.

capillary tube with a scale

Beaker of water.

You can estimate the <u>rate of transpiration</u> by measuring the <u>uptake of water</u> by a plant. This is because you can assume that <u>water uptake</u> by the plant is directly related to <u>water loss</u> by the leaves (transpiration).

Set up the apparatus as in the diagram, and then record the <u>starting position</u> of the air bubble. Start a stopwatch and record the <u>distance moved</u> by the bubble per unit time, e.g. per hour. Keep the <u>conditions constant</u> throughout the experiment, e.g. the <u>temperature</u> and <u>air humidity</u>.

This piece of apparatus is called a potometer. Setting it up is quite tough — there are some tips on page 128.

Guard Cells Are Adapted to Open and Close Stomata

guard cell

stoma (plural — stomata)

1) They have a kidney shape which <u>opens</u> and <u>closes</u> the <u>stomata</u> (page 25) in a leaf.

2) When the plant has <u>lots</u> of water the guard cells fill with it and go plump and <u>turgid</u>. This makes the stomata <u>open</u> so <u>gases</u> can be exchanged for <u>photosynthesis</u>.

3) When the plant is <u>short</u> of water, the guard cells lose water and become <u>flaccid</u>, making the stomata <u>close</u>. This helps stop too much water vapour <u>escaping</u>.

4) <u>Thin</u> outer walls and <u>thickened</u> inner walls make the opening and closing work.

5) They're also <u>sensitive to light</u> and <u>close at night</u> to save water without losing out on photosynthesis.

6) You usually find <u>more</u> stomata on the <u>undersides</u> of leaves than on the top. The <u>lower surface</u> is <u>shaded</u> and <u>cooler</u> — so <u>less water</u> is <u>lost</u> through the stomata than if they were on the upper surface.

7) Guard cells are therefore adapted for <u>gas exchange</u> and <u>controlling water loss</u> within a <u>leaf</u>.

I say stomaaarta, you say stomaaayta...

Different leaves will have different distributions of stomata. You can peel the epidermal tissue off some leaves and mount them on microscope slides (see page 13) to compare them. It's thrilling stuff.

Q1   Explain how low light intensity affects the rate of transpiration.   [3 marks]

Revision Questions for Topic 2

Well, that's <u>Topic 2</u> finished. Now it's time for *the* greatest quiz on Earth. Please hold your excitement in.

- Try these questions and <u>tick off each one</u> when you <u>get it right</u>.
- When you've done <u>all the questions</u> under a heading and are <u>completely happy</u> with it, tick it off.

<u>Cell Organisation (p.27)</u> ☑

1) What is a tissue? ☑
2) Explain what is meant by the term 'organ system'. ☑

<u>The Role of Enzymes and Food Tests (p.28-32)</u> ☑

3) Why can enzymes be described as biological catalysts? ☑
4) Why do enzymes only usually catalyse one reaction? ☑
5) What does it mean when an enzyme has been 'denatured'? ☑
6) Describe how you could investigate the effect of pH on the rate of amylase activity. ☑
7) List the three places where amylase is made in the human body. ☑
8) What is the role of lipases? ☑
9) Where is bile stored? ☑
10) Name the solution that you would use to test for the presence of lipids in a food sample. ☑

<u>The Lungs and Circulatory System (p.33-36)</u> ☑

11) Name the tubes that split off the trachea. ☑
12) Explain the role that alveoli play in gas exchange. ☑
13) Explain why the circulatory system in humans is described as a 'double circulatory system'. ☑
14) Why does the heart have valves? ☑
15) Name the four chambers of the heart. ☑
16) How is the resting heart rate controlled in a healthy heart? ☑
17) How are arteries adapted to carry blood away from the heart? ☑
18) Why do red blood cells not have a nucleus? ☑

<u>Diseases and Risk Factors (p.37-41)</u> ☐

19) Give two advantages and two disadvantages of statins. ☑
20) What is the difference between biological and mechanical replacement heart valves? ☑
21) What is meant by a non-communicable disease? ☑
22) Give an example of where different types of disease might interact in the body. ☑
23) What is meant by a risk factor of a disease? ☑
24) Which type of tumour is cancerous? ☑

<u>Plant Cell Organisation and Transport (p.42-44)</u> ☐

25) List the tissues that make up a leaf. ☑
26) Explain how the structure of the upper epidermal tissue in a leaf is related to its function. ☑
27) What is the function of phloem? ☑
28) What is transpiration? ☑
29) List the four main things that affect transpiration. ☑
30) How could you measure the rate of transpiration? ☑
31) Name the type of cell that helps open and close stomata. ☑

Communicable Disease

If you're hoping I'll ease you gently into this new topic... no such luck. Straight on to the baddies of biology.

There Are Several Types of Pathogen

1) Pathogens are <u>microorganisms</u> that enter the body and cause <u>disease</u>.
2) They cause <u>communicable</u> (infectious) diseases — diseases that can <u>easily spread</u> (see p.39).
3) Both <u>plants</u> and <u>animals</u> can be infected by pathogens.

1. Bacteria Are Very Small Living Cells

1) Bacteria are <u>very small cells</u> (about 1/100th the size of your body cells), which can reproduce rapidly inside your body.
2) They can make you <u>feel ill</u> by <u>producing toxins</u> (poisons) that <u>damage your cells and tissues</u>.

2. Viruses Are Not Cells — They're Much Smaller

1) Viruses are <u>not cells</u>. They're <u>tiny</u>, about 1/100th the size of a bacterium.
2) Like bacteria, they can <u>reproduce rapidly</u> inside your body.
3) They live inside your cells and <u>replicate themselves</u> using the cells' <u>machinery</u> to produce many <u>copies</u> of themselves. The cell will usually then <u>burst</u>, releasing all the new viruses.
4) This <u>cell damage</u> is what makes you feel ill.

A virus

A body cell

eek!

3. Protists are Single-Celled Eukaryotes

1) There are lots of different types of protists. But they're all <u>eukaryotes</u> (see page 11) and most of them are <u>single-celled</u>.
2) Some protists are <u>parasites</u>. Parasites live <u>on</u> or <u>inside</u> other organisms and can cause them <u>damage</u>. They are often transferred to the organism by a <u>vector</u>, which doesn't get the disease itself — e.g. an insect that carries the protist.

4. Fungi Come in Different Shapes

1) Some fungi are <u>single-celled</u>. Others have a <u>body</u> which is made up of <u>hyphae</u> (thread-like structures).
2) These hyphae can <u>grow</u> and <u>penetrate human skin</u> and the <u>surface of plants</u>, causing <u>diseases</u>.
3) The hyphae can produce <u>spores</u>, which can be spread to other plants and animals.

Pathogens Can Be Spread in Different Ways

Pathogens can be <u>spread</u> in many ways. Here are a few that you need to know about.

1) <u>WATER</u> — Some pathogens can be picked up by drinking or bathing in <u>dirty water</u>. E.g. <u>cholera</u> is a <u>bacterial infection</u> that's spread by <u>drinking</u> water <u>contaminated</u> with the diarrhoea of other sufferers.
2) <u>AIR</u> — Pathogens can be carried in the <u>air</u> and can then be <u>breathed in</u>. Some airborne pathogens are carried in the air in <u>droplets</u> produced when you <u>cough</u> or <u>sneeze</u> — e.g. the <u>influenza virus</u> that causes <u>flu</u> is spread this way.
3) <u>DIRECT CONTACT</u> — Some pathogens can be picked up by <u>touching</u> contaminated surfaces, including the <u>skin</u>. E.g. <u>athlete's foot</u> is a <u>fungus</u> which makes skin itch and flake off. It's most commonly spread by touching the same things as an infected person, e.g. <u>shower floors</u> and <u>towels</u>.

Hooray, I've avoided the classic 'he was a fungi to be with' joke...

Yuck, lots of nasties out there that can cause disease. Plants need to be worried too, as you'll find out.

Q1   Describe how viruses cause cell damage.   [2 marks]

Viral, Fungal and Protist Diseases

There are heaps of diseases caused by <u>viruses</u>, <u>fungi</u> and <u>protists</u>, but you just need to know about these ones.

You Need to Know About Three Viral Diseases...

1) <u>Measles</u> is a <u>viral</u> disease. It is spread by <u>droplets</u> from an infected person's sneeze or cough.
2) People with measles develop a <u>red skin rash</u>, and they'll show signs of a <u>fever</u> (a high temperature).
3) Measles can be very serious, or even fatal, if there are <u>complications</u>. For example, measles can sometimes lead to <u>pneumonia</u> (a lung infection) or a brain infection called <u>encephalitis</u>.
4) Most people are <u>vaccinated</u> against measles when they're young.

1) <u>HIV</u> is a <u>virus</u> spread by <u>sexual contact</u>, or by exchanging <u>bodily fluids</u> such as blood. This can happen when people <u>share needles</u> when taking drugs.
2) HIV initially causes <u>flu-like symptoms</u> for a few weeks. Usually, the person doesn't then experience any symptoms for several years. During this time, HIV can be controlled with <u>antiretroviral drugs</u>. These stop the virus <u>replicating</u> in the body.
3) The virus attacks the <u>immune cells</u> (see page 49).
4) If the body's immune system is badly damaged, it <u>can't cope</u> with <u>other infections</u> or <u>cancers</u>. At this stage, the virus is known as <u>late stage HIV infection</u>, or <u>AIDS</u>.

1) <u>Tobacco mosaic virus</u> (<u>TMV</u>) is a <u>virus</u> that affects many species of <u>plants</u>, e.g. <u>tomatoes</u>.
2) It causes a mosaic pattern on the leaves of the plants — parts of the leaves become <u>discoloured</u>.
3) The discolouration means the plant can't carry out <u>photosynthesis</u> as well, so the virus affects <u>growth</u>.

Photosynthesis is important for plant growth because it produces glucose — see page 57.

...a Fungal Disease...

1) <u>Rose black spot</u> is a <u>fungus</u> that causes <u>purple or black spots</u> to develop on the <u>leaves</u> of <u>rose plants</u>. Who'd have guessed. The leaves can then turn <u>yellow</u> and <u>drop off</u>.
2) This means that less <u>photosynthesis</u> can happen, so the plant doesn't <u>grow</u> very well.
3) It spreads through the environment in <u>water</u> or by the <u>wind</u>.
4) Gardeners can treat the disease using <u>fungicides</u> and by <u>stripping</u> the plant of its <u>affected leaves</u>. These leaves then need to be <u>destroyed</u> so that the fungus can't spread to other rose plants.

...and a Disease Caused by a Protist

1) <u>Malaria</u> is caused by a protist (see the previous page).
2) Part of the malarial protist's <u>life cycle</u> takes place inside the mosquito. The mosquitoes are <u>vectors</u> (see the previous page) — they <u>pick up</u> the malarial protist when they <u>feed</u> on an <u>infected animal</u>.
3) Every time the mosquito feeds on another animal, it <u>infects it</u> by inserting the protist into the animal's blood vessels.
4) Malaria causes <u>repeating</u> episodes of <u>fever</u>. It can be <u>fatal</u>.
5) The <u>spread</u> of malaria can be reduced by stopping the <u>mosquitoes</u> from <u>breeding</u>.
6) People can be protected from mosquitoes using <u>insecticides</u> and <u>mosquito nets</u>.

I've heard this page has gone viral...

The examiner could grill you on any one of these diseases, so make sure you know them all inside out.

Q1   What symptom of measles is shown on the skin? [1 mark]

Q2   How can rose black spot be treated so that it doesn't spread to other plants? [2 marks]

Bacterial Diseases and Preventing Disease

Sorry — I'm afraid there are some more diseases to learn about here. This time, they're diseases caused by bacteria. I don't know about you, but I'm starting to feel a bit itchy all over...

You Need to Know About Two Bacterial Diseases

1) Salmonella is a type of bacteria that causes food poisoning.

2) Infected people can suffer from fever, stomach cramps, vomiting and diarrhoea. Pleasant.

3) These symptoms are caused by the toxins that the bacteria produce (see page 46).

4) You can get Salmonella food poisoning by eating food that's been contaminated with Salmonella bacteria, e.g. eating chicken that caught the disease whilst it was alive, or eating food that has been contaminated by being prepared in unhygienic conditions.

5) In the UK, most poultry (e.g. chickens and turkeys) is given a vaccination against Salmonella. This is to control the spread of the disease.

1) Gonorrhoea is a sexually transmitted disease (STD).

2) STDs are passed on by sexual contact, e.g. having unprotected sex.

3) Gonorrhoea is caused by bacteria.

4) A person with gonorrhoea will get pain when they urinate. Another symptom is a thick yellow or green discharge from the vagina or the penis.

5) Gonorrhoea was originally treated with an antibiotic called penicillin, but this has become trickier now because strains of the bacteria have become resistant to it (see page 51).

6) To prevent the spread of gonorrhoea, people can be treated with antibiotics and should use barrier methods of contraception (see page 78), such as condoms.

The Spread of Disease Can Be Reduced or Prevented

There are things that we can do to reduce, and even prevent, the spread of disease. For example:

1) Being hygienic — Using simple hygiene measures can prevent the spread of disease. For example, doing things like washing your hands thoroughly before preparing food or after you've sneezed can stop you infecting another person.

2) Destroying vectors — By getting rid of the organisms that spread disease, you can prevent the disease from being passed on. Vectors that are insects can be killed using insecticides or by destroying their habitat so that they can no longer breed.

3) Isolating infected individuals — If you isolate someone who has a communicable disease, it prevents them from passing it on to anyone else.

4) Vaccination — Vaccinating people and animals against communicable diseases means that they can't develop the infection and then pass it on to someone else. There's more about how vaccination works on page 50.

The spread of disease — mouldy margarine...

OK, I promise, that's it. No more diseases to learn about in this Topic. You may be sick of them already (geddit?) but don't turn this page until you've got all the facts firmly attached to your cranial material.

Q1   What has made it harder to treat gonorrhoea? [1 mark]

Q2   It is important for chefs to wash their hands thoroughly before cooking. Suggest why. [1 mark]

Topic 3 — Infection and Response

Fighting Disease

The human body has some pretty neat features when it comes to <u>fighting disease</u>.

Your Body Has a Pretty Sophisticated Defence System

1) The human body has got features that stop a lot of nasties getting inside in the first place.
2) The <u>skin</u> acts as a <u>barrier</u> to pathogens. It also secretes <u>antimicrobial substances</u> which kill pathogens.
3) <u>Hairs</u> and <u>mucus</u> in your nose <u>trap</u> particles that could contain pathogens.
4) The <u>trachea</u> and <u>bronchi</u> (breathing pipework — see page 33) secrete <u>mucus</u> to trap pathogens.
5) The trachea and bronchi are lined with <u>cilia</u>. These are hair-like structures, which <u>waft the mucus</u> up to the back of the throat where it can be <u>swallowed</u>.
6) The <u>stomach</u> produces <u>hydrochloric acid</u>. This kills pathogens that make it that far from the mouth.

Your Immune System Can Attack Pathogens

1) If pathogens do make it into your body, your <u>immune system</u> kicks in to destroy them.
2) The most important part of your immune system is the <u>white blood cells</u>. They travel around in your blood and crawl into every part of you, constantly patrolling for microbes. When they come across an invading microbe they have three lines of attack.

1. Consuming Them

White blood cells can <u>engulf</u> foreign cells and <u>digest</u> them. This is called <u>phagocytosis</u>.

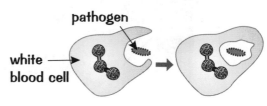

2. Producing Antibodies

1) Every invading pathogen has unique molecules (called <u>antigens</u>) on its surface.
2) When some types of white blood cell come across a <u>foreign antigen</u> (i.e. one they don't recognise), they will start to produce <u>proteins</u> called <u>antibodies</u> to lock onto the invading cells so that they can be <u>found</u> and <u>destroyed</u> by other white blood cells. The antibodies produced are specific to that type of antigen — they won't lock on to any others.
3) Antibodies are then produced <u>rapidly</u> and carried around the body to find all similar bacteria or viruses.
4) If the person is infected with the same pathogen again the white blood cells will rapidly produce the antibodies to kill it — the person is <u>naturally</u> immune to that pathogen and won't get ill.

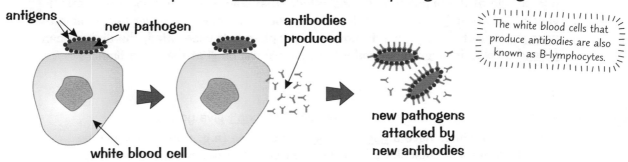

The white blood cells that produce antibodies are also known as B-lymphocytes.

3. Producing Antitoxins

These counteract toxins produced by the <u>invading bacteria</u>.

Fight disease — blow your nose with boxing gloves...

If you have a low level of white blood cells, you'll be more susceptible to infections. HIV attacks white blood cells and weakens the immune system, making it easier for other pathogens to invade.

Q1   What is phagocytosis?   [1 mark]

Q2   How are the trachea and the bronchi adapted to defend against the entry of pathogens?   [3 marks]

Fighting Disease — Vaccination

Vaccinations have changed the way we fight disease. We don't always have to deal with the problem once it's happened — we can prevent it happening in the first place.

Vaccination — Protects from Future Infections

1) When you're infected with a new pathogen, it takes your white blood cells a few days to learn how to deal with it. But by that time, you can be pretty ill.

2) Vaccinations involve injecting small amounts of dead or inactive pathogens. These carry antigens, which cause your body to produce antibodies to attack them — even though the pathogen is harmless (since it's dead or inactive). For example, the MMR vaccine contains weakened versions of the viruses that cause measles, mumps and rubella (German measles) all in one vaccine.

3) But if live pathogens of the same type appear after that, the white blood cells can rapidly mass-produce antibodies to kill off the pathogen. Cool.

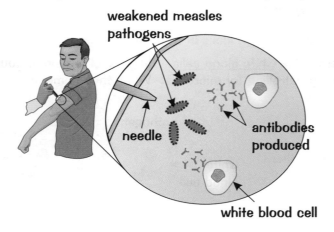

weakened measles pathogens

needle

antibodies produced

white blood cell

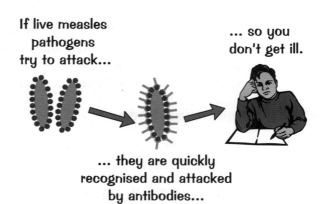

If live measles pathogens try to attack...

... so you don't get ill.

... they are quickly recognised and attacked by antibodies...

There are Pros and Cons of Vaccination

PROS

1) Vaccines have helped control lots of communicable diseases that were once common in the UK (e.g. polio, measles, whooping cough, rubella, mumps, tetanus...). Smallpox no longer occurs at all, and polio infections have fallen by 99%.

2) Big outbreaks of disease — called epidemics — can be prevented if a large percentage of the population is vaccinated. That way, even the people who aren't vaccinated are unlikely to catch the disease because there are fewer people able to pass it on. But if a significant number of people aren't vaccinated, the disease can spread quickly through them and lots of people will be ill at the same time.

CONS

1) Vaccines don't always work — sometimes they don't give you immunity.

2) You can sometimes have a bad reaction to a vaccine (e.g. swelling, or maybe something more serious like a fever or seizures). But bad reactions are very rare.

Prevention is better than cure...

Deciding whether to have a vaccination means balancing risks — the risk of catching the disease if you don't have a vaccine, against the risk of having a bad reaction if you do. As always, you need to look at the evidence. For example, if you get measles (the disease), there's about a 1 in 15 chance that you'll get complications (e.g. pneumonia) — and about 1 in 500 people who get measles actually die. However, the number of people who have a problem with the vaccine is more like 1 in 1 000 000.

Q1   What do vaccinations stimulate white blood cells to produce?   [1 mark]

Fighting Disease — Drugs

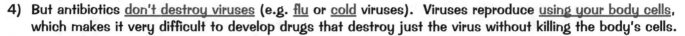

...a biscuit, nurse? Thanks very much. Sorry, couldn't face that last page — I'm squeamish about needles.*

Some Drugs Relieve Symptoms — Others Cure the Problem

1) <u>Painkillers</u> (e.g. aspirin) are drugs that relieve pain (no, really). However, they don't actually tackle the <u>cause</u> of the disease or <u>kill</u> pathogens, they just help to reduce the <u>symptoms</u>.

2) Other drugs do a similar kind of thing — reduce the <u>symptoms</u> without tackling the underlying <u>cause</u>. For example, lots of "cold remedies" don't actually <u>cure</u> colds.

3) <u>Antibiotics</u> (e.g. penicillin) work differently — they actually <u>kill</u> (or prevent the growth of) the bacteria causing the problem without killing your own body cells. <u>Different antibiotics</u> kill <u>different types</u> of bacteria, so it's important to be treated with the <u>right one</u>.

4) But antibiotics <u>don't destroy viruses</u> (e.g. <u>flu</u> or <u>cold</u> viruses). Viruses reproduce <u>using your body cells</u>, which makes it very difficult to develop drugs that destroy just the virus without killing the body's cells.

5) The use of antibiotics has <u>greatly reduced</u> the number of deaths from communicable diseases caused by bacteria.

Bacteria Can Become Resistant to Antibiotics

1) Bacteria can <u>mutate</u> — sometimes the mutations cause them to be <u>resistant</u> to (not killed by) an <u>antibiotic</u>.

2) If you have an <u>infection</u>, some of the bacteria might be <u>resistant</u> to antibiotics.

3) This means that when you <u>treat</u> the infection, only the <u>non-resistant</u> strains of bacteria will be <u>killed</u>.

4) The individual <u>resistant</u> bacteria will <u>survive</u> and <u>reproduce</u>, and the population of the resistant strain will <u>increase</u>. This is an example of natural selection (see page 96).

5) This resistant strain could cause a <u>serious infection</u> that <u>can't</u> be treated by antibiotics. E.g. <u>MRSA</u> (meticillin-resistant *Staphylococcus aureus*) causes serious wound infections and is resistant to the powerful antibiotic <u>meticillin</u>.

6) To <u>slow down</u> the <u>rate</u> of development of <u>resistant strains</u>, it's important for doctors to <u>avoid</u> <u>over-prescribing</u> antibiotics. So you <u>won't</u> get them for a <u>sore throat</u>, only for something more serious.

7) It's also important that you <u>finish</u> the <u>whole course</u> of antibiotics and don't just stop once you feel better.

Many Drugs Originally Came From Plants

1) <u>Plants</u> produce a variety of <u>chemicals</u> to <u>defend</u> themselves against <u>pests</u> and <u>pathogens</u> (see page 55).

2) Some of these chemicals can be used as <u>drugs</u> to <u>treat</u> human diseases or <u>relieve symptoms</u>. A lot of our <u>current medicines</u> were discovered by studying plants used in <u>traditional cures</u>. For example:

- <u>Aspirin</u> is used as a <u>painkiller</u> and to lower <u>fever</u>. It was developed from a chemical found in <u>willow</u>.
- <u>Digitalis</u> is used to treat <u>heart conditions</u>. It was developed from a chemical found in <u>foxgloves</u>.

3) Some drugs were extracted from <u>microorganisms</u>. For example:

- Alexander Fleming was clearing out some Petri dishes containing <u>bacteria</u>. He noticed that one of the dishes of bacteria also had <u>mould</u> on it and the <u>area around the mould</u> was <u>free of the bacteria</u>.
- He found that the <u>mould</u> (called *Penicillium notatum*) on the Petri dish was producing a <u>substance</u> that <u>killed the bacteria</u> — this substance was <u>penicillin</u>.

4) These days, drugs are made on a large scale in the <u>pharmaceutical industry</u> — they're synthesised by chemists in labs. However, the process still might start with a chemical <u>extracted</u> from a <u>plant</u>.

Ahh...Ahh... Ahhhhh Choooooooo — urghh, this page is catching...

Drug development is a big industry. And guess what — you're about to find out some more about it.

Q1   Which type of pathogen can antibiotics be used to kill?   [1 mark]

---

*That's my excuse, you'll have to think of your own.

Developing Drugs

New drugs are constantly being developed. But before they can be given to the general public, they have to go through a thorough <u>testing</u> procedure. This is what usually happens...

There are Three Main Stages in Drug Testing

(1)
1) In preclinical testing, drugs are tested on <u>human cells and tissues</u> in the lab.
2) However, you can't use human cells and tissues to test drugs that affect <u>whole</u> or <u>multiple</u> body systems, e.g. testing a drug for blood pressure must be done on a whole animal because it has an intact circulatory system.

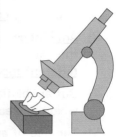

(2)
1) The next step in preclinical testing is to test the drug on <u>live animals</u>. This is to test <u>efficacy</u> (whether the drug <u>works</u> and produces the effect you're looking for), to find out about its <u>toxicity</u> (how harmful it is) and to find the best <u>dosage</u> (the concentration that should be given, and how often it should be given).
2) The law in Britain states that any new drug must be tested on <u>two</u> different <u>live mammals</u>. Some people think it's <u>cruel</u> to test on animals, but others believe this is the <u>safest</u> way to make sure a drug isn't dangerous before it's given to humans.

> But some people think that animals are so different from humans that testing on animals is pointless.

(3)
1) If the drug <u>passes</u> the tests on animals then it's tested on <u>human volunteers</u> in a <u>clinical trial</u>.
2) First, the drug is tested on <u>healthy</u> volunteers. This is to make sure that it doesn't have any <u>harmful side effects</u> when the body is working normally. At the start of the trial, a <u>very low dose</u> of the drug is given and this is gradually increased.
3) If the results of the tests on healthy volunteers are good, the drugs can be tested on people suffering from the <u>illness</u>. The <u>optimum dose</u> is found — this is the dose of drug that is the <u>most effective</u> and has <u>few side effects</u>.
4) To test how well the drug works, patients are <u>randomly</u> put into <u>two groups</u>. One is given the <u>new drug</u>, the other is given a <u>placebo</u> (a substance that's like the drug being tested but doesn't do anything). This is so the <u>doctor</u> can see the actual difference the drug makes — it allows for the <u>placebo effect</u> (when the patient expects the treatment to work and so <u>feels better</u>, even though the treatment isn't doing anything).
5) Clinical trials are <u>blind</u> — the patient in the study <u>doesn't know</u> whether they're getting the drug or the placebo. In fact, they're often <u>double-blind</u> — neither the patient nor the <u>doctor</u> knows until all the <u>results</u> have been gathered. This is so the doctors <u>monitoring</u> the patients and <u>analysing</u> the results aren't <u>subconsciously influenced</u> by their knowledge.
6) The results of drug testing and drug trials aren't published until they've been through <u>peer review</u>. This helps to prevent <u>false claims</u>.

> Peer review is when other scientists check that the work is valid and has been carried out rigorously — see page 1.

The placebo effect doesn't work with revision...

... you can't just expect to get a good mark and then magically get it. I know, I know, there's a lot of information to take in on this page, but just read it through slowly. There's nothing too tricky here — it's just a case of going over it again and again until you've got it all firmly lodged in your memory.

Q1   What is meant by the efficacy of a drug?   [1 mark]

Q2   Why do clinical trials of a new drug begin with healthy volunteers?   [1 mark]

Q3   Why must the results from drug testing be assessed by peer review?   [1 mark]

Monoclonal Antibodies

Antibodies aren't only used by the immune system — scientists have engineered them for lots of new uses.

Monoclonal Antibodies are Identical Antibodies

1) Antibodies are produced by B-lymphocytes — a type of white blood cell (see page 49).

2) Monoclonal antibodies are produced from lots of clones of a single white blood cell. This means all the antibodies are identical and will only target one specific protein antigen.

3) However, you can't just grab the lymphocyte that made the antibody and grow more — lymphocytes don't divide very easily.

4) Tumour cells, on the other hand, don't produce antibodies but divide lots — so they can be grown really easily.

5) It's possible to fuse a mouse B-lymphocyte with a tumour cell to create a cell called a hybridoma.

6) Hybridoma cells can be cloned to get lots of identical cells. These cells all produce the same antibodies (monoclonal antibodies). The antibodies can be collected and purified.

7) You can make monoclonal antibodies that bind to anything you want, e.g. an antigen that's only found on the surface of one type of cell. Monoclonal antibodies are really useful because they will only bind to (target) this molecule — this means you can use them to target a specific cell or chemical in the body.

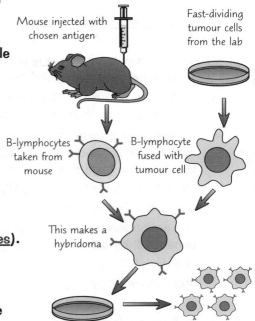

Mouse injected with chosen antigen

Fast-dividing tumour cells from the lab

B-lymphocytes taken from mouse

B-lymphocyte fused with tumour cell

This makes a hybridoma

It divides quickly to produce lots of clones that produce the monoclonal antibodies

Monoclonal Antibodies Are Used In Pregnancy Tests

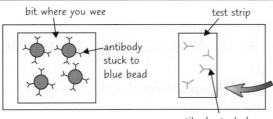

bit where you wee

test strip

antibody stuck to blue bead

antibody stuck down

If you're pregnant:

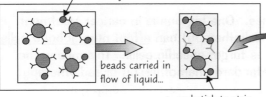

hormone stuck to antibody stuck to bead

beads carried in flow of liquid...

...and stick to strip

If you're not pregnant:

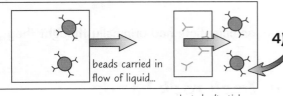

beads carried in flow of liquid...

...but don't stick

A hormone called HCG is found in the urine of women only when they are pregnant. Pregnancy testing sticks detect this hormone. Here's how they work:

1) The bit of the stick you wee on has some antibodies to the hormone, with blue beads attached.

2) The test strip (the bit of the stick that turns blue if you're pregnant) has some more antibodies to the hormone stuck onto it (so that they can't move).

3) If you're pregnant and you wee on the stick:
   - The hormone binds to the antibodies on the blue beads.
   - The urine moves up the stick, carrying the hormone and the beads.
   - The beads and hormone bind to the antibodies on the strip.
   - So the blue beads get stuck on the strip, turning it blue.

4) If you're not pregnant and you wee on the stick, the urine still moves up the stick, carrying the blue beads. But there's nothing to stick the blue beads onto the test strip, so it doesn't go blue.

The one time when you can write "wee on a stick" in an exam...

There's more on monoclonal antibodies coming next, but don't move on until you understand this page.

Q1   What is a hybridoma cell made from?   [2 marks]

More on Monoclonal Antibodies

Because monoclonal antibodies can be produced to target a specific chemical or cell, they have loads of uses.

Monoclonal Antibodies Can be Used to Treat Diseases...

1) Different cells in the body have different antigens on their cell surface. So you can make monoclonal antibodies that will bind to specific cells in the body (e.g. just liver cells).

2) Cancer cells have antigens on their cell membranes that aren't found on normal body cells. They're called tumour markers.

3) In the lab, you can make monoclonal antibodies that will bind to these tumour markers.

4) An anti-cancer drug can be attached to these monoclonal antibodies. This might be a radioactive substance, a toxic drug or a chemical which stops cancer cells growing and dividing.

5) The antibodies are given to the patient through a drip.

6) The antibodies target specific cells (the cancer cells) because they only bind to the tumour markers.

7) The drug kills the cancer cells but doesn't kill any normal body cells near the tumour.

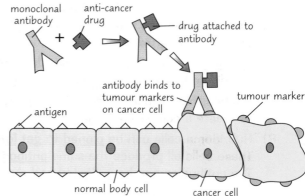

...and in Laboratories and Research to Find Specific Substances

Monoclonal antibodies can be used to:

1) Bind to hormones and other chemicals in blood to measure their levels.

2) Test blood samples in laboratories for certain pathogens.

3) Locate specific molecules on a cell or in a tissue:

> 1) First, monoclonal antibodies are made that will bind to the specific molecules you're looking for.
> 2) The antibodies are then bound to a fluorescent dye.
> 3) If the molecules are present in the sample you're analysing, the monoclonal antibodies will attach to them, and they can be detected using the dye.

Monoclonal Antibodies Do Have Some Problems Though

1) There are some obvious advantages of monoclonal antibodies. One big one is in cancer treatment. Other cancer treatments (like standard chemotherapy and radiotherapy) can affect normal body cells as well as killing cancer cells, whereas monoclonal antibodies target specific cells. This means the side effects of an antibody-based drug are lower than for standard chemotherapy or radiotherapy.

2) However, monoclonal antibodies do cause more side effects than were originally expected, e.g. they can cause fever, vomiting and low blood pressure. When they were first developed, scientists thought that because they targeted a very specific cell or molecule, they wouldn't create a lot of side effects.

3) This means that they are not as widely used as treatments as scientists had originally thought they might be.

Bonoclonal antibodies — used to detect Irish rock bands...

As you've just found out, monoclonal antibodies are really useful for finding stuff. Imagine having a horde of trained fireflies to search for your lost keys, or phone, or remote control. Instead of you having to search under everything, you just release the fireflies and wait for them to cluster around your lost stuff, in a big obvious glowing mass. Genius.

Q1   List three things that can be bound to a monoclonal antibody to treat cancer.   [3 marks]

Plant Diseases and Defences

It's not just us humans that can get diseases — plants get their fair share too.

Plants Need Mineral Ions

Plants need mineral ions from the soil. If there aren't enough, plants suffer deficiency symptoms.

1) Nitrates are needed to make proteins and therefore for growth. A lack of nitrates causes stunted growth.

2) Magnesium ions are needed for making chlorophyll, which is needed for photosynthesis. Plants without enough magnesium suffer from chlorosis and have yellow leaves.

Plants Can Get Diseases

1) Plants can be infected by viral, bacterial and fungal pathogens — see page 47 for some examples. They can also be infested and damaged by insects. For example, aphids are an insect that can cause huge damage to plants.

2) It's usually pretty clear that a plant has a disease. The common signs are:

| 1) Stunted growth | 2) Spots on the leaves | 3) Patches of decay (rot) |
| 4) Abnormal growths, e.g. lumps | 5) Malformed stems or leaves | 6) Discolouration |

3) Infestations of pests are easy to spot too — you should be able to see them on the plants.

4) Different plant diseases have different signs. They can be identified by:

1) Looking up the signs in a gardening manual or on a gardening website.
2) Taking the infected plant to a laboratory, where scientists can identify the pathogen.
3) Using testing kits that identify the pathogen using monoclonal antibodies (see page 53).

Plants Have Physical, Chemical and Mechanical Defences...

PHYSICAL DEFENCES

1) Most plant leaves and stems have a waxy cuticle, which provides a barrier to stop pathogens entering.

2) Plant cells themselves are surrounded by cell walls made from cellulose. These form a physical barrier against pathogens that make it past the waxy cuticle.

3) Plants have layers of dead cells around their stems, for example, the outer part of the bark on trees. These act as a barrier to stop pathogens entering.

CHEMICAL DEFENCES

1) Some can produce antibacterial chemicals which kill bacteria — e.g. the mint plant and witch hazel.

2) Other plants produce poisons which can deter herbivores (organisms that eat plants) — e.g. tobacco plants, foxgloves and deadly nightshade.

MECHANICAL DEFENCES

1) Some plants have adapted to have thorns and hairs. These stop animals from touching and eating them.

2) Other plants have leaves that droop or curl when something touches them. This means that they can prevent themselves from being eaten by knocking insects off themselves and moving away from things.

3) Some plants can cleverly mimic other organisms. E.g. the passion flower has bright yellow spots on its leaves which look like butterfly eggs. This stops other butterflies laying their eggs there. Several species of plant in the 'ice plant family' in southern Africa look like stones and pebbles. This tricks other organisms into not eating them.

Symptoms of revision deficiency include nagging parents...

You've made it to the end of the Topic. But don't run off just yet — have a go at this question first.

Q1 How could you tell that a plant has a nitrate deficiency? [1 mark]

Revision Questions for Topic 3

Well, that wraps up Topic 3 — time to put yourself to the test and find out how much you really know.
- Try these questions and tick off each one when you get it right.
- When you've done all the questions under a heading and are completely happy with it, tick it off.

Types of Disease (p.46-48) ☑

1) How can bacteria make us feel ill? ☐

2) Give one way that fungi can cause disease. ☐

3) How does tobacco mosaic virus affect a plant's growth? ☐

4) How are mosquitoes involved in the spread of malaria? ☐

5) What are the symptoms of gonorrhoea? ☐

6) How can destroying vectors help to prevent the spread of disease? ☐

Fighting Disease (p.49-52) ☑

7) What does the stomach produce that can kill pathogens? ☐

8) Give three ways that the white blood cells can defend against pathogens. ☐

9) Give one pro and one con of vaccination. ☐

10) Why is it difficult to develop drugs that kill viruses without also damaging body tissues? ☐

11) Which plant does the painkiller aspirin originate from? ☐

12) What two things are drugs tested on in preclinical testing? ☐

13) What is meant by a drug's toxicity? ☐

Antibodies (p.53-54) ☑

14) What is a monoclonal antibody? ☐

15) Where are the B-lymphocytes taken from when making monoclonal antibodies? ☐

16) Why might a fluorescent dye be added to a monoclonal antibody? ☐

17) Why aren't monoclonal antibodies used as drugs as much as scientists hoped they would be? ☐

Plant Diseases and Defences (p.55) ☑

18) What do plants use magnesium ions for? ☐

19) Give one way of identifying a plant disease. ☐

20) Give one mechanical defence that a plant may have to defend itself. ☐

Photosynthesis and Limiting Factors

First, photosynthesis equations. Then there are some more bits 'n' bobs you should know...

Photosynthesis Produces Glucose Using Light

1) Photosynthesis uses energy to change carbon dioxide and water into glucose and oxygen.
2) It takes place in chloroplasts in green plant cells — they contain pigments like chlorophyll that absorb light.
3) Energy is transferred to the chloroplasts from the environment by light.
4) Photosynthesis is endothermic — this means energy is transferred from the environment in the process.
5) The word equation for photosynthesis is:

$$\text{carbon dioxide} + \text{water} \xrightarrow{\text{light}} \text{glucose} + \text{oxygen}$$

6) Here's the symbol equation too:

$$6CO_2 + 6H_2O \xrightarrow{\text{light}} C_6H_{12}O_6 + 6O_2$$

Plants Use Glucose in Five Main Ways...

1) For respiration — This transfers energy from glucose (see p.61) which enables the plants to convert the rest of the glucose into various other useful substances.
2) Making cellulose — Glucose is converted into cellulose for making strong plant cell walls (see p.11).
3) Making amino acids — Glucose is combined with nitrate ions (absorbed from the soil) to make amino acids, which are then made into proteins.
4) Stored as oils or fats — Glucose is turned into lipids (fats and oils) for storing in seeds.
5) Stored as starch — Glucose is turned into starch and stored in roots, stems and leaves, ready for use when photosynthesis isn't happening, like in the winter. Starch is insoluble, which makes it much better for storing than glucose — a cell with lots of glucose in would draw in loads of water and swell up.

Limiting Factors Affect the Rate of Photosynthesis

1) The rate of photosynthesis is affected by intensity of light, concentration of CO_2 and temperature.
2) Any of these three factors can become the limiting factor — this just means that it's stopping photosynthesis from happening any faster.
3) These factors have a combined effect on the rate of photosynthesis, but which factor is limiting at a particular time depends on the environmental conditions:
   • at night it's pretty obvious that light is the limiting factor,
   • in winter it's often the temperature,
   • if it's warm enough and bright enough, the amount of CO_2 is usually limiting.
4) Chlorophyll can also be a limiting factor of photosynthesis.

> The amount of chlorophyll in a plant can be affected by disease (e.g. infection with the tobacco mosaic virus) or environmental stress, such as a lack of nutrients. These factors can cause chloroplasts to become damaged or to not make enough chlorophyll. This means the rate of photosynthesis is reduced because they can't absorb as much light.

Now you'll have something to bore the great-grandkids with...

You'll be able to tell them how, in your day, all you needed was a bit of carbon dioxide and some water and you could make your own entertainment. But at the moment you need to learn this page...

Q1   Name the products of photosynthesis.   [2 marks]

Q2   Apart from temperature, name three other limiting factors of photosynthesis.   [3 marks]

The Rate of Photosynthesis

Now that you know light, CO_2 and temperature all <u>affect</u> the <u>rate of photosynthesis</u>, you also need to know <u>how</u> they affect the rate, so you can take a gander at a load of lovely pictures... well, graphs. I've also thrown an <u>experiment</u> and an <u>equation</u> in for good measure. I can tell these pages are going to be your favourites...

Three Important Graphs for Rate of Photosynthesis

1) Not Enough Light Slows Down the Rate of Photosynthesis

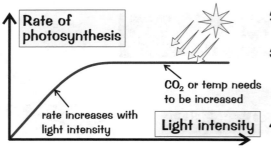

1) Light provides the <u>energy</u> needed for photosynthesis.
2) As the <u>light level</u> is raised, the rate of photosynthesis <u>increases steadily</u> — but only up to a <u>certain point</u>.
3) Beyond that, it <u>won't</u> make any difference — as light intensity increases, the rate will <u>no longer increase</u>. This is because it'll be either the <u>temperature</u> or the <u>CO_2 level</u> which is now the limiting factor, not light.
4) In the lab you can change the light intensity by <u>moving a lamp</u> closer to or further away from your plant (see the next page for this experiment).
5) But if you just plot the rate of photosynthesis against "distance of lamp from the plant", you get a <u>weird-shaped graph</u>. To get a graph like the one above you either need to <u>measure</u> the light intensity at the plant using a <u>light meter</u> or do a bit of nifty maths with your results.

2) Too Little Carbon Dioxide Also Slows it Down

1) CO_2 is one of the <u>raw materials</u> needed for photosynthesis.
2) As with light intensity, the amount of <u>CO_2</u> will only increase the rate of photosynthesis up to a point. After this the graph <u>flattens out</u> — as the amount of CO_2 increases, the rate <u>no longer increases</u>. This shows that CO_2 is no longer the <u>limiting factor</u>.
3) As long as <u>light</u> and <u>CO_2</u> are in plentiful supply then the factor limiting photosynthesis must be <u>temperature</u>.

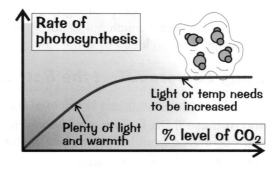

3) The Temperature has to be Just Right

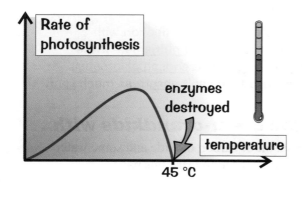

1) Usually, if the temperature is the <u>limiting factor</u> it's because it's <u>too low</u> — the <u>enzymes</u> needed for photosynthesis work more <u>slowly</u> at low temperatures.
2) But if the plant gets <u>too hot</u>, the enzymes it needs for photosynthesis and its other reactions will be <u>damaged</u>.
3) This happens at about <u>45 °C</u> (which is pretty hot for outdoors, although <u>greenhouses</u> can get that hot if you're not careful).

The Rate of Photosynthesis

One Graph May Show the Effect of Many Limiting Factors

You could get a graph that shows <u>more than one</u> limiting factor on the rate of photosynthesis, for example:

1) The graph on the right shows how the rate of photosynthesis is affected by <u>light intensity</u> and <u>temperature</u>.

2) At the start, both of the lines show that as the light intensity <u>increases</u>, the rate of photosynthesis <u>increases steadily</u>.

3) But the lines <u>level off</u> when <u>light</u> is <u>no longer</u> the limiting factor. The line at <u>25 °C</u> levels off at a <u>higher point</u> than the one at 15 °C, showing that <u>temperature</u> must have been a <u>limiting factor</u> at 15 °C.

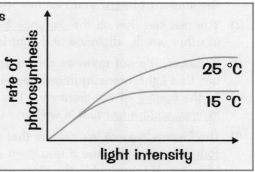

1) The graph on the right shows how the rate of photosynthesis is affected by <u>light intensity</u> and <u>CO$_2$ concentration</u>.

2) Again, both the lines <u>level off</u> when <u>light</u> is <u>no longer</u> the limiting factor.

3) The line at the <u>higher CO$_2$ concentration of 0.4%</u> levels off at a <u>higher point</u> than the one at 0.04%. This means <u>CO$_2$ concentration</u> must have been a <u>limiting factor</u> at 0.04% CO$_2$. The limiting factor here <u>isn't temperature</u> because it's the <u>same</u> for both lines (25 °C).

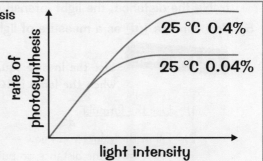

Oxygen Production Shows the Rate of Photosynthesis

PRACTICAL

<u>Canadian pondweed</u> can be used to measure the effect of <u>light intensity</u> on the <u>rate of photosynthesis</u>. The rate at which the pondweed produces <u>oxygen</u> corresponds to the rate at which it's photosynthesising — the <u>faster</u> the rate of oxygen production, the <u>faster</u> the rate of photosynthesis.

Here's how the experiment works:

1) A source of <u>white light</u> is placed at a <u>specific distance</u> from the pondweed.

2) The pondweed is left to photosynthesise for a <u>set amount of time</u>. As it photosynthesises, the oxygen released will collect in the <u>capillary tube</u>.

3) At the end of the experiment, the <u>syringe</u> is used to draw the gas bubble in the tube up alongside a ruler and the <u>length</u> of the <u>gas bubble</u> is <u>measured</u>. This is <u>proportional</u> to the <u>volume of O$_2$</u> produced.

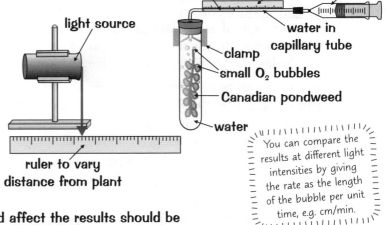

You can compare the results at different light intensities by giving the rate as the length of the bubble per unit time, e.g. cm/min.

4) For this experiment, any <u>variables</u> that could affect the results should be <u>controlled</u>, e.g. the <u>temperature</u> and <u>time</u> the pondweed is left to photosynthesise.

5) The experiment is <u>repeated</u> twice with the <u>light source</u> at the <u>same</u> distance and the <u>mean</u> volume of O$_2$ produced is calculated.

6) Then the whole experiment is repeated with the <u>light source</u> at <u>different distances</u> from the pondweed.

The apparatus above can be altered to measure the effect of <u>temperature</u> or <u>CO$_2$</u> on photosynthesis. E.g. the test tube of pondweed can be put into a <u>water bath</u> at a <u>set temperature</u>, or a measured amount of <u>sodium hydrogencarbonate</u> can be dissolved in the water (which <u>gives off</u> CO$_2$). The experiment can then be repeated with different temperatures of water / concentrations of sodium hydrogencarbonate.

The Rate of Photosynthesis

The Inverse Square Law Links Light Intensity and Distance

1) In the experiment on the previous page, when the <u>lamp</u> is <u>moved away</u> from the pondweed, the amount of <u>light</u> that reaches the pondweed <u>decreases</u>.

2) You can say that as the <u>distance increases</u>, the <u>light intensity decreases</u>. In other words, distance and light intensity are <u>inversely proportional</u> to each other.

3) However, it's not quite as simple as that. It turns out that light intensity decreases in <u>proportion</u> to the <u>square</u> of the distance. This is called the <u>inverse square law</u> and is written out like this:

This is the 'proportional to' symbol.

Putting one over the distance shows the <u>inverse</u>.

$$\text{light intensity} \propto \frac{1}{\text{distance (d)}^2}$$

The distance is <u>squared</u>.

4) The inverse square law means that if you <u>halve</u> the <u>distance</u>, the <u>light intensity</u> will be <u>four times greater</u> and if you <u>third</u> the distance, the light intensity will be <u>nine times greater</u>. Likewise, if you <u>double</u> the distance, the light intensity will be <u>four times smaller</u> and if you <u>treble</u> the distance, the light intensity will be <u>nine times smaller</u>.

5) You can use $1/d^2$ as a measure of light intensity.

EXAMPLE: Use the inverse square law to calculate the light intensity when the lamp is 10 cm from the pondweed.

1) <u>Use the formula</u> $\frac{1}{d^2}$.

$$\text{light intensity} = \frac{1}{d^2}$$

2) Fill in the <u>values</u> you know — you're given the distance, so put that in.

$$\text{light intensity} = \frac{1}{10^2}$$

3) Calculate the <u>answer</u>.

$$= 0.01 \text{ a.u.}$$

'a.u.' stands for 'arbitrary units'.

You can Artificially Create the Ideal Conditions for Farming

1) The most common way to artificially create the <u>ideal environment</u> for plants is to grow them in a <u>greenhouse</u>.

2) Greenhouses help to <u>trap</u> the Sun's <u>heat</u>, and make sure that the <u>temperature</u> doesn't become <u>limiting</u>. In winter a farmer or gardener might use a <u>heater</u> as well to keep the temperature at the ideal level. In summer it could get <u>too hot</u>, so they might use <u>shades</u> and <u>ventilation</u> to cool things down.

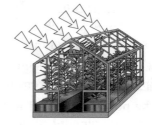

3) <u>Light</u> is always needed for photosynthesis, so commercial farmers often supply <u>artificial light</u> after the Sun goes down to give their plants more quality photosynthesis time.

4) Farmers and gardeners can also increase the level of <u>carbon dioxide</u> in the greenhouse. E.g. by using a <u>paraffin heater</u> to heat the greenhouse. As the paraffin burns, it makes carbon dioxide as a <u>by-product</u>.

5) Keeping plants <u>enclosed</u> in a greenhouse also makes it easier to keep them free from <u>pests</u> and <u>diseases</u>. The farmer can add <u>fertilisers</u> to the soil as well, to provide all the <u>minerals</u> needed for healthy growth.

6) Sorting all this out <u>costs money</u> — but if the farmer can keep the conditions <u>just right</u> for photosynthesis, the plants will grow much <u>faster</u> and a <u>decent crop</u> can be harvested much more <u>often</u>, which can then be <u>sold</u>. It's important that a farmer supplies just the <u>right amount</u> of heat, light, etc. — enough to make the plants grow well, but <u>not</u> more than the plants <u>need</u>, as this would just be <u>wasting money</u>.

Don't blame it on the sunshine, don't blame it on the CO_2...

Now don't let the inverse square law put you off learning everything on these past three pages.

Q1 An experiment was carried out to find out the effect of temperature on the rate of photosynthesis. Name two variables that should have been controlled in this experiment. [2 marks]

Q2 Write down the inverse square law. [1 mark]

Respiration and Metabolism

You need <u>energy</u> to keep your body going. Energy comes from <u>food</u>, and it's <u>transferred</u> by <u>respiration</u>.

Respiration is NOT "Breathing In and Out"

<u>Respiration</u> involves many reactions. These are really important reactions, as respiration transfers the <u>energy</u> that the cell needs to do just about everything — this energy is used for <u>all living processes</u>.

1) <u>Respiration</u> is <u>not</u> breathing in and breathing out, as you might think.

2) <u>Respiration</u> is the process of <u>transferring energy</u> from the <u>breakdown of glucose</u> (sugar) — and it goes on in <u>every cell</u> in your body <u>continuously</u>.

3) It happens in <u>plants</u> too. <u>All</u> living things <u>respire</u>. It's how they transfer <u>energy</u> from their <u>food</u> to their <u>cells</u>.

> <u>RESPIRATION</u> is the process of <u>TRANSFERRING ENERGY FROM GLUCOSE</u>, which goes on <u>IN EVERY CELL</u>.

4) Respiration is <u>exothermic</u> — it <u>transfers energy</u> to the <u>environment</u>.

Respiration Transfers Energy for All Kinds of Things

Here are <u>three examples</u> of how organisms <u>use</u> the <u>energy</u> transferred by respiration:

1) To build up <u>larger molecules</u> from <u>smaller</u> ones (like proteins from amino acids — see below).

2) In animals it's used to allow the <u>muscles</u> to <u>contract</u> (so they can <u>move</u> about).

3) In <u>mammals</u> and <u>birds</u> the energy is used to keep their <u>body temperature</u> steady in colder surroundings. (Unlike other animals, mammals and birds keep their bodies constantly warm.)

Metabolism is ALL the Chemical Reactions in an Organism

1) In a <u>cell</u> there are <u>lots</u> of <u>chemical reactions</u> happening <u>all the time</u>, which are controlled by <u>enzymes</u>.

2) Many of these reactions are <u>linked together</u> to form <u>bigger reactions</u>:

reactant →enzyme→ product →enzyme→ product →enzyme→ product

Enzymes are biological catalysts — see p.28.

3) In some of these reactions, <u>larger molecules</u> are <u>made</u> from smaller ones. For example:

- Lots of small <u>glucose</u> molecules are <u>joined together</u> in reactions to form <u>starch</u> (a storage molecule in plant cells), <u>glycogen</u> (a storage molecule in animal cells) and <u>cellulose</u> (a component of plant cell walls).
- <u>Lipid</u> molecules are each made from <u>one molecule</u> of <u>glycerol</u> and <u>three fatty acids</u>.
- <u>Glucose</u> is combined with <u>nitrate ions</u> to make <u>amino acids</u>, which are then made into <u>proteins</u>.

4) In other reactions, larger molecules are <u>broken down</u> into smaller ones. For example:

- <u>Glucose</u> is broken down in <u>respiration</u>. Respiration transfers energy to power <u>all</u> the reactions in the body that <u>make molecules</u>.
- <u>Excess protein</u> is <u>broken down</u> in a <u>reaction</u> to produce <u>urea</u>. Urea is then <u>excreted</u> in <u>urine</u>.

5) The <u>sum</u> (total) of <u>all</u> of the <u>reactions</u> that happen in a <u>cell</u> or the <u>body</u> is called its <u>metabolism</u>.

Don't stop respirin' — hold onto that feelin'...

Isn't it strange to think that each individual living cell in your body is respiring every second of every day, transferring energy from the food you eat. This energy is used to make molecules that our cells need.

Q1 Give two examples of how animals use the energy transferred by respiration. [2 marks]

Q2 What is metabolism? [1 mark]

Aerobic and Anaerobic Respiration

There are <u>two types</u> of <u>respiration</u>, don't cha know...

Aerobic Respiration Needs Plenty of Oxygen

1) <u>Aerobic respiration</u> is respiration using <u>oxygen</u>.
   It's the most <u>efficient</u> way to transfer energy from glucose.

2) Aerobic respiration goes on <u>all the time</u> in <u>plants</u> and <u>animals</u>.

3) Most of the reactions in <u>aerobic respiration</u> happen inside <u>mitochondria</u> (see page 11).

4) Here are the <u>word</u> and <u>symbol equations</u> for aerobic respiration:

$$\text{glucose} + \text{oxygen} \longrightarrow \text{carbon dioxide} + \text{water}$$

$$C_6H_{12}O_6 + 6O_2 \longrightarrow 6CO_2 + 6H_2O$$

Anaerobic Respiration is Used if There's Not Enough Oxygen

When you do vigorous exercise and your body can't supply enough <u>oxygen</u> to your muscles,
they start doing <u>anaerobic respiration</u> as well as aerobic respiration.

1) "Anaerobic" just means "<u>without</u> oxygen". It's the <u>incomplete breakdown</u> of glucose, making <u>lactic acid</u>.

2) Here's the <u>word equation</u> for anaerobic respiration in muscle cells:

$$\text{glucose} \longrightarrow \text{lactic acid}$$

3) <u>Anaerobic respiration</u> does <u>not transfer nearly as much energy</u> as aerobic respiration.
   This is because glucose <u>isn't fully oxidised</u> (because it doesn't combine with oxygen).

4) So, anaerobic respiration is only useful in <u>emergencies</u>, e.g. during exercise when it allows you to keep
   on using your muscles for a while longer.

Anaerobic Respiration in Plants and Yeast is Slightly Different

1) <u>Plants</u> and <u>yeast cells</u> can respire <u>without oxygen</u> too, but they produce <u>ethanol</u> (alcohol)
   and <u>carbon dioxide</u> instead of lactic acid.

2) Here is the <u>word equation</u> for anaerobic respiration in <u>plants</u> and <u>yeast cells</u>:

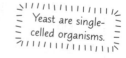

Yeast are single-celled organisms.

$$\text{glucose} \longrightarrow \text{ethanol} + \text{carbon dioxide}$$

3) Anaerobic respiration in <u>yeast cells</u> is called <u>fermentation</u>.

4) In the <u>food and drinks industry</u>, <u>fermentation</u> by yeast is of <u>great value</u>
   because it's used to make <u>bread</u> and <u>alcoholic drinks</u>, e.g. beer and wine.

5) In <u>bread-making</u>, it's the <u>carbon dioxide</u> from fermentation that makes bread <u>rise</u>.

6) In <u>beer</u> and <u>wine-making</u>, it's the fermentation process that produces <u>alcohol</u>.

I'd like a ham and fermentation sandwich please... yum

Fermentation is a really important process because of its use in making alcoholic drinks and bread.
We drink and eat so much of these that making them is big bucks. And it's all down to tiny yeast cells.

Q1   What are the reactants of aerobic respiration?   [2 marks]

Q2   What is the process of anaerobic respiration in yeast called?   [1 mark]

Exercise

When you exercise, your body responds in different ways to get enough energy to your cells.

When You Exercise You Respire More

1) Muscles need energy from respiration to contract. When you exercise, some of your muscles contract more frequently than normal so you need more energy. This energy comes from increased respiration.

2) The increase in respiration in your cells means you need to get more oxygen into them.

3) Your breathing rate and breath volume increase to get more oxygen into the blood, and your heart rate increases to get this oxygenated blood around the body faster. This removes CO_2 more quickly at the same time.

4) When you do really vigorous exercise (like sprinting) your body can't supply oxygen to your muscles quickly enough, so they start respiring anaerobically (see the previous page).

5) This is NOT the best way to transfer energy from glucose because lactic acid builds up in the muscles, which gets painful.

6) Long periods of exercise also cause muscle fatigue — the muscles get tired and then stop contracting efficiently.

> Remember, lactic acid is formed from the incomplete oxidation of glucose.

Anaerobic Respiration Leads to an Oxygen Debt

1) After resorting to anaerobic respiration, when you stop exercising you'll have an "oxygen debt".

2) An oxygen debt is the amount of extra oxygen your body needs to react with the build up of lactic acid and remove it from the cells. Oxygen reacts with the lactic acid to form harmless CO_2 and water.

3) In other words you have to "repay" the oxygen that you didn't get to your muscles in time, because your lungs, heart and blood couldn't keep up with the demand earlier on.

4) This means you have to keep breathing hard for a while after you stop, to get more oxygen into your blood, which is transported to the muscle cells.

5) The pulse and breathing rate stay high whilst there are high levels of lactic acid and underline{CO_2}.

6) Your body also has another way of coping with the high level of lactic acid — the blood that enters your muscles transports the lactic acid to the liver. In the liver, the lactic acid is converted back to glucose.

You Can Investigate The Effect of Exercise on The Body

1) You can measure breathing rate by counting breaths, and heart rate by taking the pulse.

2) E.g. you could take your pulse after:
   - sitting down for 5 minutes,
   - then after 5 minutes of gentle walking,
   - then again after 5 minutes of slow jogging,
   - then again after running for 5 minutes,
   and plot your results in a bar chart.

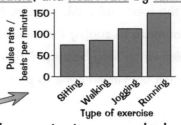

> You put two fingers on the inside of your wrist or your neck and count the number of pulses in 1 minute.

3) Your pulse rate will increase the more intense the exercise is, as your body needs to get more oxygen to the muscles and take more carbon dioxide away from the muscles.

4) To reduce the effect of any random errors on your results, do it as a group and plot the average pulse rate for each exercise.

> There's more about random error on page 5.

Oxygen debt — cheap to pay back...

At the end of a sprinting race you often see athletes breathing hard — now you know this is to get rid of the lactic acid that's built up in the muscles. But remember, the liver plays a role in breaking it down too.

Q1   What causes muscle fatigue?   [1 mark]

Q2   Explain what an "oxygen debt" is.   [1 mark]

Revision Questions for Topic 4

Well, it's all over for <u>Topic 4</u> folks — but I know how much you'll miss it, so here are some questions on it...

- Try these questions and <u>tick off each one</u> when you <u>get it right</u>.
- When you've done <u>all the questions</u> under a heading and are <u>completely happy</u> with it, tick it off.

<u>Photosynthesis (p.57-60)</u> ☐

1) Where in a plant cell does photosynthesis take place? ☑
2) How is energy transferred to a plant from its environment for photosynthesis? ☑
3) What is an endothermic reaction? ☑
4) What is the word equation for photosynthesis? ☑
5) What type of molecule is formed from combining glucose molecules with nitrate ions? ☑
6) Why do plants store glucose as starch? ☑
7) What is meant by a 'limiting factor' of photosynthesis? ☑
8) What effect would a low carbon dioxide concentration have on the rate of photosynthesis? ☑
9) What effect would a temperature above 45 °C have on the rate of photosynthesis? ☑
10) Describe a method that could be used to measure the effect of light intensity on the rate of photosynthesis. ☑
11) In the inverse square law, how are light intensity and distance linked? ☑
12) Give one way that the temperature can be decreased in a greenhouse. ☑
13) Give one way that the level of carbon dioxide can be increased in a greenhouse. ☑

<u>Respiration and Metabolism (p.61-63)</u> ☑

14) What is respiration? ☑
15) What is an exothermic reaction? ☑
16) What process transfers energy to make new molecules in cells? ☑
17) Give three examples of metabolic reactions. ☑
18) Name the products of aerobic respiration. ☑
19) What is produced by anaerobic respiration in muscle cells? ☑
20) What is the word equation for anaerobic respiration in yeast cells? ☑
21) Name two products of the food and drink industry that fermentation is needed for. ☑
22) Give three things that increase to supply the muscles with more oxygenated blood during exercise. ☑
23) What happens to muscles when they become fatigued? ☑
24) In what organ is lactic acid converted back to glucose? ☑

Homeostasis

Homeostasis — a word that strikes fear into the heart of many a GCSE student. But it's really not that bad at all. This page is a brief <u>introduction</u> to the topic, so you need to <u>nail all of this</u> before you can move on.

Homeostasis — Maintaining a Stable Internal Environment

1) The conditions inside your body need to be kept <u>steady</u>, even when the <u>external environment changes</u>. This is really important because your <u>cells</u> need the <u>right conditions</u> in order to <u>function properly</u>, including the right conditions for <u>enzyme action</u> (see p.28).

2) <u>Homeostasis</u> is all about the <u>regulation</u> of the conditions inside your body (and cells) to <u>maintain a stable internal environment</u>, in response to <u>changes</u> in both internal and external conditions.

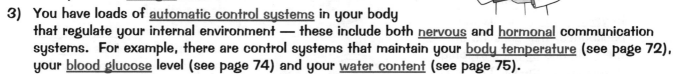

I'm not really a doctor — this clipboard isn't holding anything. But take it from me, homeostasis is one important topic.

3) You have loads of <u>automatic control systems</u> in your body that regulate your internal environment — these include both <u>nervous</u> and <u>hormonal</u> communication systems. For example, there are control systems that maintain your <u>body temperature</u> (see page 72), your <u>blood glucose</u> level (see page 74) and your <u>water content</u> (see page 75).

4) All your automatic control systems are made up of <u>three main components</u> which work together to maintain a steady condition — cells called <u>receptors</u>, <u>coordination centres</u> (including the brain, spinal cord and pancreas) and <u>effectors</u>.

Negative Feedback Counteracts Changes

Your automatic control systems keep your internal environment stable using a mechanism called <u>negative feedback</u>. When the level of something (e.g. water or temperature) gets <u>too high</u> or <u>too low</u>, your body uses negative feedback to bring it back to <u>normal</u>.

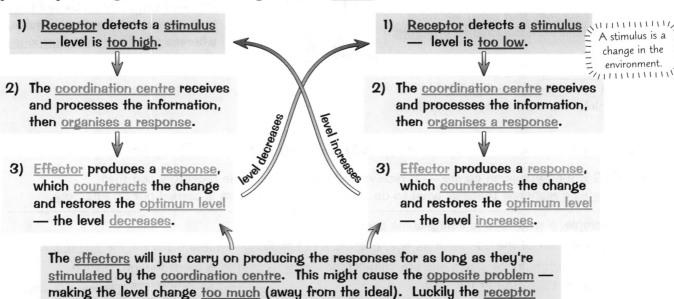

1) <u>Receptor</u> detects a <u>stimulus</u> — level is <u>too high</u>.

2) The <u>coordination centre</u> receives and processes the information, then <u>organises a response</u>.

3) <u>Effector</u> produces a <u>response</u>, which <u>counteracts</u> the change and restores the <u>optimum level</u> — the level <u>decreases</u>.

level decreases   level increases

1) <u>Receptor</u> detects a <u>stimulus</u> — level is <u>too low</u>.

A stimulus is a change in the environment.

2) The <u>coordination centre</u> receives and processes the information, then <u>organises a response</u>.

3) <u>Effector</u> produces a <u>response</u>, which <u>counteracts</u> the change and restores the <u>optimum level</u> — the level <u>increases</u>.

The <u>effectors</u> will just carry on producing the responses for as long as they're <u>stimulated</u> by the <u>coordination centre</u>. This might cause the <u>opposite problem</u> — making the level change <u>too much</u> (away from the ideal). Luckily the <u>receptor</u> detects if the level becomes <u>too different</u> and negative feedback <u>starts again</u>.

This process happens without you thinking about it — it's all <u>automatic</u>.

If you do enough revision, you can avoid negative feedback...

Negative feedback is a fancy-sounding name for a not-very-complicated idea. It's common sense really. For example, if you looked sad, I'd try and cheer you up. And if you looked really happy, I'd probably start to annoy you by flicking the backs of your ears. It stops things getting out of balance, I think.

Q1   Why do the internal conditions of your body need to be regulated?   [1 mark]

Q2   Name the component of a control system that detects stimuli.   [1 mark]

The Nervous System

Organisms need to <u>respond to stimuli</u> (changes in the environment) in order to <u>survive</u>. A <u>single-celled</u> organism can just <u>respond</u> to its environment, but the cells of <u>multicellular</u> organisms need to <u>communicate</u> with each other first. So as multicellular organisms evolved, they developed <u>nervous</u> and <u>hormonal communication systems</u>.

The Nervous System Detects and Reacts to Stimuli

The <u>nervous system</u> means that humans can <u>react to their surroundings</u> and <u>coordinate their behaviour</u>.

The Nervous System is made up of Different Parts

Central Nervous System (CNS)

In <u>vertebrates</u> (animals with backbones) this consists of the <u>brain</u> and <u>spinal cord</u> only. In <u>mammals</u>, the CNS is connected to the body by <u>sensory neurones</u> and <u>motor neurones</u>.

Sensory Neurones

The <u>neurones</u> that carry information as electrical impulses from the <u>receptors</u> to the CNS.

Motor Neurones

The <u>neurones</u> that carry electrical impulses from the CNS to <u>effectors</u>.

Effectors

All your <u>muscles</u> and <u>glands</u>, which respond to nervous impulses.

Receptors and Effectors can form part of Complex Organs

1) <u>Receptors</u> are the cells that <u>detect stimuli</u>.

2) There are many <u>different types</u> of receptors, such as <u>taste</u> receptors on the tongue and <u>sound</u> receptors in the ears.

3) Receptors can form part of <u>larger</u>, <u>complex organs</u>, e.g. the <u>retina</u> of the <u>eye</u> is covered in <u>light receptor cells</u>.

4) <u>Effectors respond</u> to nervous impulses and bring about a change.

5) Muscles and glands are known as <u>effectors</u> — they respond in different ways. <u>Muscles contract</u> in response to a nervous impulse, whereas <u>glands secrete hormones</u>.

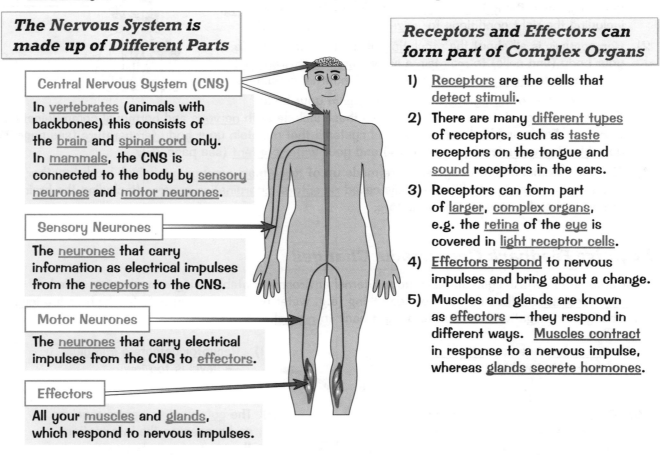

The Central Nervous System (CNS) Coordinates the Response

The CNS is a <u>coordination centre</u> — it receives information from the <u>receptors</u> and then <u>coordinates a response</u> (decides what to do about it). The response is carried out by <u>effectors</u>.

For example, a small bird is eating some seed...

1) ...when, out of the corner of its eye, it spots a cat skulking towards it (this is the <u>stimulus</u>).

2) The <u>receptors</u> in the bird's eye are <u>stimulated</u>. <u>Sensory neurones</u> carry the information from the <u>receptors</u> to the <u>CNS</u>.

3) The CNS <u>decides</u> what to do about it.

4) The CNS sends information to the muscles in the bird's wings (the <u>effectors</u>) along <u>motor neurones</u>. The muscles contract and the bird flies away to safety.

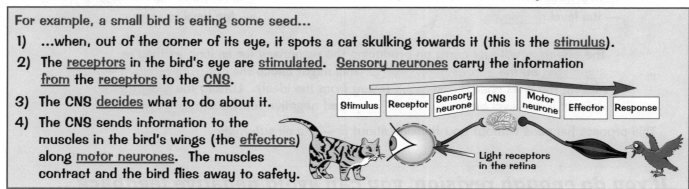

Stimulus | Receptor | Sensory neurone | CNS | Motor neurone | Effector | Response

Light receptors in the retina

Don't let the thought of exams play on your nerves...

Don't forget that it's only large animals like mammals and birds that have complex nervous systems. Simple animals like jellyfish don't — everything they do is a reflex response (see next page).

Q1 Name two types of effector. [2 marks]

Synapses and Reflexes

Neurones transmit information <u>very quickly</u> to and from the brain, and your brain <u>quickly decides</u> how to respond to a stimulus. But <u>reflexes</u> are even quicker...

Synapses *Connect Neurones*

1) The <u>connection</u> between <u>two neurones</u> is called a <u>synapse</u>.

2) The nerve signal is transferred by <u>chemicals</u> which <u>diffuse</u> (move) across the gap.

3) These chemicals then set off a <u>new electrical signal</u> in the <u>next</u> neurone.

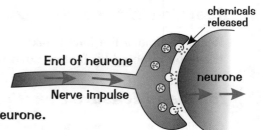

Reflexes *Help Prevent Injury*

1) <u>Reflexes</u> are <u>rapid</u>, <u>automatic</u> responses to certain stimuli that <u>don't involve</u> the <u>conscious</u> part of the brain — they can reduce the chances of being injured.

2) For example, if someone shines a <u>bright light</u> in your eyes, your <u>pupils</u> automatically get smaller so that less light gets into the eye — this stops it getting <u>damaged</u>.

3) Or if you get a shock, your body releases the <u>hormone</u> adrenaline automatically — it doesn't wait for you to <u>decide</u> that you're shocked.

4) The passage of information in a reflex (from receptor to effector) is called a <u>reflex arc</u>.

The Reflex Arc Goes Through the Central Nervous System

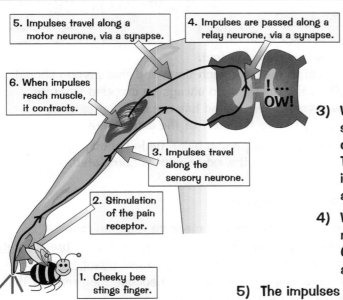

5. Impulses travel along a motor neurone, via a synapse.

4. Impulses are passed along a relay neurone, via a synapse.

6. When impulses reach muscle, it contracts.

3. Impulses travel along the sensory neurone.

2. Stimulation of the pain receptor.

1. Cheeky bee stings finger.

!... OW!

1) The neurones in reflex arcs go through the <u>spinal cord</u> or through an <u>unconscious part of the brain</u>.

2) When a <u>stimulus</u> (e.g. a painful bee sting) is detected by receptors, <u>impulses</u> are sent along a <u>sensory neurone</u> to a <u>relay neurone</u> in the CNS.

3) When the impulses reach a <u>synapse</u> between the sensory neurone and the relay neurone, they trigger chemicals to be released (see above). These chemicals cause impulses to be sent along the <u>relay neurone</u>.

Relay neurones connect sensory neurones to motor neurones.

4) When the impulses reach a <u>synapse</u> between the relay neurone and a motor neurone, the same thing happens. Chemicals are released and cause impulses to be sent along the <u>motor neurone</u>.

5) The impulses then travel along the motor neurone to the <u>effector</u> (which is usually a <u>muscle</u>, like in this example).

6) The <u>muscle</u> then <u>contracts</u> and moves your hand away from the bee.

7) Because you don't have to think about the response (which takes time) it's <u>quicker</u> than normal responses.

Don't get all twitchy — just learn it...

Reflexes bypass your conscious brain completely when a quick response is essential — your body just gets on with things. If you had to stop and think first, you'd end up a lot more sore (or worse).

Q1 What is a reflex action? [1 mark]

Q2 A chef touches a hot tray. A reflex reaction causes him to immediately move his hand away.
a) State the effector in this reflex reaction. [1 mark]
b) Describe the pathway of the reflex from stimulus to effector. [4 marks]

 **PRACTICAL** # Investigating Reaction Time

On your marks... get set... read this page.

Reaction Time is How Quickly You Respond

Reaction time is the time it takes to <u>respond to a stimulus</u> — it's often <u>less</u> than a <u>second</u>.
It can be <u>affected</u> by factors such as <u>age</u>, <u>gender</u> or <u>drugs</u>.

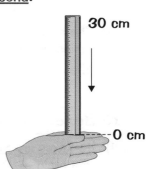

30 cm

You Can Measure Reaction Time

<u>Caffeine</u> is a drug that can <u>speed up</u> a person's reaction time.
The <u>effect of caffeine</u> on reaction time can be <u>measured</u> like this...

1) The person being tested should sit with their arm resting on the edge of a table
(this should stop them moving their arm up or down during the test).

2) Hold a <u>ruler</u> vertically between their thumb and forefinger. Make sure
that the <u>zero end</u> of the ruler is <u>level</u> with their thumb and finger.
Then <u>let go</u> without giving any warning.

0 cm

3) The person being tested should try to <u>catch the ruler</u>
as quickly as they can — as soon as they see it fall.

4) Reaction time is measured by the <u>number</u> on the ruler where it's caught.
The number should be read from the <u>top</u> of the <u>thumb</u>. The further down the
ruler it's caught (i.e. the higher the number), the slower their reaction time.

14 cm

5) <u>Repeat</u> the test several times then calculate the
<u>mean distance</u> that the ruler fell.

6) The person being tested should then have a <u>caffeinated drink</u>
(e.g. 300 ml of cola). After <u>ten minutes</u>, repeat steps 1 to 5.

With a little bit of maths, it's possible to work out the reaction time in seconds using the mean distance.

7) You need to <u>control any variables</u> to make sure that this is a fair test.
For example, you should use the <u>same person</u> to catch the ruler each time, and that person should
always use the <u>same hand</u> to catch the ruler. Also, the ruler should always be dropped from the
<u>same height</u>, and you should make sure that the person being tested has not had <u>any caffeine</u>
(or anything else that may affect their reaction time) before the start of the experiment.

8) Too much caffeine can cause <u>unpleasant side-effects</u>, so the person being tested should
avoid drinking <u>any more caffeine</u> for the rest of the day after the experiment is completed.

Reaction Time Can Be Measured Using a Computer

1) Simple <u>computer tests</u> can also be used to measure reaction time.
For example, the person being tested has to <u>click the mouse</u> (or <u>press a key</u>)
as soon as they see a stimulus on the screen, e.g. a box <u>change colour</u>.

2) Computers can give a <u>more precise</u> reaction time because they remove the
possibility of <u>human error</u> from the measurement.

3) As the computer can record the reaction time in <u>milliseconds</u>,
it can also give a more <u>accurate</u> measurement.

4) Using a computer can also remove the possibility that the person can
<u>predict</u> when to respond — using the ruler test, the catcher may learn
to <u>anticipate</u> the drop by reading the tester's <u>body language</u>.

Ready... Steady...

... Ah, too slow.

Q1 A student was measuring her reaction time using a computer test. She had to click the mouse when
the screen changed from red to green. She repeated the test five times. Her results were as follows:
242 ms, 256 ms, 253 ms, 249 ms, 235 ms.
Calculate the mean reaction time of the student.

[2 marks]

Topic 5 — Homeostasis and Response

The Brain

Scientists know a bit about the <u>brain</u> but <u>not as much</u> as they'd like. Their knowledge is improving with the invention of new <u>gadgetry</u> that helps them study the brain. Read on, it's pretty amazing stuff.

The Brain is Responsible for Complex Behaviours

1) Along with the spinal cord, the brain is part of the <u>central nervous system</u>.

2) It's made up of <u>billions</u> of <u>interconnected neurones</u> (neurones that are connected together).

3) The brain is in charge of all of our <u>complex behaviours</u>. It controls and coordinates everything you do — running, breathing, sleeping, remembering your gym kit...

4) We know that <u>different regions</u> of the brain carry out <u>different functions</u>:

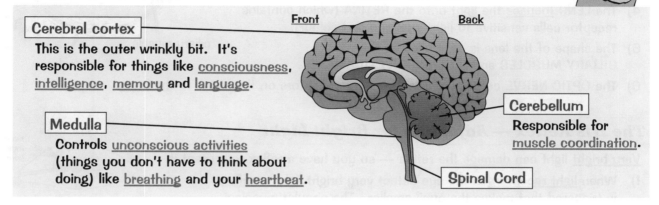

Cerebral cortex
This is the outer wrinkly bit. It's responsible for things like <u>consciousness</u>, <u>intelligence</u>, <u>memory</u> and <u>language</u>.

Front   Back

Cerebellum
Responsible for <u>muscle coordination</u>.

Medulla
Controls <u>unconscious activities</u> (things you don't have to think about doing) like <u>breathing</u> and your <u>heartbeat</u>.

Spinal Cord

Scientists Use a Range of Methods to Study the Brain

Scientists use a few different methods to study the brain and map out <u>which bits do what</u>:

Scientists that study the brain are called neuroscientists.

Studying patients with brain damage	If a <u>small</u> part of the brain has been <u>damaged</u>, the <u>effect</u> this has on the patient can tell you a lot about what the damaged part of the brain does. E.g. if an area at the back of the brain was damaged by a stroke and the patient went <u>blind</u>, you know that that area has something to do with <u>vision</u>.
Electrically stimulating the brain	The brain can be <u>stimulated electrically</u> by pushing a tiny <u>electrode</u> into the tissue and giving it a small zap of electricity. By observing what stimulating <u>different parts</u> of the brain does, it's possible to get an idea of what those parts do. E.g. when a certain part of the brain (known as the <u>motor area</u>) is stimulated, it causes <u>muscle contraction</u> and <u>movement</u>.
MRI Scans	A <u>magnetic resonance imaging (MRI) scanner</u> is a big fancy tube-like machine that can produce a very <u>detailed picture</u> of the brain's structures. Scientists use it to find out what areas of the brain are <u>active</u> when people are doing things like listening to music or trying to recall a memory. 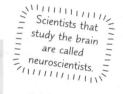

Messing With the Brain Can Have Consequences

1) Knowledge of how the brain works has led to the development of <u>treatments</u> for <u>disorders</u> of the nervous system. For example, <u>electrical stimulation</u> of the brain can help reduce <u>muscle tremors</u> caused by nervous system disorders such as Parkinson's disease.

2) However, the brain is incredibly <u>complex</u> and <u>delicate</u> — the investigation of brain function and any treatment of brain damage or disease is difficult. It also carries <u>risks</u>, such as <u>physical damage</u> to the brain or <u>increased problems</u> with brain function (e.g. difficulties with speech).

A whole page dedicated to that squidgy thing in your head...

...lucky you. But actually it's really fascinating stuff. It'll make it that bit easier to learn...

Q1   Name the region of the brain that controls coordinated movement.   [1 mark]

The Eye

The eye is a sense organ. There are several parts you need to learn about, so get focused.

Learn the Eye with All Its Labels

1) The SCLERA is the tough, supporting wall of the eye.
2) The CORNEA is the transparent outer layer found at the front of the eye. It refracts (bends) light into the eye.
3) The IRIS contains muscles that allow it to control the diameter of the PUPIL (the hole in the middle) and therefore how much light enters the eye.
4) The LENS focuses the light onto the RETINA (which contains receptor cells sensitive to light intensity and colour).
5) The shape of the lens is controlled by the CILIARY MUSCLES and SUSPENSORY LIGAMENTS.
6) The OPTIC NERVE carries impulses from the receptors on the retina to the brain.

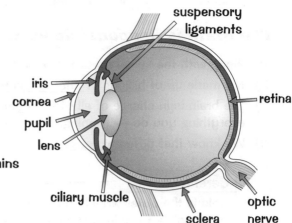

The Iris Reflex — Adjusting for Bright Light

Very bright light can damage the retina — so you have a reflex to protect it.

1) When light receptors in the eye detect very bright light, a reflex is triggered that makes the pupil smaller. The circular muscles in the iris contract and the radial muscles relax. This reduces the amount of light that can enter the eye.
2) The opposite process happens in dim light. This time, the radial muscles contract and the circular muscles relax, which makes the pupil wider.

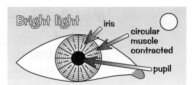

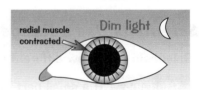

Focusing on Near and Distant Objects — Another Reflex

The eye focuses light on the retina by changing the shape of the lens — this is known as accommodation.

To look at near objects:

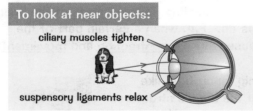

ciliary muscles tighten

suspensory ligaments relax

1) The ciliary muscles contract, which slackens the suspensory ligaments.
2) The lens becomes fat (more curved).
3) This increases the amount by which it refracts light.

To look at distant objects:

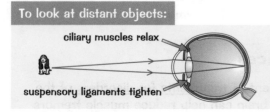

ciliary muscles relax

suspensory ligaments tighten

1) The ciliary muscles relax, which allows the suspensory ligaments to pull tight.
2) This makes the lens go thin (less curved).
3) So it refracts light by a smaller amount.

As you get older, your eye's lens loses flexibility, so it can't easily spring back to a round shape. This means light can't be focused well for near viewing, so older people often have to use reading glasses.

If the lens cannot refract the light by the right amount (so that it focuses on the retina), the person will be short- or long-sighted — see the next page for more.

Eye eye, Captain...

It doesn't matter how good you are at blagging in the exam — you need to learn those diagrams of the eye.

Q1   What name is given to the transparent layer at the front of the eye?   [1 mark]

Q2   Explain how the eye focuses on an object that's close to it.   [4 marks]

Topic 5 — Homeostasis and Response

Correcting Vision Defects

As you can see on the previous page, the way the eye works is quite <u>complex</u>. It's not surprising really that sometimes it <u>doesn't work so well</u>. Thankfully, we have ways of <u>correcting</u> it...

Some People are Long- or Short-Sighted

<u>Long-sighted</u> people are <u>unable to focus</u> on <u>near</u> objects:

1) This occurs when the <u>lens</u> is the wrong shape and doesn't <u>refract</u> (bend) the light enough or the <u>eyeball</u> is too <u>short</u>.

2) The images of near objects are brought into focus <u>behind</u> the <u>retina</u>.

3) You can use glasses with a <u>convex lens</u> (a lens which <u>curves outwards</u>) to correct it. The lens <u>refracts</u> the light rays so they focus on the <u>retina</u>.

4) The medical term for long-sightedness is <u>hyperopia</u>.

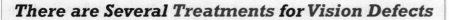

<u>Short-sighted</u> people are <u>unable to focus</u> on <u>distant</u> objects:

1) This occurs when the <u>lens</u> is the wrong shape and refracts the light <u>too much</u> or the <u>eyeball</u> is too <u>long</u>.

2) The images of distant objects are brought into focus <u>in front</u> of the <u>retina</u>.

3) You can use glasses with a <u>concave lens</u> (a lens which <u>curves inwards</u>) to correct it, so that the light rays focus on the <u>retina</u>.

4) The medical term for short-sightedness is <u>myopia</u>.

There are Several Treatments for Vision Defects

Wearing glasses isn't for everyone. You need to know about these <u>alternatives</u>:

<u>CONTACT LENSES</u>: <u>Contact lenses</u> are thin lenses that sit on the <u>surface</u> of the eye and are shaped to <u>compensate</u> for the fault in focusing. They're popular because they are <u>lightweight</u> and almost <u>invisible</u>. They're also more <u>convenient</u> than glasses for activities like <u>sports</u>. The two main types of contact lenses are <u>hard lenses</u> and <u>soft lenses</u>. Soft lenses are generally more <u>comfortable</u>, but carry a higher risk of <u>eye infections</u> than hard lenses.

<u>LASER EYE SURGERY</u>: Bad eyesight can sometimes be corrected with <u>laser eye surgery</u>. A laser can be used to <u>vaporise tissue</u>, changing the <u>shape</u> of the cornea (and so changing how strongly it refracts light into the eye). <u>Slimming it down</u> makes it <u>less powerful</u> and can improve <u>short sight</u>. <u>Changing the shape</u> so that it's <u>more powerful</u> will improve <u>long sight</u>. The surgeon can <u>precisely</u> control how much tissue the laser takes off, completely correcting the vision. However, like all <u>surgical procedures</u>, there is a risk of <u>complications</u>, such as infection or the eye reacting in a way that makes your vision worse than before.

<u>REPLACEMENT LENS SURGERY</u>: Sometimes long-sightedness may be more effectively treated by <u>replacing</u> the lens of the eye (rather than altering the shape of the cornea with laser eye surgery). In <u>replacement lens surgery</u>, the natural lens of the eye is <u>removed</u> and an <u>artificial lens</u>, made of <u>clear plastic</u>, is inserted in its place. As it involves work <u>inside</u> the eye, replacing a lens carries <u>higher risks</u> than laser eye surgery, including possible damage to the <u>retina</u> (which could lead to loss of sight).

I think I'm a little long-sighted...

If you can read this you've got better eyesight than me!

You won't have to draw those diagrams for different lenses in the exam, but you may have to interpret them, so it's probably for the best that you make sure you totally understand what's going on in each one.

Q1   Explain the cause of short-sightedness.   [2 marks]

Q2   How can glasses help a long-sighted person focus on something nearby?   [1 mark]

Controlling Body Temperature

The body has to keep its insides at around <u>37 °C</u> — the <u>optimum temperature</u> for <u>enzymes</u> in the body.

Body Temperature Must be Kept Constant

Core body temperature is the temperature inside your body, where your internal organs are.

1) The body has to <u>balance</u> the amount of <u>energy gained</u> (e.g. through respiration) and <u>lost</u> to keep the <u>core body temperature constant</u>.

2) There is a <u>thermoregulatory centre</u> in the <u>brain</u>, which contains <u>receptors</u> that are sensitive to the temperature of the <u>blood</u> flowing through the brain.

3) The thermoregulatory centre also receives impulses from <u>temperature receptors</u> in the <u>skin</u>, giving information about <u>skin temperature</u>.

1) <u>Temperature receptors</u> detect that core body temperature is <u>too high</u>.

2) The <u>thermoregulatory centre</u> acts as a <u>coordination centre</u> — it receives information from the temperature receptors and <u>triggers</u> the <u>effectors</u> automatically.

3) <u>Effectors</u>, e.g. sweat glands, produce a <u>response</u> (see below) and <u>counteract</u> the change.

body cools down *body warms up*

1) <u>Temperature receptors</u> detect that core body temperature is <u>too low</u>.

2) The <u>thermoregulatory centre</u> acts as a <u>coordination centre</u> — it receives information from the temperature receptors and <u>triggers</u> the <u>effectors</u> automatically.

3) <u>Effectors</u>, e.g. muscles, produce a <u>response</u> (see below) and <u>counteract</u> the change.

Some effectors work <u>antagonistically</u>, e.g. one effector heats and another cools — they'll work at the same time to achieve a very precise temperature. This mechanism allows a <u>more sensitive response</u>.

The Body has Some Nifty Tricks for Altering its Temperature

<u>Different responses</u> are produced by <u>effectors</u> to <u>counteract</u> an increase or decrease in <u>body temperature</u>.

When you're TOO HOT:

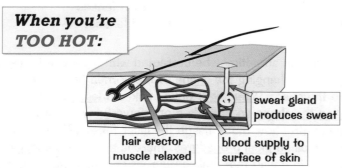
sweat gland produces sweat
hair erector muscle relaxed
blood supply to surface of skin

1) <u>Sweat</u> is produced by sweat glands and <u>evaporates</u> from the skin. This transfers energy to the <u>environment</u>.

2) The <u>blood vessels</u> supplying the skin <u>dilate</u> so more blood flows close to the surface of the skin. This is called <u>vasodilation</u>. This helps <u>transfer energy</u> from the skin to the environment.

When you're TOO COLD:

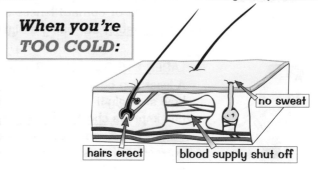
no sweat
hairs erect
blood supply shut off

1) <u>Hairs</u> stand up to trap an <u>insulating layer</u> of <u>air</u>.

2) <u>No sweat</u> is produced.

3) Blood vessels supplying skin capillaries <u>constrict</u> to <u>close off</u> the skin's blood supply. This is called <u>vasoconstriction</u>.

4) When you're <u>cold</u> you <u>shiver</u> too (your muscles contract automatically). This needs <u>respiration</u>, which transfers some <u>energy</u> to <u>warm</u> the body.

Shiver me timbers — it's a wee bit nippy in here...

People who are exposed to extreme cold for a long time without protection can get frostbite — the blood supply to the fingers and toes is cut off to reduce the amount of energy lost (but this kills the cells, and they go black)... yuk.

Q1 Name the area of the brain that controls body temperature. [1 mark]

Topic 5 — Homeostasis and Response

The Endocrine System

The other way to send information around the body (apart from along nerves) is by using hormones.

Hormones *Are Chemical Messengers* Sent in the Blood

1) Hormones are chemical molecules released directly into the blood. They are carried in the blood to other parts of the body, but only affect particular cells in particular organs (called target organs). Hormones control things in organs and cells that need constant adjustment.

2) Hormones are produced in (and secreted by) various glands, called endocrine glands. These glands make up your endocrine system.

3) Hormones tend to have relatively long-lasting effects.

4) Here are some examples of glands:

THE PITUITARY GLAND

The pituitary gland produces many hormones that regulate body conditions. It is sometimes called the 'master gland' because these hormones act on other glands, directing them to release hormones that bring about change.

OVARIES — females only

Produce oestrogen, which is involved in the menstrual cycle (see page 77).

TESTES — males only

Produce testosterone, which controls puberty and sperm production in males (see page 77).

THYROID

This produces thyroxine, which is involved in regulating things like the rate of metabolism, heart rate and temperature.

ADRENAL GLAND

This produces adrenaline, which is used to prepare the body for a 'fight or flight' response (see page 80).

THE PANCREAS

This produces insulin, which is used to regulate the blood glucose level (see next page).

Hormones *and Nerves Have Differences*

NERVES:
- Very FAST action.
- Act for a very SHORT TIME.
- Act on a very PRECISE AREA.

HORMONES:
- SLOWER action.
- Act for a LONG TIME.
- Act in a more GENERAL way.

So if you're not sure whether a response is nervous or hormonal, have a think...

1) If the response is really quick, it's probably nervous. Some information needs to be passed to effectors really quickly (e.g. pain signals, or information from your eyes telling you about the lion heading your way), so it's no good using hormones to carry the message — they're too slow.

2) But if a response lasts for a long time, it's probably hormonal. For example, when you get a shock, a hormone called adrenaline is released into the body (causing the fight or flight response, where your body is hyped up ready for action). You can tell it's a hormonal response (even though it kicks in pretty quickly) because you feel a bit wobbly for a while afterwards.

Nerves, hormones — no wonder revision makes me tense...

Hormones control various organs and cells in the body, though they tend to control things that aren't immediately life-threatening (so things like sexual development, blood sugar level, water content, etc.).

Q1 Why is the pituitary gland referred to as the 'master gland'? [1 mark]

Controlling Blood Glucose

Blood glucose is also controlled as part of homeostasis. Insulin and glucagon are the two hormones involved.

Insulin and Glucagon Control Blood Glucose Level

1) Eating foods containing carbohydrate puts glucose (a type of sugar) into the blood from the gut.

2) The normal metabolism of cells removes glucose from the blood.

3) Vigorous exercise removes much more glucose from the blood.

4) Excess glucose can be stored as glycogen in the liver and in the muscles.

5) The level of glucose in the blood must be kept steady. Changes are monitored and controlled by the pancreas, using the hormones insulin and glucagon, in a negative feedback cycle:

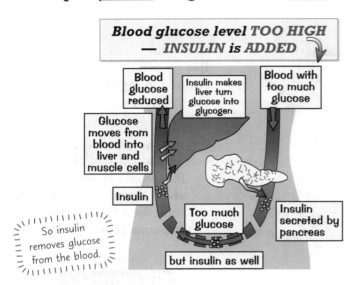

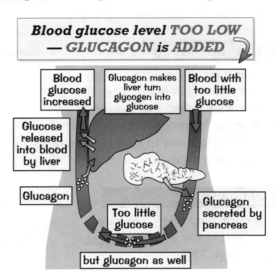

With Diabetes, You Can't Control Your Blood Sugar Level

Diabetes is a condition that affects your ability to control your blood sugar level. There are two types:

1) Type 1 diabetes is where the pancreas produces little or no insulin. This means a person's blood glucose level can rise to a level that can kill them. People with Type 1 diabetes need insulin therapy — this usually involves several injections of insulin throughout the day, most likely at mealtimes. This makes sure that glucose is removed from the blood quickly once the food has been digested, stopping the level getting too high. It's a very effective treatment. The amount of insulin that needs to be injected depends on the person's diet and how active they are. As well as insulin therapy, people with Type 1 diabetes need to think about limiting the intake of food rich in simple carbohydrates, e.g. sugars (which cause the blood glucose to rise rapidly) and taking regular exercise (which helps to remove excess glucose from the blood).

2) Type 2 diabetes is where a person becomes resistant to their own insulin (they still produce insulin, but their body's cells don't respond properly to the hormone). This can also cause a person's blood sugar level to rise to a dangerous level. Being overweight can increase your chance of developing Type 2 diabetes, as obesity is a major risk factor in the development of the disease. Type 2 diabetes can be controlled by eating a carbohydrate-controlled diet and getting regular exercise.

And people used to think the pancreas was just a cushion... (true)

This stuff can seem a bit confusing at first, but if you learn those two diagrams, it should get a bit easier. In the exam, you might be given a graph showing the effect of insulin on blood glucose level and be asked to interpret the data — if you do, just use what you know about reading graphs. Easy really.

Q1   Describe how the blood glucose level is returned to normal when it is too high.   [3 marks]

The Kidneys

The kidneys are really important in this whole homeostasis thing.

Kidneys Basically Act as Filters to "Clean the Blood"

The kidneys make urine by taking waste products (and other unwanted substances) out of your blood. Substances are filtered out of the blood as it passes through the kidneys. This process is called filtration. Useful substances like glucose, some ions and the right amount of water are then absorbed back into the blood. This process is called selective reabsorption. The substances that are removed from the body in urine include:

1 UREA

1) Proteins (and the amino acids that they are broken down into) can't be stored by the body — so any excess amino acids are converted into fats and carbohydrates, which can be stored. This occurs in the liver and involves a process called deamination.

2) Ammonia is produced as a waste product from this process.

3) Ammonia is toxic so it's converted to urea in the liver. Urea is then transported to the kidneys, where it's filtered out of the blood and excreted from the body in urine.

A small, unregulated amount of urea is also lost from the skin in sweat.

2 IONS

1) Ions such as sodium are taken into the body in food, and then absorbed into the blood.

2) If the ion (or water) content of the body is wrong, this could upset the balance between ions and water, meaning too much or too little water is drawn into cells by osmosis (see page 21). Having the wrong amount of water can damage cells or mean they don't work as well as normal.

3) Some ions are lost in sweat (which tastes salty, you may have noticed). However, this amount is not regulated, so the right balance of ions in the body must be maintained by the kidneys. The right amount of ions is reabsorbed into the blood after filtration and the rest is removed from the body in urine.

3 WATER

1) The body has to constantly balance the water coming in against the water going out.

2) We lose water from the skin in sweat and from the lungs when breathing out.

3) We can't control how much we lose in these ways, so the amount of water is balanced by the amount we consume and the amount removed by the kidneys in urine.

The Concentration of Urine is Controlled by a Hormone

1) The concentration of urine is controlled by a hormone called anti-diuretic hormone (ADH). This is released into the bloodstream by the pituitary gland.

2) The brain monitors the water content of the blood and instructs the pituitary gland to release ADH into the blood according to how much is needed.

3) The whole process of water content regulation is controlled by negative feedback (see page 65). This means that if the water content gets too high or too low a mechanism will be triggered that brings it back to normal.

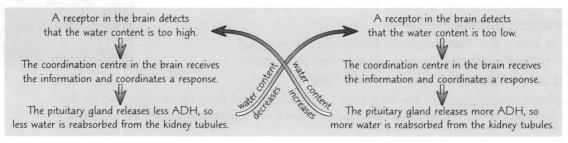

Adjusting water content — blood, sweat and, erm, wee...

The kidneys excrete about 547.5 litres of urine a year... that's five baths full. (Not that you should put it there.)

Q1   Alcohol suppresses the production of ADH. Suggest how this can lead to dehydration.   [2 marks]

Kidney Failure

If someone's kidneys stop working, there are basically two treatments — regular dialysis or a transplant.

The Kidneys Remove Waste Substances from the Blood

1) If the kidneys don't work properly, waste substances build up in the blood and you lose your ability to control the levels of ions and water in your body. Eventually, this results in death.

2) People with kidney failure can be kept alive by having dialysis treatment — where machines do the job of the kidneys. Or they can have a kidney transplant.

The kidneys are incredibly important — if they don't work as they should, you can get problems in the heart, bones, nervous system, stomach, mouth, etc.

Dialysis Machines Filter the Blood

1) Dialysis has to be done regularly to keep the concentrations of dissolved substances in the blood at normal levels, and to remove waste substances.

2) In a dialysis machine the person's blood flows between partially permeable membranes, surrounded by dialysis fluid. It's permeable to things like ions and waste substances, but not big molecules like proteins (just like the membranes in the kidney).

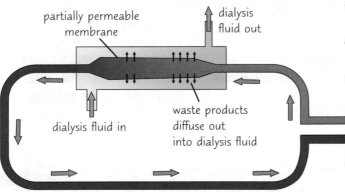

partially permeable membrane

dialysis fluid out

waste products diffuse out into dialysis fluid

dialysis fluid in

from person

back to person

3) The dialysis fluid has the same concentration of dissolved ions and glucose as healthy blood.

4) This means that useful dissolved ions and glucose won't be lost from the blood during dialysis.

5) Only waste substances (such as urea) and excess ions and water diffuse across the barrier.

6) Many patients with kidney failure have to have a dialysis session three times a week. Each session takes 3-4 hours — not much fun.

7) Plus, dialysis may cause blood clots or infections.

8) Being on a dialysis machine is not a pleasant experience and it is expensive for the NHS to run.

9) However, dialysis can buy a patient with kidney failure valuable time until a donor organ is found.

Kidney Transplants are a Cure, but can be Rejected

1) At the moment, the only cure for kidney failure is to have a kidney transplant.

2) Healthy kidneys are usually transplanted from people who have died suddenly.

3) The person who died has to be on the organ donor register or carry a donor card (provided their relatives agree too).

4) Kidneys can also be transplanted from people who are still alive (as we all have two of them) but there is a small risk to the person donating the kidney.

5) There is also a risk that the donor kidney can be rejected by the patient's immune system. The patient is treated with drugs to prevent this but it can still happen.

6) Transplants are cheaper (in the long run) than dialysis and they can put an end to the hours patients have to spend on dialysis, but there are long waiting lists for kidneys.

Dialysis or transplant? Both have their downsides...

Donor kidneys are ideally matched by blood type (and a few other things) to the recipient, which make them less likely to be rejected. However, it means a potentially long waiting time for a suitable kidney.

Q1   What is the purpose of the partially permeable membrane in a dialysis machine?   [2 marks]

Topic 5 — Homeostasis and Response

Puberty and the Menstrual Cycle

The monthly release of an egg from a woman's ovaries is part of the menstrual cycle.

Hormones Promote Sexual Characteristics at Puberty

At puberty, your body starts releasing sex hormones that trigger off secondary sexual characteristics (such as the development of facial hair in men and breasts in women) and cause eggs to mature in women.

- In men, the main reproductive hormone is testosterone. It's produced by the testes and stimulates sperm production.
- In women, the main reproductive hormone is oestrogen. It's produced by the ovaries. As well as bringing about physical changes, oestrogen is also involved in the menstrual cycle.

The Menstrual Cycle Has Four Stages

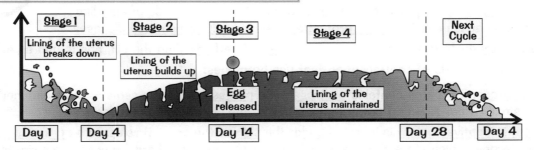

Stage 1 Day 1 — menstruation starts. The uterus lining breaks down for about four days.

Stage 2 The uterus lining builds up again, from day 4 to day 14, into a thick spongy layer full of blood vessels, ready to receive a fertilised egg.

Stage 3 An egg develops and is released from the ovary at day 14 — this is called ovulation.

Stage 4 The wall is then maintained for about 14 days until day 28. If no fertilised egg has landed on the uterus wall by day 28, the spongy lining starts to break down and the whole cycle starts again.

It's Controlled by Four Hormones

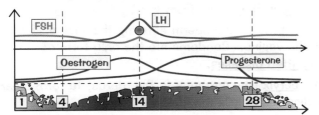

1 FSH (Follicle-Stimulating Hormone)
  1) Produced in the pituitary gland.
  2) Causes an egg to mature in one of the ovaries, in a structure called a follicle.
  3) Stimulates the ovaries to produce oestrogen.

2 Oestrogen
  1) Produced in the ovaries.
  2) Causes the lining of the uterus to grow.
  3) Stimulates the release of LH (which causes the release of an egg) and inhibits release of FSH.

3 LH (Luteinising Hormone)
  1) Produced by the pituitary gland.
  2) Stimulates the release of an egg at day 14 (ovulation).

4 Progesterone
  1) Produced in the ovaries by the remains of the follicle after ovulation.
  2) Maintains the lining of the uterus during the second half of the cycle. When the level of progesterone falls, the lining breaks down.
  3) Inhibits the release of LH and FSH.

Which came first — the chicken or the luteinising hormone...

Female or not, learn this page... till you know what hormone does what and understand that there graph.

Q1 Name the hormone that stimulates an egg to mature in the ovary. [1 mark]

Q2 Where is testosterone produced in the male body? [1 mark]

Controlling Fertility

Pregnancy can happen if sperm reaches the ovulated egg. Contraception tries to stop this happening.

Hormones Can Be Used to Reduce Fertility

1) Oestrogen can be used to prevent the release of an egg — so it can be used as a method of contraception.

2) This may seem kind of strange (since naturally oestrogen helps stimulate the release of eggs). But if oestrogen is taken every day to keep the level of it permanently high, it inhibits the production of FSH, and after a while egg development and production stop and stay stopped.

3) Progesterone also reduces fertility, e.g. by stimulating the production of thick mucus which prevents any sperm getting through and reaching an egg.

4) The pill is an oral contraceptive containing oestrogen and progesterone (known as the combined oral contraceptive pill).

5) It's over 99% effective at preventing pregnancy, but it can cause side effects like headaches and nausea and it doesn't protect against sexually transmitted diseases.

6) There's also a progesterone-only pill — it has fewer side effects than the pill, and is just as effective.

7) There are other methods of contraception that use hormones:

- The contraceptive patch contains oestrogen and progesterone (the same as the combined pill). It's a small (5 cm × 5 cm) patch that's stuck to the skin. Each patch lasts one week.
- The contraceptive implant is inserted under the skin of the arm. It releases a continuous amount of progesterone, which stops the ovaries releasing eggs, makes it hard for sperm to swim to the egg, and stops any fertilised egg implanting in the uterus. An implant can last for three years.
- The contraceptive injection also contains progesterone. Each dose lasts 2 to 3 months.
- An intrauterine device (IUD) is a T-shaped device that is inserted into the uterus to kill sperm and prevent implantation of a fertilised egg. There are two main types — plastic IUDs that release progesterone and copper IUDs that prevent the sperm surviving in the uterus.

Barriers Stop Egg and Sperm Meeting

1) Non-hormonal forms of contraception are designed to stop the sperm from getting to the egg.

2) Condoms are worn over the penis during intercourse to prevent the sperm entering the vagina. There are also female condoms that are worn inside the vagina. Condoms are the only form of contraception that will protect against sexually transmitted diseases.

3) A diaphragm is a shallow plastic cup that fits over the cervix (the entrance to the uterus) to form a barrier. It has to be used with spermicide (a substance that disables or kills the sperm).

4) Spermicide can be used alone as a form of contraception, but it is not as effective (only about 70-80%).

There are More Drastic Ways to Avoid Pregnancy

STERILISATION — Sterilisation involves cutting or tying the fallopian tubes (which connect the ovaries to the uterus) in a female, or the sperm duct (the tube between the testes and penis) in a male. This is a permanent procedure. However, there is a very small chance that the tubes can rejoin.

'NATURAL' METHODS — Pregnancy may be avoided by finding out when in the menstrual cycle the woman is most fertile and avoiding sexual intercourse on those days. It's popular with people who think that hormonal and barrier methods are unnatural, but it's not very effective.

ABSTINENCE — The only way to be completely sure that sperm and egg don't meet is to not have intercourse.

The winner of best contraceptive ever — just not doing it...

You might be asked to evaluate the different hormonal and non-hormonal methods of contraception in your exam. If you do, make sure you weigh up and write about both the pros and the cons of each method. Exciting stuff.

Q1   Name two forms of contraception that reduce fertility by releasing oestrogen.   [2 marks]

More on Controlling Fertility

Scientific advances in <u>understanding fertility</u> have led to many <u>infertile</u> women being helped to <u>have babies</u>.

Hormones Can Be Used to Increase Fertility

1) Some women have levels of <u>FSH</u> (follicle-stimulating hormone) that are <u>too low</u> to cause their <u>eggs to mature</u>. This means that <u>no eggs</u> are <u>released</u> and the women <u>can't get pregnant</u>.

2) The hormones <u>FSH</u> and <u>LH</u> can be given to women in a <u>fertility drug</u> to stimulate <u>ovulation</u>.

PROS | It helps a lot of women to <u>get pregnant</u> when previously they couldn't... pretty obvious.

CONS | It <u>doesn't always work</u> — some women may have to do it many times, which can be <u>expensive</u>.
<u>Too many eggs</u> could be stimulated, resulting in unexpected <u>multiple pregnancies</u> (twins, triplets, etc.).

IVF Can Also Help Couples to Have Children

If a woman cannot get pregnant using medication, she may chose to try <u>IVF</u> ("*in vitro* fertilisation").

1) IVF involves collecting <u>eggs</u> from the woman's ovaries and fertilising them in a <u>lab</u> using the man's <u>sperm</u>.

2) IVF treatment can also involve a technique called <u>Intra-Cytoplasmic Sperm Injection (ICSI)</u>, where the sperm is <u>injected</u> directly into an egg. It's useful if the man has a very low sperm count.

3) The fertilised eggs are then grown into <u>embryos</u> in a laboratory incubator.

4) Once the embryos are <u>tiny balls of cells</u>, one or two of them are <u>transferred</u> to the woman's uterus to improve the chance of <u>pregnancy</u>.

5) <u>FSH</u> and <u>LH</u> are given before egg collection to <u>stimulate several eggs to mature</u> (so more than one egg can be collected).

PRO | Fertility treatment can give an infertile couple <u>a child</u> — a pretty obvious <u>benefit</u>.

CONS | <u>Multiple births</u> can happen if more than one embryo grows into a baby — these are <u>risky</u> for the mother and babies (there's a higher risk of miscarriage, stillbirth...).
The success rate of IVF is <u>low</u> — the average success rate in the UK is about **26%**. This makes the process incredibly <u>stressful</u> and often <u>upsetting</u>, especially if it ends in <u>multiple failures</u>.
As well as being <u>emotionally stressful</u>, the process is also <u>physically stressful</u> for the woman.
Some women have a strong <u>reaction</u> to the hormones — e.g. <u>abdominal pain</u>, <u>vomiting</u>, <u>dehydration</u>.

Advances in <u>microscope techniques</u> have helped to improve the techniques (and therefore the <u>success rate</u>) of IVF. Specialised <u>micro-tools</u> have been developed to use on the eggs and sperm under the microscope. They're also used to <u>remove</u> single cells from the embryo for <u>genetic testing</u> (to check that it is <u>healthy</u> — see page 93). More recently, the development of <u>time-lapse imaging</u> (using a microscope and camera built into the incubator) means that the growth of the embryos can be <u>continuously monitored</u> to help identify those that are more likely to result in a <u>successful pregnancy</u>.

Some People Are Against IVF

1) The process of IVF often results in <u>unused</u> embryos that are eventually destroyed. Because of this, some people think it is <u>unethical</u> because each embryo is a <u>potential human life</u>.

2) The <u>genetic testing</u> of embryos before implantation also raises ethical issues as some people think it could lead to the selection of <u>preferred characteristics</u>, such as gender or eye colour.

Nothing funny here, sorry...

Fertility treatment can help to increase the chance of pregnancy, but it can be hard on those involved.

Q1   What is the role of FSH and LH during IVF?   [1 mark]

Q2   Give one drawback to using hormones to increase fertility.   [1 mark]

Adrenaline and Thyroxine

You've met a lot of <u>human hormones</u> so far, but <u>two more</u> won't hurt. Then that's it, I promise...

Adrenaline *Prepares You for "Fight or Flight"*

1) <u>Adrenaline</u> is a hormone released by the <u>adrenal glands</u>, which are <u>just above the kidneys</u> (see p.73).

2) Adrenaline is released in response to <u>stressful or scary situations</u> — your brain detects fear or stress and sends <u>nervous impulses</u> to the adrenal glands, which respond by secreting adrenaline.

3) It gets the body ready for '<u>fight or flight</u>' by triggering mechanisms that <u>increase</u> the supply of <u>oxygen</u> and <u>glucose</u> to cells in the <u>brain</u> and <u>muscles</u>. For example, adrenaline <u>increases heart rate</u>.

Hormone Release *can be Affected by Negative Feedback*

Your body can <u>control</u> the levels of hormones (and other substances) in the blood using <u>negative feedback</u> <u>systems</u>. When the body detects that the level of a substance has gone <u>above or below</u> the <u>normal level</u>, it <u>triggers a response</u> to bring the level <u>back to normal</u> again. Here's an example of just that:

Thyroxine *Regulates Metabolism*

1) <u>Thyroxine</u> is a hormone released by the <u>thyroid gland</u>, which is in the <u>neck</u> (see p.73).

Thyroxine is made in the thyroid gland from iodine and amino acids.

2) It plays an important role in regulating the <u>basal metabolic rate</u> — the speed at which chemical reactions in the body occur while the body is at <u>rest</u>. Thyroxine is also important for loads of processes in the body, such as stimulating <u>protein synthesis</u> for <u>growth</u> and <u>development</u>.

3) Thyroxine is released in response to <u>thyroid stimulating hormone</u> (TSH), which is released from the <u>pituitary gland</u>.

4) A <u>negative feedback system</u> keeps the amount of thyroxine in the blood at the right level — when the level of thyroxine in the blood is <u>higher than normal</u>, the secretion of <u>TSH</u> from the pituitary gland is <u>inhibited</u> (stopped). This <u>reduces</u> the amount of <u>thyroxine</u> released from the thyroid gland, so the level in the blood <u>falls</u> back towards <u>normal</u>.

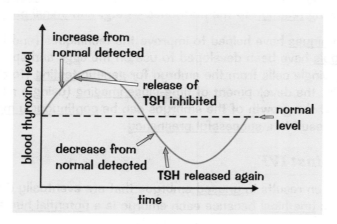

Negative feedback sucks, especially from your science teacher...

You can think about negative feedback working like a thermostat — if the temperature gets too low, the thermostat will turn the heating on, then if the temperature gets too high, it'll turn the heating off again.

Q1 Name the gland that releases thyroxine. [1 mark]

Q2 Describe the response if the level of thyroxine in the blood gets too high. [3 marks]

Plant Hormones

Plants <u>don't</u> just grow randomly. Plant hormones make sure they grow in the <u>right direction</u>.

Auxin is a Plant Growth Hormone

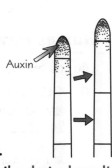

1) <u>Auxin</u> is a <u>plant hormone</u> that controls <u>growth</u> near the <u>tips</u> of <u>shoots</u> and <u>roots</u>.
2) It controls the growth of a plant in response to <u>light</u> (<u>phototropism</u>) and <u>gravity</u> (<u>gravitropism</u> or <u>geotropism</u>).
3) Auxin is produced in the <u>tips</u> and <u>moves backwards</u> to stimulate the <u>cell elongation</u> <u>(enlargement) process</u> which occurs in the cells <u>just behind</u> the tips.
4) If the tip of a shoot is <u>removed</u>, no auxin is available and the shoot may <u>stop growing</u>.
5) Extra auxin <u>promotes</u> growth in the <u>shoot</u> but <u>inhibits</u> growth in the <u>root</u> — producing the <u>desired result</u>...

Shoots grow towards light

1) When a <u>shoot tip</u> is exposed to <u>light</u>, <u>more auxin</u> accumulates on the side that's in the <u>shade</u> than the side that's in the light.
2) This makes the cells grow (elongate) <u>faster</u> on the <u>shaded side</u>, so the shoot bends <u>towards</u> the light.

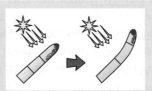

Shoots grow away from gravity and roots grow towards gravity

1) When a <u>shoot</u> is growing sideways, <u>gravity</u> produces an unequal distribution of auxin in the tip, with <u>more auxin</u> on the <u>lower side</u>.
2) This causes the lower side to grow <u>faster</u>, bending the shoot <u>upwards</u>.
3) A <u>root</u> growing sideways will also have more auxin on its <u>lower side</u>.
4) But in a root the <u>extra</u> auxin <u>inhibits</u> growth. This means the cells on <u>top</u> elongate faster, and the root bends <u>downwards</u>.

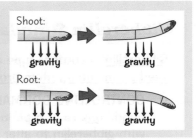

You can Investigate Plant Growth Responses

PRACTICAL

You can investigate the effect of <u>light</u> on the <u>growth</u> of cress seeds like this...

1) Put <u>10 cress seeds</u> into three different Petri dishes, each lined with <u>moist filter paper</u>. (Remember to label your dishes, e.g. A, B, C.)

2) Shine a <u>light</u> onto one of the dishes from <u>above</u> and two of the dishes from <u>different directions</u>.

3) Leave your poor little cress seeds alone for <u>one week</u> until you can <u>observe</u> their <u>responses</u> — and hey presto, you'll find the seedlings <u>grow towards the light</u>.

4) You know that the <u>growth response</u> of the cress seeds is due to <u>light</u> only, if you <u>control</u> all other variables. Examples of variables to <u>control</u> are:

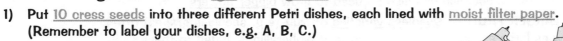

You can also investigate the effect of gravity on plant growth. Just place four seedlings on damp cotton wool in a Petri dish, each with their roots pointing in a different direction, and store the Petri dish vertically for a few days in the dark. You should find that the roots of each seedling grow downwards.

VARIABLE	HOW TO CONTROL IT
number of seeds	use the same number of seeds in each dish
type of seed	use seeds that all come from the same packet
temperature	keep your Petri dishes in a place where the temperature is stable (i.e. away from heat sources and draughts)
water	use a measuring cylinder to add the same amount of water
light intensity	keep the distance between the bulb and dish the same

A plant auxin to a bar — 'ouch'...

You need to be able to draw labelled diagrams to show the results of your experiment. Make sure you do it neatly.

Q1   Explain what causes plant shoots to grow towards light.   [2 marks]

Commercial Uses of Plant Hormones

Plant hormones can be extracted, or artificial copies can be made. They can then be used to do all kinds of useful things, including killing weeds, growing cuttings and ripening fruit.

Auxins Have Many Uses

Auxins are useful for controlling plant growth. Here are some of the ways they come in handy:

Unhappy weeds

1) KILLING WEEDS — Most weeds growing in fields of crops or in a lawn are broad-leaved, in contrast to grasses and cereals which have very narrow leaves. Selective weedkillers have been developed using auxins, which only affect the broad-leaved plants. They totally disrupt their normal growth patterns, which soon kills them, whilst leaving the grass and crops untouched.

2) GROWING FROM CUTTINGS WITH ROOTING POWDER — A cutting is part of a plant that has been cut off it, like the end of a branch with a few leaves on it. Normally, if you stick cuttings in the soil they won't grow, but if you add rooting powder, which contains auxins, they will produce roots rapidly and start growing as new plants. This enables growers to produce lots of clones (exact copies) of a really good plant very quickly.

3) GROWING CELLS IN TISSUE CULTURE — Tissue culture can be used to grow clones of a plant from a few of its cells. To do this, hormones such as auxins need to be added to the growth medium (along with nutrients) to stimulate the cells to divide to form both roots and shoots.

Gibberellin Stimulates Plant Stems to Grow

Gibberellin is another type of plant growth hormone. It stimulates seed germination, stem growth and flowering. Its uses include:

Seed germination is when a seed starts to grow into a plant.

1) CONTROLLING DORMANCY — Lots of seeds won't germinate until they've been through certain conditions (e.g. a period of cold or of dryness). This is called dormancy. Seeds can be treated with gibberellin to alter dormancy and make them germinate at times of year that they wouldn't normally. It also helps to make sure all the seeds in a batch germinate at the same time.

2) INDUCING FLOWERING — Some plants require certain conditions to flower, such as longer days or low temperatures. If these plants are treated with gibberellin, they will flower without any change in their environment. Gibberellin can also be used to grow bigger flowers.

3) GROWING LARGER FRUIT — Seedless varieties of fruit (e.g. seedless grapes) often do not grow as large as seeded fruit. However, if gibberellin is added to these fruit, they will grow larger to match the normal types.

Ethene Stimulates Ripening of Fruit

Some fruit will produce more ethene as it ripens.

1) Ethene is a gas produced by aging parts of a plant. It influences the growth of the plant by controlling cell division. It also stimulates enzymes that cause fruit to ripen.

2) Commercially, it can be used to speed up the ripening of fruits — either while they are still on the plant, or during transport to the shops.

3) This means that fruit can be picked while it's still unripe (and therefore firmer and less easily damaged). The gas is then added to the fruit on the way to the supermarket so that it will be perfect just as it reaches the shelves.

4) Ripening can also be delayed while the fruit is in storage by adding chemicals that block ethene's effect on the fruit or reduce the amount of ethene that the fruit can produce. Alternatively, some chemicals can be used that react with ethene to remove it from the air.

You will ripen when I SAY you can ripen — and NOT BEFORE...

Three different hormones, many different uses. Bet you didn't know plant hormones could be so useful...

Q1   Give one way that gibberellin is used commercially.   [1 mark]

Revision Questions for Topic 5

Congratulations, you've made it to the end of Topic 5 — now for some questions to make sure you've been paying attention...

- Try these questions and tick off each one when you get it right.
- When you've done all the questions under a heading and are completely happy with it, tick it off.

Homeostasis and the Nervous System (p.65-72) ☑

1) What is a stimulus?
2) Explain how negative feedback helps to maintain a stable internal environment.
3) What makes up the central nervous system and what does it do?
4) What is a synapse?
5) What is the purpose of a reflex action?
6) What is a reaction time?
7) Give one thing the cerebral cortex is responsible for.
8) Give three methods used by scientists to study the brain.
9) Explain the roles of the following parts of the eye:
   a) cornea   b) iris   c) lens
10) Describe the iris reflex. Why is this needed?
11) What is the medical term for short-sightedness?
12) Give three things that the body can do to reduce heat loss if it gets too cold.

Hormones in Humans (p.73-80) ☑

13) What is a hormone?
14) Give two differences between nervous and hormonal responses.
15) Where is excess glucose stored in the body?
16) What effect does the hormone glucagon have on blood glucose level?
17) What is the difference between how type 1 and type 2 diabetes are usually controlled?
18) Name three things that are reabsorbed by kidneys.
19) What hormone controls the amount of water reabsorbed by the kidneys?
20) What are the advantages and disadvantages of a kidney transplant over dialysis?
21) Draw a timeline of the 28 day menstrual cycle.
    Label the four stages of the cycle and label when the egg is released.
22) Describe two effects of FSH on the body.
23) Which of the following is a hormonal contraceptive — condom, plastic IUD or diaphragm?
24) Briefly describe how IVF is carried out.
25) How does adrenaline prepare the body for 'fight or flight'?

Plant Hormones (p.81-82) ☑

26) What is auxin?
27) What is: a) phototropism?   b) gravitropism?
28) Explain how auxin causes plant roots to grow downwards.
29) Give three ways that auxin can be used commercially.
30) Which plant hormone is responsible for fruit ripening?

DNA

The first step in understanding genetics is getting to grips with DNA and genes.

Chromosomes Are Really Long Molecules of DNA

1) DNA stands for deoxyribonucleic acid. It's the chemical that all of the genetic material in a cell is made up from.

2) It contains coded information — basically all the instructions to put an organism together and make it work.

3) So it's what's in your DNA that determines what inherited characteristics you have.

4) DNA is found in the nucleus of animal and plant cells, in really long structures called chromosomes.

5) Chromosomes normally come in pairs.

6) DNA is a polymer. It's made up of two strands coiled together in the shape of a double helix.

Head to the next page for more on the structure of DNA.

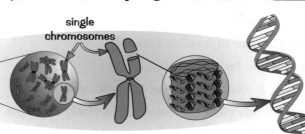

single chromosomes

nucleus

A DNA molecule with a double helix structure (a double-stranded spiral).

A Gene Codes for a Specific Protein

1) A gene is a small section of DNA found on a chromosome.

2) Each gene codes for (tells the cells to make) a particular sequence of amino acids which are put together to make a specific protein.

3) Only 20 amino acids are used, but they make up thousands of different proteins.

4) Genes simply tell cells in what order to put the amino acids together (more on this on the next page).

5) DNA also determines what proteins the cell produces, e.g. haemoglobin, keratin.

6) That in turn determines what type of cell it is, e.g. red blood cell, skin cell.

Every Organism Has a Genome

1) Genome is just the fancy term for the entire set of genetic material in an organism.

2) Scientists have worked out the complete human genome.

3) Understanding the human genome is a really important tool for science and medicine for many reasons.

1) It allows scientists to identify genes in the genome that are linked to different types of disease.

2) Knowing which genes are linked to inherited diseases could help us to understand them better and could help us to develop effective treatments for them.

3) Scientists can look at genomes to trace the migration of certain populations of people around the world. All modern humans are descended from a common ancestor who lived in Africa, but humans can now be found all over the planet. The human genome is mostly identical in all individuals, but as different populations of people migrated away from Africa, they gradually developed tiny differences in their genomes. By investigating these differences, scientists can work out when new populations split off in a different direction and what route they took.

Insert joke about genes and jeans here...

There are so many, I thought you could come up with your own as a bit of light relief.
Make sure that you're clued up on this stuff about DNA, genes and proteins before you move on.

Q1   What is a gene?   [3 marks]

Q2   What is an organism's genome?   [1 mark]

The Structure of DNA and Protein Synthesis

So here's how life works — DNA molecules contain a genetic code that determines which proteins are built.

DNA is Made Up of Nucleotides

1) DNA strands are polymers made up of lots of repeating units called nucleotides.

2) Each nucleotide consists of one sugar molecule, one phosphate molecule and one 'base'.

3) The sugar and phosphate molecules in the nucleotides form a 'backbone' to the DNA strands. The sugar and phosphate molecules alternate. One of four different bases — A, T, C or G — joins to each sugar.

4) Each base links to a base on the opposite strand in the helix.

5) A always pairs up with T, and C always pairs up with G. This is called complementary base pairing.

6) It's the order of bases in a gene that decides the order of amino acids in a protein.

7) Each amino acid is coded for by a sequence of three bases in the gene.

8) The amino acids are joined together to make various proteins, depending on the order of the gene's bases.

9) There are parts of DNA that don't code for proteins. Some of these non-coding parts switch genes on and off, so they control whether or not a gene is expressed (used to make a protein).

Part of a DNA strand

sugar-phosphate backbone

sugar

base

phosphate

nucleotide

Part of a DNA molecule

strands

base on one strand is joined to a base on the other strand

bases

mRNA Carries The Code to The Ribosomes

1) Proteins are made in the cell cytoplasm on tiny structures called ribosomes.

2) To make proteins, ribosomes use the code in the DNA. DNA is found in the cell nucleus and can't move out of it because it's really big. So the cell needs to get the code from the DNA to the ribosome.

3) This is done using a molecule called mRNA — which is made by copying the code from DNA. The mRNA acts as a messenger between the DNA and the ribosome — it carries the code between the two.

4) The correct amino acids are brought to the ribosomes in the correct order by carrier molecules.

Proteins Have Many Different Functions

When a chain of amino acids has been assembled, it folds into a unique shape which allows the protein to perform the task it's meant to do. Here are a few examples of types of protein:

1) ENZYMES — act as biological catalysts to speed up chemical reactions in the body (see page 28).

2) HORMONES — used to carry messages around the body. E.g. insulin is a hormone released into the blood by the pancreas to regulate the blood sugar level.

3) STRUCTURAL PROTEINS — are physically strong. E.g. collagen is a structural protein that strengthens connective tissues (like ligaments and cartilage).

Q: What do DNA and a game of rounders have in common?

A: four bases. Remember — the order of these bases in the DNA is copied into mRNA, which then moves to the ribosomes. Here, the chain of amino acids is assembled according to the order of the bases.

Q1   Which bases pair up according to complementary base pairing?   [2 marks]

Mutations

Sometimes the <u>sequence</u> of <u>DNA bases</u> can be changed. These changes are called <u>mutations</u>. Read on...

Mutations are Changes to the Genetic Code

1) <u>Occasionally</u> a gene may <u>mutate</u>. A mutation is a random <u>change</u> in an organism's <u>DNA</u>. They can sometimes be <u>inherited</u>.

2) Mutations occur <u>continuously</u>. They can occur <u>spontaneously</u>, e.g. when a chromosome isn't quite replicated properly. However, the <u>chance</u> of mutation is <u>increased</u> by exposure to certain <u>substances</u> or <u>some types of radiation</u>.

3) Mutations <u>change the sequence</u> of the <u>DNA bases</u> in a gene, which produces a <u>genetic variant</u> (a different form of the gene). As the <u>sequence</u> of DNA bases <u>codes</u> for the sequence of <u>amino acids</u> that make up a <u>protein</u> (see page 84), mutations to a gene <u>sometimes</u> lead to <u>changes</u> in the protein that it codes for.

4) <u>Most</u> mutations have <u>very little</u> or <u>no effect</u> on the <u>protein</u>. Some will change it to such a <u>small extent</u> that its <u>function</u> or <u>appearance</u> is <u>unaffected</u>.

5) However, some mutations can <u>seriously affect</u> a protein. Sometimes, the mutation will code for an altered protein with a change in its <u>shape</u>. This could affect its ability to perform its <u>function</u>. E.g.

> 1) If the shape of an <u>enzyme's active site</u> is changed, its <u>substrate</u> may <u>no longer</u> be able to <u>bind</u> to it.
>
> *Enzymes are proteins — see page 28.*
>
> 2) <u>Structural proteins</u> like collagen could <u>lose</u> their <u>strength</u> if their shape is changed, making them pretty <u>useless</u> at providing structure and support.

There's more on non-coding DNA on the previous page.

6) If there's a mutation in the <u>non-coding DNA</u>, it can alter how genes are <u>expressed</u>.

There Are Different Types of Mutation, For Example...

Insertions

1) <u>Insertions</u> are where a <u>new base</u> is <u>inserted</u> into the DNA base sequence where it shouldn't be.

2) You should remember from page 85 that every <u>three bases</u> in a DNA base sequence <u>codes</u> for a particular <u>amino acid</u>.

3) An insertion <u>changes</u> the way the groups of <u>three bases</u> are '<u>read</u>', which can change the <u>amino acids</u> that they code for.

4) Insertions can change <u>more than one</u> amino acid as they have a <u>knock-on effect</u> on the bases further on in the sequence.

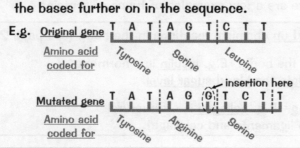

Deletions

1) <u>Deletions</u> are when a random base is <u>deleted</u> from the DNA base sequence.

2) Like insertions, they <u>change</u> the way that the <u>base sequence</u> is '<u>read</u>' and have <u>knock-on effects</u> further down the sequence.

Substitutions

<u>Substitution</u> mutations are when a random base in the DNA base sequence is <u>changed</u> to a different base.

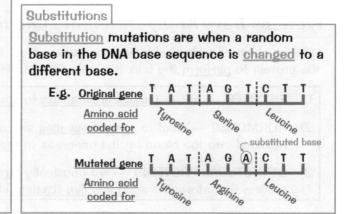

Mutations — sometimes known to give ninja superpowers...

Remember, changes in bases can affect the amino acid sequence, and therefore the protein coded for.

Q1   What is a mutation?   [1 mark]

Q2   Explain why the function of a protein may be affected by a gene mutation.   [3 marks]

Topic 6 — Inheritance, Variation and Evolution

Reproduction

Ooo err, reproduction... Surely you knew it'd come up at some point. It can happen in two different ways...

Sexual Reproduction Produces Genetically Different Cells

1) Sexual reproduction is where genetic information from two organisms (a father and a mother) is combined to produce offspring which are genetically different to either parent.

2) In sexual reproduction, the mother and father produce gametes by meiosis (see next page) — e.g. egg and sperm cells in animals.

3) In humans, each gamete contains 23 chromosomes — half the number of chromosomes in a normal cell. (Instead of having two of each chromosome, a gamete has just one of each.)

4) The egg (from the mother) and the sperm cell (from the father) then fuse together (fertilisation) to form a cell with the full number of chromosomes (half from the father, half from the mother).

> SEXUAL REPRODUCTION involves the fusion of male and female gametes.
> Because there are TWO parents, the offspring contain a mixture of their parents' genes.

Fertilisation:

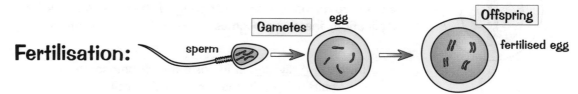

5) This is why the offspring inherits features from both parents — it's received a mixture of chromosomes from its mum and its dad (and it's the chromosomes that decide how you turn out).

6) This mixture of genetic information produces variation in the offspring. Pretty cool, eh.

7) Flowering plants can reproduce in this way too. They also have egg cells, but their version of sperm is known as pollen. Hmm... I'm having second thoughts about frolicking in that meadow now.

Asexual Reproduction Produces Genetically Identical Cells

1) In asexual reproduction there's only one parent so the offspring are genetically identical to that parent.

2) Asexual reproduction happens by mitosis — an ordinary cell makes a new cell by dividing in two (see page 15).

3) The new cell has exactly the same genetic information (i.e. genes) as the parent cell — it's called a clone.

> In ASEXUAL REPRODUCTION there's only ONE parent. There's no fusion of gametes, no mixing of chromosomes and no genetic variation between parent and offspring. The offspring are genetically identical to the parent — they're clones.

4) Bacteria, some plants and some animals reproduce asexually.

A handsome bunch — even if I do say so myself...

You need to reproduce these facts in the exam...

The main messages on this page are that: 1) sexual reproduction needs two parents and forms cells that are genetically different to the parents, so there's lots of genetic variation. And 2) asexual reproduction needs just one parent to make genetically identical cells, so there's no genetic variation in the offspring.

Q1   What type of cell division is involved in asexual reproduction?   [1 mark]

Q2   Suggest why there is variation in the offspring of sexual reproduction.   [2 marks]

Meiosis

Now I bet you're wondering how gametes end up with <u>half</u> the number of <u>chromosomes</u> of a normal cell... or maybe you're not. Well, I'm going to tell you anyway. Step forward the marvellous process of meiosis.

Gametes Are Produced by Meiosis

1) As you know from the previous page, <u>gametes</u> only have <u>one copy</u> of each <u>chromosome</u>, so that when <u>gamete fusion</u> takes place, you get the <u>right amount</u> of <u>chromosomes</u> again (two copies of each).

2) To make gametes which only have <u>half</u> the original number of chromosomes, cells divide by <u>meiosis</u>. This process involves <u>two cell divisions</u>. In humans, it <u>only</u> happens in the <u>reproductive organs</u> (the ovaries in females and testes in males).

Meiosis Produces Cells Which Have Half the Normal Number of Chromosomes

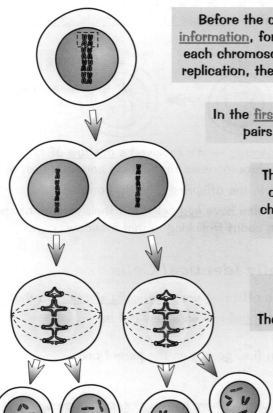

Before the cell starts to divide, it <u>duplicates</u> its <u>genetic information</u>, forming two armed chromosomes — one arm of each chromosome is an <u>exact copy</u> of the other arm. After replication, the chromosomes arrange themselves into <u>pairs</u>.

The genetic information is stored in DNA — see p.84.

In the <u>first division</u> in meiosis the chromosome pairs <u>line up</u> in the centre of the cell.

The pairs are then <u>pulled apart</u> so each new cell only has one copy of each chromosome. <u>Some</u> of the father's chromosomes (shown in blue) and <u>some</u> of the mother's chromosomes (shown in red) go into each new cell.

In the <u>second division</u>, the chromosomes <u>line up</u> again in the centre of the cell. The arms of the chromosomes are <u>pulled apart</u>.

You get four gametes, each with only a <u>single set</u> of chromosomes in it. Each of the gametes is <u>genetically different</u> from the others because the chromosomes all get <u>shuffled up</u> during meiosis and each gamete only gets <u>half</u> of them, at random.

The Cell Produced by Gamete Fusion Replicates Itself

1) After two <u>gametes</u> have fused during fertilisation, the resulting new cell <u>divides</u> by <u>mitosis</u> to make a <u>copy</u> of itself.

2) Mitosis <u>repeats many times</u> to produce <u>lots</u> of new cells in an embryo.

3) As the embryo develops, these cells then start to <u>differentiate</u> (see page 14) into the <u>different types</u> of <u>specialised cell</u> that make up a <u>whole organism</u>.

There's loads on mitosis on page 15.

Now that I have your undivided attention...

Remember, in humans, meiosis only occurs in reproductive organs where gametes are being made.

Q1   How many cell divisions take place in meiosis?   [1 mark]

Topic 6 — Inheritance, Variation and Evolution

More on Reproduction

As the line in Oliver Twist goes, "Please sir, I want some more... information about the types of reproduction". Something like that anyway. I'm feeling like a generous workhouse master today, so here's a full page.

Sexual Reproduction Has Advantages Over Asexual Reproduction

1) Offspring from sexual reproduction have a <u>mixture</u> of two sets of chromosomes. The organism inherits genes (and therefore features) from <u>both</u> parents, which produces <u>variation</u> in the offspring (see p.87).

2) Variation <u>increases</u> the chance of a species <u>surviving</u> a <u>change in the environment</u>. While a change in the environment could <u>kill</u> some <u>individuals</u>, it's likely that <u>variation</u> will have led to <u>some</u> of the offspring being able to <u>survive</u> in the new environment. They have a <u>survival advantage</u>.

3) Because individuals with characteristics that make them <u>better adapted</u> to the environment have a <u>better</u> chance of <u>survival</u>, they are <u>more likely</u> to breed <u>successfully</u> and pass the genes for the characteristics on. This is known as <u>natural selection</u> (see p.96).

4) We can use <u>selective breeding</u> to <u>speed up</u> natural selection. This allows us to produce animals with <u>desirable characteristics</u>. Selective breeding is where individuals with a desirable characteristic are bred to produce <u>offspring</u> that have the desirable characteristic too (see p.98). This means that we can <u>increase food production</u>, e.g. by breeding animals that produce a lot of meat.

Asexual Reproduction Has Advantages Over Sexual Reproduction

1) There only needs to be <u>one parent</u>.

2) This means that asexual reproduction uses <u>less energy</u> than sexual reproduction, because organisms <u>don't</u> have to <u>find a mate</u>.

3) This also means that asexual reproduction is <u>faster</u> than sexual reproduction.

4) <u>Many</u> identical offspring can be produced in <u>favourable conditions</u>.

Some Organisms Can Reproduce by Both Methods

Some organisms can reproduce sexually or asexually depending on their <u>circumstances</u>. You need to know these examples:

1) <u>Malaria</u> is caused by a <u>parasite</u> that's spread by <u>mosquitoes</u> — see page 47. When a mosquito carrying the parasite <u>bites</u> a human, the parasite can be <u>transferred</u> to the <u>human</u>. The parasite reproduces <u>sexually</u> when it's in the <u>mosquito</u> and <u>asexually</u> when it's in the <u>human</u> host.

2) Many species of fungus can reproduce both sexually and asexually. These species release <u>spores</u>, which can become <u>new</u> fungi when they land in a suitable place. Spores can be produced sexually and asexually. <u>Asexually-produced</u> spores form fungi that are <u>genetically identical</u> to the parent fungus. <u>Sexually-produced</u> spores introduce <u>variation</u> and are often produced in response to an unfavourable <u>change</u> in the <u>environment</u>, increasing the chance that the population will <u>survive</u> the change.

3) Loads of species of plant <u>produce seeds sexually</u>, but can also reproduce <u>asexually</u>. <u>Asexual</u> reproduction can take place in <u>different</u> ways. For example, strawberry plants produce 'runners'. These are stems that grow horizontally on the <u>surface</u> of the soil away from a plant. At various points along the runner, a <u>new</u> strawberry plant forms that is <u>identical</u> to the original plant. Another example is in plants that grow from <u>bulbs</u> (e.g. daffodils). <u>New bulbs</u> can form from the main bulb and <u>divide</u> off. Each new bulb can grow into a new <u>identical plant</u>.

Well that's reproduction sorted... Well that's reproduction sorted...

It's key here to remember that both types of reproduction have their own different advantages. Make sure you also know about organisms that can reproduce by both methods.

Q1 Give three advantages of asexual reproduction over sexual reproduction. [3 marks]

X and Y Chromosomes

Now for a couple of <u>very</u> important little chromosomes...

Your Chromosomes Control Whether You're Male or Female

There are <u>23 pairs</u> of chromosomes in every human body cell (page 15). Of these, <u>22</u> are <u>matched pairs</u> of chromosomes that just control <u>characteristics</u>. The <u>23rd pair</u> are labelled <u>XY</u> or <u>XX</u>. They're the two chromosomes that <u>decide</u> your <u>sex</u> — whether you turn out <u>male</u> or <u>female</u>.

<u>Males</u> have an <u>X</u> and a <u>Y</u> chromosome: XY
The <u>Y chromosome</u> causes <u>male characteristics</u>.

<u>Females</u> have <u>two X chromosomes</u>: XX
The <u>XX combination</u> allows <u>female characteristics</u> to develop.

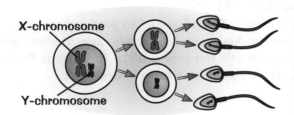

When making sperm, the X and Y chromosomes are drawn apart in the first division in <u>meiosis</u> (see page 88). There's a <u>50% chance</u> each sperm cell gets an <u>X-chromosome</u> and a <u>50% chance</u> it gets a <u>Y-chromosome</u>.

A similar thing happens when making eggs. But the original cell has two X-chromosomes, so all the eggs have one X-chromosome.

Genetic Diagrams Show the Possible Gamete Combinations

1) To find the <u>probability</u> of getting a boy or a girl, you can draw a <u>genetic diagram</u>.

2) Genetic diagrams are just <u>models</u> that are used to show all the possible genetic <u>outcomes</u> when you <u>cross together</u> different genes or chromosomes.

3) Put the <u>possible gametes</u> (eggs or sperm) from <u>one</u> parent down the side, and those from the <u>other</u> parent along the top.

4) Then in each middle square you <u>fill in</u> the letters from the top and side that line up with that square. The <u>pairs of letters</u> in the middle show the possible combinations of the gametes.

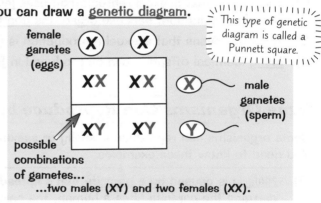

This type of genetic diagram is called a Punnett square.

...two males (XY) and two females (XX).

5) There are <u>two XX results</u> and <u>two XY results</u>, so there's the same probability of getting a boy or a girl.

6) Don't forget that this <u>50:50 ratio</u> is only a <u>probability</u> at each pregnancy.

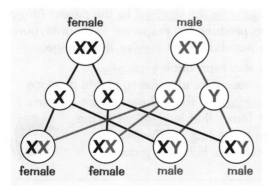

The other type of genetic diagram looks a bit more complicated, but it shows exactly the same thing.

1) At the top are the <u>parents</u>.

2) The middle circles show the <u>possible gametes</u> that are formed. One gamete from the female combines with one gamete from the male (during fertilisation).

3) The criss-cross lines show <u>all</u> the <u>possible</u> ways the X and Y chromosomes <u>could</u> combine. The <u>possible combinations</u> of the offspring are shown in the bottom circles.

4) Remember, only <u>one</u> of these possibilities would <u>actually happen</u> for any one offspring.

Have you got the Y-factor...

Most genetic diagrams you'll see in exams concentrate on a gene instead of a chromosome. But the principle's the same. Don't worry — there are loads of other examples on the following pages.

Q1   What combination of sex chromosomes do human females have?   [1 mark]

Topic 6 — Inheritance, Variation and Evolution

Genetic Diagrams

Genetic diagrams, eh. They're not as scary as they look — you just need to <u>practise</u> them...

Some Characteristics are Controlled by Single Genes

1) What <u>genes</u> you <u>inherit</u> control what <u>characteristics</u> you <u>develop</u>.

2) <u>Different</u> genes control <u>different</u> characteristics. <u>Some</u> characteristics are controlled by a <u>single</u> gene, e.g. <u>mouse fur colour</u> and <u>red-green colour blindness</u> in humans.

3) However, most characteristics are controlled by <u>several genes interacting</u>.

4) All genes exist in different <u>versions</u> called <u>alleles</u> (which are represented by <u>letters</u> in genetic diagrams).

5) You have <u>two</u> versions (alleles) of <u>every gene</u> in your body — <u>one</u> on <u>each chromosome</u> in a pair.

6) If an organism has <u>two alleles</u> for a particular gene that are <u>the same</u>, then it's <u>homozygous</u> for that trait. If its two alleles for a particular gene are <u>different</u>, then it's <u>heterozygous</u>.

7) If the two alleles are <u>different</u>, only one can determine what <u>characteristic</u> is present. The allele for the <u>characteristic that's shown</u> is called the <u>dominant</u> allele (use a capital letter for dominant alleles — e.g. 'C'). The other one is called <u>recessive</u> (and you show these with small letters — e.g. 'c').

8) For an organism to display a <u>recessive</u> characteristic, <u>both</u> its alleles must be <u>recessive</u> (e.g. cc). But to display a <u>dominant</u> characteristic the organism can be <u>either</u> CC or Cc, because the dominant allele <u>overrules</u> the recessive one if the plant/animal/other organism is heterozygous.

9) Your <u>genotype</u> is the combination of <u>alleles</u> you have. Your alleles work at a molecular level to determine what characteristics you have — your <u>phenotype</u>.

Genetic Diagrams Show the Possible Alleles of Offspring

Suppose you start breeding <u>hamsters</u> with <u>superpowers</u>. The allele which causes hamsters to have superpowers is <u>recessive</u> ("b"), whilst <u>normal</u> (boring) behaviour is due to a <u>dominant</u> allele ("B").

1) A <u>superpowered</u> hamster <u>must</u> have the <u>genotype bb</u>. But a <u>normal</u> hamster could be <u>BB or Bb</u>.

2) Here's what happens if you breed from two <u>homozygous</u> hamsters:

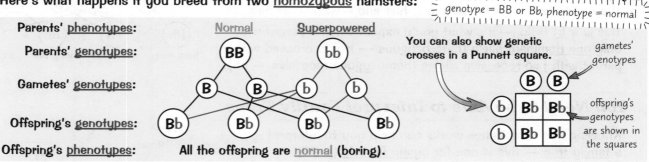

genotype = BB or Bb, phenotype = normal

You can also show genetic crosses in a Punnett square.

gametes' genotypes

offspring's genotypes are shown in the squares

3) If two of these <u>offspring</u> now <u>breed</u>, you'll get the next generation:

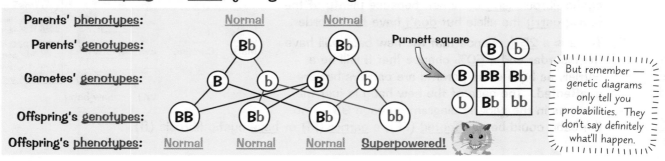

Punnett square

But remember — genetic diagrams only tell you probabilities. They don't say definitely what'll happen.

4) That's a <u>3:1 ratio</u> of normal to superpowered offspring in this generation (a <u>1 in 4</u> or <u>25%</u> probability of superpowers).

Your meanotype determines how nice you are to your sibling...

You need to be able to produce and interpret both of these types of genetic diagram for the exam.

Q1   Define genotype and phenotype.   [2 marks]

More Genetic Diagrams

You've got to be able to <u>predict</u> and <u>explain</u> the outcomes of crosses between individuals for each <u>possible</u> <u>combination</u> of <u>dominant</u> and <u>recessive alleles</u> of a gene. You should be able to draw a <u>genetic diagram</u> and <u>work it out</u> — but it'll be easier if you've seen them all before. So here are a couple more examples for you. You also need to know how to interpret another type of genetic diagram called a <u>family tree</u>...

All the Offspring are Normal

For a reminder on the terms homozygous and heterozygous, head to page 91.

Let's take another look at the <u>superpowered hamster</u> example from page 91:

In this cross, a <u>homozygous dominant</u> hamster (BB) is crossed with a <u>homozygous recessive</u> hamster (bb). <u>All</u> the offspring are normal (boring).

But, if you crossed a <u>homozygous dominant</u> hamster (BB) with a <u>heterozygous</u> hamster (Bb), you would also get <u>all</u> normal (boring) offspring.

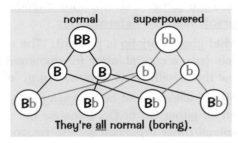

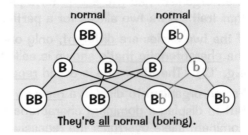

To find out <u>which</u> it was you'd have to <u>breed the offspring together</u> and see what kind of <u>ratio</u> you got that time — then you'd have a good idea. If it was <u>3:1</u>, it's likely that you originally had BB and bb.

There's a 1:1 Ratio in the Offspring

A cat with <u>long hair</u> was bred with another cat with <u>short hair</u>. The long hair is caused by a <u>dominant</u> allele 'H', and the short hair by a <u>recessive</u> allele 'h'.

They had 8 kittens — 4 with long hair and 4 with short hair.

This is a <u>1:1</u> ratio — it's what you'd expect when a parent with only <u>one dominant allele</u> (heterozygous — Hh) is crossed with a parent with <u>two recessive alleles</u> (homozygous recessive — hh).

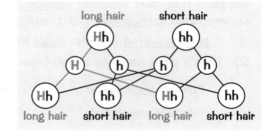

You Need to be Able to Interpret Family Trees

Knowing how inheritance works can help you to interpret a <u>family tree</u> — this is one for <u>cystic fibrosis</u> (p.93).

1) From the family tree, you can tell that the allele for cystic fibrosis <u>isn't</u> dominant because plenty of the family <u>carry</u> the allele but <u>don't</u> have the disorder.

2) There is a <u>25%</u> chance that the new baby will have the disorder and a <u>50%</u> chance that it will be a carrier, as both of its parents are carriers but are unaffected. The case of the new baby is just the same as in the genetic diagram on page <u>93</u> — so the baby could be <u>unaffected</u> (FF), a <u>carrier</u> (Ff) or <u>have</u> cystic fibrosis (ff).

It's enough to make you go cross-eyed...

In the exam, you might get a family tree showing the inheritance of a dominant allele — in this case, there won't be any carriers shown. Now, here's a practice question from the realm of mythical creatures.

Q1   In merpeople, the dominant allele, T, causes a long tail and the recessive allele, t, causes a short tail. Using a Punnett square, predict the ratio of long to short tailed merbabies for a cross between a heterozygous merman and a mermaid who is homozygous recessive for tail length.

[3 marks]

Topic 6 — Inheritance, Variation and Evolution

Inherited Disorders

Some disorders can be <u>inherited</u> from your parents. Many of these can be <u>screened</u> for in embryos.

Cystic Fibrosis is Caused by a Recessive Allele

<u>Cystic fibrosis</u> is a <u>genetic disorder</u> of the <u>cell membranes</u>. It <u>results</u> in the body producing a lot of thick sticky <u>mucus</u> in the <u>air passages</u> and in the <u>pancreas</u>.

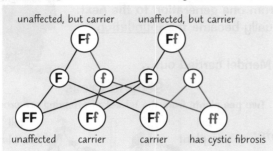

unaffected, but carrier   unaffected, but carrier

Ff   **Ff**

F **f**   **F** **f**

FF   **Ff**   **Ff**   **ff**

unaffected   carrier   carrier   has cystic fibrosis

1) The allele which causes cystic fibrosis is a <u>recessive allele</u>, 'f', carried by about <u>1 person in 25</u>.

2) Because it's recessive, people with only <u>one copy</u> of the allele <u>won't</u> have the disorder — they're known as <u>carriers</u>.

3) For a child to have the disorder, <u>both parents</u> must be either <u>carriers</u> or have the disorder <u>themselves</u>.

4) As the diagram shows, there's a <u>1 in 4 chance</u> of a child having the disorder if <u>both</u> parents are <u>carriers</u>.

Polydactyly is Caused by a Dominant Allele

<u>Polydactyly</u> is a <u>genetic disorder</u> where a baby's born with <u>extra fingers or toes</u>. It doesn't usually cause any other problems so <u>isn't life-threatening</u>.

1) The disorder is caused by a <u>dominant allele</u>, 'D', and so can be inherited if just <u>one parent</u> carries the defective allele.

2) The <u>parent</u> that <u>has</u> the defective allele <u>will have</u> the condition too since the allele is dominant.

3) As the genetic diagram shows, there's a <u>50% chance</u> of a child having the disorder if <u>one</u> parent has <u>one</u> D allele.

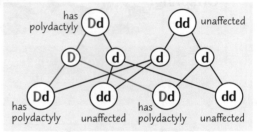

has polydactyly **Dd**   **dd** unaffected

D **d**   **d** **d**

Dd   **dd**   **Dd**   **dd**

has polydactyly   unaffected   has polydactyly   unaffected

Embryos Can Be Screened for Genetic Disorders

1) During *in vitro* fertilisation (IVF), embryos are fertilised in a <u>laboratory</u>, and then <u>implanted</u> into the mother's womb.

2) Before being implanted, it's possible to <u>remove a cell</u> from each embryo and <u>analyse</u> its <u>genes</u>.

3) Many <u>genetic disorders</u> can be <u>detected</u> in this way, such as cystic fibrosis.

4) It's also possible to get DNA from an embryo <u>in the womb</u> and test that for disorders.

5) There are lots of <u>ethical</u>, <u>social</u> and <u>economic</u> concerns surrounding embryo screening.

6) Embryonic screening is quite <u>controversial</u> because of the <u>decisions</u> it can lead to.

7) For embryos produced by <u>IVF</u> — after screening, embryos with '<u>bad</u>' alleles would be <u>destroyed</u>.

8) For embryos in the <u>womb</u> — screening could lead to the decision to <u>terminate</u> the pregnancy.

9) Here are some more arguments <u>for</u> and <u>against</u> screening:

<u>Against Embryonic Screening</u>	<u>For Embryonic Screening</u>
1) It implies that <u>people</u> with <u>genetic problems</u> are 'undesirable' — this could increase <u>prejudice</u>.	1) It will help to stop people <u>suffering</u>.
2) There may come a point where everyone wants to screen their embryos so they can pick the most '<u>desirable</u>' one, e.g. they want a blue-eyed, blond-haired, intelligent boy.	2) Treating disorders costs the Government (and the taxpayers) a lot of <u>money</u>.
3) Screening is <u>expensive</u>.	3) There are <u>laws</u> to stop it going too far. At the moment parents cannot even select the sex of their baby (unless it's for health reasons).

Embryo screening — it's a tricky one...

Try writing a balanced argument for and against embryo screening — it's good practice.

Q1   Why won't someone heterozygous for the cystic fibrosis allele have the disorder?   [3 marks]

The Work of Mendel

Some people forget about Mendel but I reckon he's the <u>Granddaddy of Genetics</u>. Here's a whole page on him.

Mendel Did Genetic Experiments with Pea Plants

<u>Gregor Mendel</u> was an Austrian monk who trained in <u>mathematics</u> and <u>natural history</u> at the University of Vienna. On his garden plot at the monastery in the <u>mid 19th century</u>, Mendel noted how <u>characteristics</u> in <u>plants</u> were <u>passed on</u> from one generation to the next. The results of his research were published in <u>1866</u> and eventually became the <u>foundation</u> of modern <u>genetics</u>.

The diagrams show two <u>crosses for height</u> in <u>pea plants</u> that Mendel carried out...

peas out

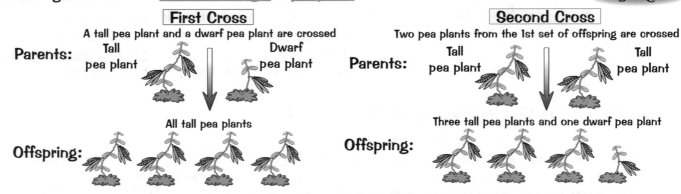

First Cross
A tall pea plant and a dwarf pea plant are crossed
Parents:
Tall pea plant
Dwarf pea plant
All tall pea plants
Offspring:

Second Cross
Two pea plants from the 1st set of offspring are crossed
Parents:
Tall pea plant
Tall pea plant
Three tall pea plants and one dwarf pea plant
Offspring:

Mendel had shown that the height characteristic in pea plants was determined by separately inherited "<u>hereditary units</u>" passed on from each parent. The ratios of tall and dwarf plants in the offspring showed that the unit for tall plants, <u>T</u>, was <u>dominant</u> over the unit for dwarf plants, <u>t</u>.

Mendel Reached Three Important Conclusions

Mendel reached these three important conclusions about <u>heredity in plants</u>:

1) Characteristics in plants are determined by "<u>hereditary units</u>".
2) Hereditary units are passed on to offspring <u>unchanged</u> from both parents, <u>one unit</u> from <u>each parent</u>.
3) Hereditary units can be <u>dominant</u> or <u>recessive</u> — if an individual has <u>both</u> the dominant and the recessive unit for a characteristic, the <u>dominant</u> characteristic will be expressed.

It Took a While For People to Understand His Work

1) Mendel's work was <u>cutting edge</u> and <u>new</u> to the scientists of the day. They didn't have the background knowledge to <u>properly understand</u> his findings — they had <u>no idea</u> about <u>genes</u>, <u>DNA</u> and <u>chromosomes</u>.
2) It wasn't until <u>after his death</u> that people realised how <u>significant</u> his work was.
3) Using Mendel's work as a starting point, the observations of <u>many</u> different scientists have contributed to the <u>understanding</u> of genes that we have <u>today</u>. For example:

> 1) In the <u>late 1800s</u>, scientists became familiar with <u>chromosomes</u>. They were able to observe how they <u>behaved</u> during <u>cell division</u>.
>
> 2) Then in the <u>early 20th century</u>, scientists realised that there were striking <u>similarities</u> in the way that <u>chromosomes</u> and <u>Mendel's "units"</u> acted. Based on this, it was proposed that the "units" were <u>found</u> on the <u>chromosomes</u>. We now know these "units" as <u>genes</u>.
>
> 3) In <u>1953</u>, the <u>structure</u> of <u>DNA</u> was determined (see page 85). This allowed scientists to go on and find out exactly how <u>genes work</u>.

Clearly, being a monk in the 1800s was a right laugh...

There was no TV in those days, you see, so Mendel filled his time by growing lots and lots of pea plants.

Q1   Suggest why the importance of Mendel's work wasn't realised straight away.   [1 mark]

Variation

You'll probably have noticed that not all people are identical. There are reasons for this.

Organisms of the Same Species Have Differences

1) Different species look... well... different — my dog definitely doesn't look like a daisy.

2) But even organisms of the <u>same species</u> will usually look at least <u>slightly</u> different — e.g. in a room full of people you'll see different <u>colour hair</u>, individually <u>shaped noses</u>, etc.

3) These differences are called the <u>variation</u> within a species, and there are <u>two</u> types of variation — <u>genetic variation</u> and <u>environmental variation</u>.

Different Genes Cause Genetic Variation

1) All plants and animals have <u>characteristics</u> that are in some ways similar to their <u>parents'</u>.

2) This is because an organism's <u>characteristics</u> are determined by the <u>genes inherited</u> from their <u>parents</u>. (Genes are the <u>codes</u> inside your cells that <u>control</u> how you're made — more about these on page 84).

3) These genes are passed on in <u>sex cells</u> (<u>gametes</u>), from which the offspring develop (see page 87).

4) Most animals (and quite a lot of plants) get <u>some</u> genes from the <u>mother</u> and <u>some</u> from the <u>father</u>.

5) This combining of genes from two parents causes <u>genetic variation</u> — no two of the species are <u>genetically identical</u> (other than identical twins).

6) <u>Some</u> characteristics are determined <u>only</u> by genes (e.g. violet flower colour). In <u>animals</u> these include: <u>eye colour</u>, <u>blood group</u> and <u>inherited disorders</u> (e.g. haemophilia or cystic fibrosis).

Characteristics are also Influenced by the Environment

1) The <u>environment</u>, including the <u>conditions</u> that organisms <u>live and grow</u> in, also causes <u>differences</u> between members of the same species — this is called <u>environmental variation</u>.

2) For example, a plant grown in plenty of <u>sunlight</u> would be <u>luscious</u> and <u>green</u>, but the <u>same</u> plant grown in <u>darkness</u> would grow <u>tall</u> and <u>spindly</u> and have <u>yellow leaves</u>. These are environmental variations.

3) Environmental variation covers a <u>wide range</u> of differences — from <u>losing your toes</u> in a piranha attack, to getting a <u>suntan</u>, to having <u>yellow leaves</u> (never happened to me yet though), and so on.

Most Characteristics are Due to Genes AND the Environment

1) <u>Most characteristics</u> (e.g. body weight, height, skin colour, condition of teeth, academic or athletic prowess, etc.) are determined by a <u>mixture</u> of <u>genetic</u> and <u>environmental</u> factors.

2) For example, the <u>maximum height</u> that an animal or plant could grow to is determined by its <u>genes</u>. But whether it actually grows that tall depends on its <u>environment</u> (e.g. how much food it gets).

Mutations Introduce Variation

Mutations are covered in loads more detail on page 86.

1) Mutations are <u>changes</u> to the <u>sequence of bases</u> in <u>DNA</u>. As you saw on page 86, mutations can lead to <u>changes</u> in the <u>protein</u> that a gene codes for. <u>Most mutations</u> have <u>no effect</u> on the <u>protein</u> the gene codes for, so <u>most mutations</u> have <u>no effect</u> on the organism's <u>phenotype</u>. Some have a <u>small influence</u> on phenotype and so only alter characteristics <u>slightly</u>. However, although it's very rare, mutations can result in a <u>new phenotype</u> being seen in a species.

2) If the <u>environment changes</u>, and the new phenotype makes an <u>individual more suited</u> to the new environment, it can become common <u>throughout</u> the species <u>relatively quickly</u> by natural selection — see the next page.

My mum's got no trousers — cos I've got her jeans...

So you can't blame all of your faults on your parents — the environment usually plays a role too.

Q1   Explain what is meant by environmental variation.   [2 marks]

Evolution

THEORY OF EVOLUTION: All of today's species have evolved from simple life forms that first started to develop over three billion years ago.

Only the Fittest Survive

Charles Darwin came up with a really important theory about evolution. He used the observations he made on a huge round-the-world trip, along with experiments, discussions and new knowledge of fossils and geology, to suggest the theory of evolution by natural selection.

Charles Darwin

1) Darwin knew that organisms in a species show wide variation in their characteristics (phenotypic variation). He also knew that organisms have to compete for limited resources in an ecosystem.

2) Darwin concluded that the organisms with the most suitable characteristics for the environment would be more successful competitors and would be more likely to survive. This idea is called the 'survival of the fittest'.

3) The successful organisms that survive are more likely to reproduce and pass on the genes for the characteristics that made them successful to their offspring.

4) The organisms that are less well adapted would be less likely to survive and reproduce, so they are less likely to pass on their genes to the next generation.

5) Over time, beneficial characteristics become more common in the population and the species changes — it evolves.

New Discoveries Have Helped to Develop the Theory

1) Darwin's theory wasn't perfect. Because the relevant scientific knowledge wasn't available at the time, he couldn't give a good explanation for why new characteristics appeared or exactly how individual organisms passed on beneficial adaptations to their offspring.

2) We now know that phenotype is controlled by genes. New phenotypic variations arise because of genetic variants produced by mutations (changes in DNA — see page 86). Beneficial variations are passed on to future generations in the genes that parents contribute to their offspring.

The Development of a New Species is Called Speciation

1) Over a long period of time, the phenotype of organisms can change so much because of natural selection that a completely new species is formed. This is called speciation.

2) Speciation happens when populations of the same species change enough to become reproductively isolated — this means that they can't interbreed to produce fertile offspring.

There's more on speciation on p.102.

Extinction is When No Individuals of a Species Remain

The fossil record contains many species that don't exist any more — these species are said to be extinct.

Species become extinct for these reasons:
1) The environment changes too quickly (e.g. destruction of habitat).
2) A new predator kills them all (e.g. humans hunting them).
3) A new disease kills them all.
4) They can't compete with another (new) species for food.
5) A catastrophic event happens that kills them all (e.g. a volcanic eruption or a collision with an asteroid).

> Dodos are now extinct. Humans not only hunted them, but introduced other animals which ate all their eggs, and we destroyed the forest where they lived — they really didn't stand a chance...

"Natural selection" — sounds like vegan chocolates...

Natural selection's all about the organisms with the best characteristics surviving to pass on their genes.

Q1 Give three factors that can lead to a species becoming extinct. [3 marks]

More About Evolution

There's a lot of evidence for the theory of evolution by natural selection.
But back in the day, poor Charlie Darwin didn't have half as much evidence to convince people.

Not Everyone Agreed with Darwin...

When Darwin proposed his theory in his book "On the Origin of Species" in 1859,
his idea was very controversial for various reasons...

It went against common religious beliefs about how life on Earth developed — it was the
first plausible explanation for the existence of life on earth without the need for a "Creator" (God).

Darwin couldn't explain why these new, useful characteristics appeared or how they were
passed on from individual organisms to their offspring. But then he didn't know anything about
genes or mutations — they weren't discovered 'til 50 years after his theory was published.

There wasn't enough evidence to convince many scientists, because not
many other studies had been done into how organisms change over time.

...and Lamarck had Different Ideas

There were different scientific hypotheses about evolution around at the same time, such as Lamarck's:

1) Jean-Baptiste Lamarck (1744-1829) argued that changes that an organism acquires during
   its lifetime will be passed on to its offspring — e.g. he thought that if a characteristic
   was used a lot by an organism, then it would become more developed during its
   lifetime, and the organism's offspring would inherit the acquired characteristic.

2) For example, using this theory, if a rabbit used its legs to run a lot (to escape predators), then
   its legs would get longer. The offspring of that rabbit would then be born with longer legs.

Scientists Develop Different Hypotheses from Observations

1) Often scientists come up with different hypotheses to explain similar observations.

2) Scientists might develop different hypotheses because they have different beliefs
   (e.g. religious) or they have been influenced by different people (e.g. other
   scientists and their way of thinking)... or they just darn well think differently.

There's more about making hypotheses on page 1.

3) The only way to find out whose hypothesis is right is to find evidence to support
   or disprove each one.

4) For example, Lamarck and Darwin both had different hypotheses to explain how evolution happens.
   In the end...

   • Lamarck's hypothesis was eventually rejected because experiments didn't support
     his hypothesis. You can see it for yourself, e.g. if you dye a hamster's fur bright pink
     (not recommended), its offspring will still be born with the normal fur colour because
     the new characteristic won't have been passed on.
   • The discovery of genetics supported Darwin's idea because it provided an explanation of
     how organisms born with beneficial characteristics can pass them on (i.e. via their genes).
     Other evidence was also found by looking at fossils of different ages (the fossil record) —
     this allows you to see how changes in organisms developed slowly over time. The relatively
     recent discovery of how bacteria are able to evolve to become resistant to antibiotics also
     further supports evolution by natural selection.

5) There's so much evidence for Darwin's idea that it's now an accepted hypothesis (a theory).

Here's to crazy new ideas...

Science is fuelled by new ideas. Without them, we'd still think the world is flat and that mullets are cool.

Q1   Explain why Darwin's theory was considered controversial when it was first proposed.   [3 marks]

Selective Breeding

'Selective breeding' sounds like it has the potential to be a tricky topic, but it's actually dead simple.
You take the best plants or animals and breed them together to get the best possible offspring. That's it.

Selective Breeding is Very Simple

Selective breeding is when humans artificially select the plants or animals that are
going to breed so that the genes for particular characteristics remain in the population.
Organisms are selectively bred to develop features that are useful or attractive,
for example:

- Animals that produce more meat or milk.
- Crops with disease resistance.
- Dogs with a good, gentle temperament.
- Decorative plants with big or unusual flowers.

lovely

This is the basic process involved in selective breeding:

1) From your existing stock, select the ones which have the characteristics you're after.

2) Breed them with each other.

3) Select the best of the offspring, and breed them together.

4) Continue this process over several generations, and the desirable trait gets
stronger and stronger. Eventually, all the offspring will have the characteristic.

Selective breeding is also known as 'artificial selection'.

> In agriculture (farming), selective breeding can be used to improve yields. E.g. to improve
> meat yields, a farmer could breed together the cows and bulls with the best characteristics
> for producing meat, e.g. large size. After doing this for several generations the farmer
> would get cows with a very high meat yield.

5) Selective breeding is nothing new — people have been doing it for thousands of years.
It's how we ended up with edible crops from wild plants and how we got domesticated
animals like cows and dogs.

The Main Drawback is a Reduction in the Gene Pool

1) The main problem with selective breeding is that it reduces the gene pool — the number of different
alleles (forms of a gene) in a population. This is because the farmer keeps breeding from the "best"
animals or plants — which are all closely related. This is known as inbreeding.

2) Inbreeding can cause health problems because there's more chance of the organisms inheriting
harmful genetic defects when the gene pool is limited. Some dog breeds are particularly susceptible to
certain defects because of inbreeding — e.g. pugs often have breathing problems.

3) There can also be serious problems if a new disease appears, because there's not much variation in the
population. All the stock are closely related to each other, so if one of them is going to be killed by a
new disease, the others are also likely to succumb to it.

| Selective Breeding | → | Reduction in the number of different alleles (forms of a gene) | → | Less chance of any resistant alleles being present in the population |

Oh Eck!

I use the same genes all the time too — they flatter my hips...

Different breeds of dog came from selective breeding. For example, somebody thought 'I really like this small,
yappy wolf — I'll breed it with this other one'. After thousands of generations, we got poodles.

Q1   Why might a plant nursery use selective breeding?   [1 mark]

Q2   What potential issues can selective breeding cause?   [3 marks]

Genetic Engineering

Genetic engineering is an interesting area of science with <u>exciting possibilities</u>, but there might be <u>dangers</u> too...

Genetic Engineering Transfers Genes Between Organisms

The basic idea of genetic engineering is to <u>transfer</u> a <u>gene</u> responsible for a <u>desirable characteristic</u> from one organism's genome into <u>another</u> organism, so that it also has the <u>desired characteristic</u>.

1) A useful gene is <u>isolated</u> (cut) from one organism's genome using <u>enzymes</u> and is inserted into a <u>vector</u>.

2) The vector is usually a <u>virus</u> or a <u>bacterial plasmid</u> (a fancy piece of circular DNA found in bacterial cells), depending on the type of organism that the gene is being transferred to.

3) When the vector is <u>introduced</u> to the target organism, the <u>useful gene</u> is <u>inserted</u> into its cell(s).

4) Scientists use this method to do <u>all sorts</u> of things. For example:

> 1) <u>Bacteria</u> have been genetically modified to produce <u>human insulin</u> that can be used to treat <u>diabetes</u>.
>
> 2) <u>Genetically modified</u> (GM) <u>crops</u> have had their genes modified, e.g. to improve the size and quality of their fruit, or make them <u>resistant</u> to <u>disease</u>, <u>insects</u> and <u>herbicides</u> (chemicals used to kill weeds).
>
> 3) <u>Sheep</u> have been genetically engineered to produce substances, like drugs, in their <u>milk</u> that can be used to treat <u>human diseases</u>.
>
> 4) Scientists are researching genetic modification treatments for <u>inherited diseases</u> caused by faulty genes, e.g. by <u>inserting working genes</u> into people with the disease. This is called <u>gene therapy</u>.

5) In some cases, the transfer of the gene is carried out when the organism receiving the gene is at an <u>early stage</u> of <u>development</u> (e.g. egg or embryo). This means that the organism <u>develops</u> with the <u>characteristic</u> coded for by the gene.

Genetic Engineering is a Controversial Topic

1) Genetic engineering is an <u>exciting area of science</u>, which has the <u>potential</u> for solving many of our problems (e.g. treating diseases, more efficient food production etc.), but not everyone thinks it's a great idea.

2) There are <u>worries</u> about the long-term effects of genetic engineering — that changing an organism's genes might <u>accidentally</u> create unplanned <u>problems</u>, which could get passed on to <u>future generations</u>.

There Are Pros and Cons of GM Crops

1) Some people say that growing GM crops will affect the number of <u>wild flowers</u> (and so the population of <u>insects</u>) that live in and around the crops — <u>reducing</u> farmland <u>biodiversity</u>.

2) Not everyone is convinced that GM crops are <u>safe</u> and some people are concerned that we might not <u>fully understand</u> the effects of eating them on <u>human health</u>. E.g. people are worried they may develop <u>allergies</u> to the food — although there's probably no more risk for this than for eating usual foods.

3) A big concern is that <u>transplanted genes</u> may get out into the <u>natural environment</u>. For example, the <u>herbicide resistance</u> gene may be picked up by weeds, creating a new '<u>superweed</u>' variety.

4) On the plus side, the characteristics chosen for GM crops can <u>increase the yield</u>, making more food.

5) People living in developing nations often lack <u>nutrients</u> in their diets. GM crops could be <u>engineered</u> to contain the nutrient that's <u>missing</u>. For example, 'golden rice' is a GM rice crop that contains beta-carotene — lack of this substance causes <u>blindness</u>.

6) GM crops are already being grown in some places, often <u>without any problems</u>.

If only there was a gene to make revision easier...

Make sure you've got everything on this page firmly in your noggin. You need to understand the lot.

Q1   Outline one benefit and one concern about GM crops.   [2 marks]

Topic 6 — Inheritance, Variation and Evolution

Cloning

We can clone plants and animals in several different ways. Cool. But some of them have potential problems...

Plants Can Be Cloned by Tissue Culture and from Cuttings

TISSUE CULTURE
This is where a few plant cells are put in a growth medium with hormones, and they grow into new plants — clones of the parent plant. These plants can be made very quickly, in very little space, and be grown all year. Tissue culture is used by scientists to preserve rare plants that are hard to reproduce naturally and by plant nurseries to produce lots of stock quickly.

CUTTINGS
1) Gardeners can take cuttings from good parent plants, and then plant them to produce genetically identical copies (clones) of the parent plant.
2) These plants can be produced quickly and cheaply. This is an older, simpler method than tissue culture.

You Can Make Animal Clones Using Embryo Transplants

Farmers can produce cloned offspring from their best bull and cow — using embryo transplants.

1) Sperm cells are taken from a prize bull and egg cells are taken from a prize cow. The sperm are then used to artificially fertilise an egg cell. The embryo that develops is then split many times (to form clones) before any cells become specialised.
2) These cloned embryos can then be implanted into lots of other cows where they grow into baby calves (which will all be genetically identical to each other).
3) Hundreds of "ideal" offspring can be produced every year from the best bull and cow.

Adult Cell Cloning is Another Way to Make a Clone

1) Adult cell cloning involves taking an unfertilised egg cell and removing its nucleus. The nucleus is then removed from an adult body cell (e.g. skin cell) and is inserted into the 'empty' egg cell.
2) The egg cell is then stimulated by an electric shock — this makes it divide, just like a normal embryo.
3) When the embryo is a ball of cells, it's implanted into the womb of an adult female. It grows into a genetically identical copy (clone) of the original adult body cell as it has the same genetic information.
4) This technique was used to create Dolly — the famous cloned sheep.

There are Many Issues Surrounding Cloning

1) Cloning quickly gets you lots of "ideal" offspring. But you also get a "reduced gene pool" — this means there are fewer different alleles in a population. If a population are all closely related and a new disease appears, they could all be wiped out — there may be no allele in the population giving resistance to it.
2) But the study of animal clones could lead to greater understanding of the development of the embryo, and of ageing and age-related disorders.
3) Cloning could also be used to help preserve endangered species.
4) However, it's possible that cloned animals might not be as healthy as normal ones, e.g. Dolly the sheep had arthritis, which tends to occur in older sheep (but the jury's still out on if this was due to cloning).
5) Some people worry that humans might be cloned in the future. If it was allowed, any success may follow many unsuccessful attempts, e.g. children born severely disabled.

Thank goodness they didn't do that with my little brother...

Cloning can be controversial — especially when it's to do with cloning animals (and especially humans).

Q1 Describe how animals can be cloned by adult cell cloning. [5 marks]

Fossils

Fossils are great. If they're <u>well-preserved</u>, you can see what oldy-worldy creatures <u>looked</u> like.
They also show how living things have <u>evolved</u>. Although we're not sure how life started in the first place...

Fossils *are the Remains of Plants and Animals*

Fossils are the <u>remains</u> of organisms from <u>many thousands of years ago</u>, which are found in <u>rocks</u>.
They provide the <u>evidence</u> that organisms lived ages ago. Fossils can tell us a lot about <u>how much</u> or
<u>how little</u> organisms have <u>changed</u> (<u>evolved</u>) over time. Fossils form in rocks in one of <u>three</u> ways:

1) FROM <u>GRADUAL REPLACEMENT</u> BY MINERALS   (Most fossils happen this way.)

1) Things like <u>teeth</u>, <u>shells</u>, <u>bones</u> etc., which <u>don't decay</u> easily, can last a long time when <u>buried</u>.

2) They're eventually <u>replaced by minerals</u> as they decay,
   forming a <u>rock-like substance</u> shaped like the original hard part.

3) The surrounding sediments also turn to rock, but the fossil stays
   <u>distinct</u> inside the rock and eventually someone <u>digs it up</u>.

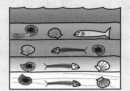

2) FROM <u>CASTS</u> AND <u>IMPRESSIONS</u>

1) Sometimes, fossils are formed when an organism is <u>buried</u> in a <u>soft</u> material like clay.
   The clay later <u>hardens</u> around it and the organism decays, leaving a <u>cast</u> of itself.
   An animal's <u>burrow</u> or a plant's <u>roots</u> (<u>rootlet traces</u>) can be preserved as casts.

2) Things like footprints can also be <u>pressed</u> into these materials when soft, leaving an
   <u>impression</u> when it hardens.

3) FROM <u>PRESERVATION</u> IN PLACES WHERE NO DECAY HAPPENS

1) In <u>amber</u> (a clear yellow 'stone' made from fossilised resin) and <u>tar pits</u>
   there's no <u>oxygen</u> or <u>moisture</u> so <u>decay microbes</u> can't survive.

2) In <u>glaciers</u> it's too <u>cold</u> for the <u>decay microbes</u> to work.

3) <u>Peat bogs</u> are too <u>acidic</u> for <u>decay microbes</u>.
   (A fully preserved man they named 'Pete Marsh' was found in a bog.)

But No One Knows How Life Began

Fossils show how much or how little different organisms have changed (<u>evolved</u>) as life has developed on
Earth over millions of years. But where did the <u>first</u> living thing come from...

1) There are various <u>hypotheses</u> suggesting how life first came into being, but no one really <u>knows</u>.

2) Maybe the first life forms came into existence in a primordial <u>swamp</u> (or under the <u>sea</u>) here on <u>Earth</u>.
   Maybe simple organic molecules were brought to Earth on <u>comets</u> — these could have then become
   more <u>complex</u> organic molecules, and eventually very simple <u>life forms</u>.

3) These hypotheses can't be supported or disproved because there's a <u>lack</u> of good, <u>valid</u> evidence:

   - Many early forms of life were <u>soft-bodied</u>, and soft tissue tends to
     decay away <u>completely</u> — so the fossil record is <u>incomplete</u>.

   - Fossils that did form millions of years ago may have been
     <u>destroyed</u> by <u>geological activity</u>, e.g. the movement of tectonic
     plates may have crushed fossils already formed in the rock.

Don't get bogged down by all this information...

It's a bit mind-boggling really how fossils can still exist even millions of years after the organism died.
They really are fascinating things, and scientists have learned a whole lot from studying them in detail.

Q1   Suggest what makes low-oxygen environments suitable for the formation of fossils.   [2 marks]

Speciation

Evolution (see page 96) leads to the development of lots of <u>different species</u>. This process is called <u>speciation</u>.

Speciation is the Development of a New Species

1) A species is a group of <u>similar organisms</u> that can <u>reproduce</u> to give <u>fertile offspring</u>.

2) <u>Speciation</u> is the development of a <u>new species</u>.

3) Speciation occurs when <u>populations</u> of the <u>same species</u> become so <u>different</u> that they can <u>no longer successfully interbreed</u> to produce <u>fertile offspring</u>.

Isolation and Natural Selection Lead to Speciation

<u>Isolation</u> is where <u>populations</u> of a species are <u>separated</u>. This can happen due to a <u>physical barrier</u>. E.g. floods and earthquakes can cause barriers that <u>geographically isolate</u> some individuals from the main population. <u>Conditions</u> on either side of the barrier will be <u>slightly different</u>, e.g. they may have <u>different climates</u>. Because the environment is <u>different</u> on each side, <u>different characteristics</u> will become more common in each population due to <u>natural selection</u> operating <u>differently</u> on the populations.

1) Each population shows <u>genetic variation</u> because they have a wide range of <u>alleles</u>.

2) In each population, individuals with characteristics that make them better adapted to their environment have a <u>better chance of survival</u> and so are more likely to <u>breed</u> successfully.

3) So the <u>alleles</u> that control the <u>beneficial characteristics</u> are more likely to be <u>passed on</u> to the <u>next generation</u>.

Eventually, individuals from the different populations will have <u>changed</u> so much that they <u>won't</u> be able to <u>breed</u> with one another to produce fertile offspring. The two groups will have become <u>separate species</u>.

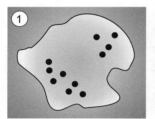 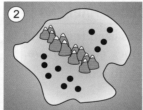 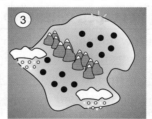 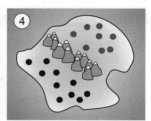

Two populations of ⟹ Physical barriers ⟹ Populations ⟹ Development of
the same species   separate populations.   adapt to new   a new species.
● = individual organism   environments.

Wallace Was a Pioneer of the Theory of Speciation

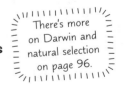
There's more on Darwin and natural selection on page 96.

1) <u>Alfred Russel Wallace</u> was a scientist working at the <u>same time</u> as Charles Darwin. He was one of the <u>early</u> scientists working on the idea of <u>speciation</u>. His observations greatly <u>contributed</u> to how we understand speciation <u>today</u>. Our current understanding <u>developed</u> as <u>more evidence</u> became available over time.

2) During his career, Wallace <u>independently</u> came up with the idea of <u>natural selection</u> and published work on the subject <u>together</u> with Darwin in <u>1858</u>. This then prompted Darwin to publish '<u>On the Origin of Species</u>' in <u>1859</u>.

3) <u>Observations</u> made by Wallace as he travelled the world provided lots of <u>evidence</u> to support the theory of evolution by natural selection. For example, he realised that <u>warning colours</u> are used by some species (e.g. butterflies) to <u>deter predators</u> from eating them and that this was an example of a <u>beneficial characteristic</u> that had evolved by natural selection.

4) It's this work on <u>warning colours</u> and his work on <u>speciation</u> that he's <u>most famous</u> for.

If only Darwin's name had been Gromit...

Well isn't speciation riveting... Put some time into learning this page, then maybe grab a biscuit.

Q1   Why might natural selection work differently on two isolated populations of a species?   [3 marks]

Antibiotic-Resistant Bacteria

The discovery of antibiotics, like penicillin, was a huge benefit to medicine — suddenly bacterial infections that had often been fatal could be cured. But unfortunately they might not be a permanent solution.

Bacteria can Evolve and Become Antibiotic-Resistant

1) Like all organisms, bacteria sometimes develop random mutations (see p.86) in their DNA. These can lead to changes in the bacteria's characteristics, e.g. being less affected by a particular antibiotic. This can lead to antibiotic-resistant strains forming as the gene for antibiotic resistance becomes more common in the population.

The gene for antibiotic resistance becomes more common in the population because of natural selection — see page 96 for more.

2) To make matters worse, because bacteria are so rapid at reproducing, they can evolve quite quickly.

3) For the bacterium, the ability to resist antibiotics is a big advantage. It's better able to survive, even in a host who's being treated to get rid of the infection, and so it lives for longer and reproduces many more times. This increases the population size of the antibiotic-resistant strain.

4) Antibiotic-resistant strains are a problem for people who become infected with these bacteria because they aren't immune to the new strain and there is no effective treatment. This means that the infection easily spreads between people. Sometimes drug companies can come up with a new antibiotic that's effective, but 'superbugs' that are resistant to most known antibiotics are becoming more common.

5) MRSA is a relatively common 'superbug' that's really hard to get rid of. It often affects people in hospitals and can be fatal if it enters their bloodstream.

Antibiotic Resistance is Becoming More Common

1) For the last few decades, we've been able to deal with bacterial infections pretty easily using antibiotics. The death rate from infectious bacterial diseases (e.g. pneumonia) has fallen dramatically.

2) But the problem of antibiotic resistance is getting worse — partly because of the overuse and inappropriate use of antibiotics, e.g. doctors prescribing them for non-serious conditions or infections caused by viruses.

Antibiotics don't kill viruses — see p.51.

3) The more often antibiotics are used, the bigger the problem of antibiotic resistance becomes, so it's important that doctors only prescribe antibiotics when they really need to:

> It's not that antibiotics actually cause resistance — they create a situation where naturally resistant bacteria have an advantage and so increase in numbers.

4) It's also important that you take all the antibiotics a doctor prescribes for you:

> Taking the full course makes sure that all the bacteria are destroyed, which means that there are none left to mutate and develop into antibiotic-resistant strains.

5) In farming, antibiotics can be given to animals to prevent them becoming ill and to make them grow faster. This can lead to the development of antibiotic-resistant bacteria in the animals which can then spread to humans, e.g. during meat preparation and consumption. Increasing concern about the overuse of antibiotics in agriculture has led to some countries restricting their use.

6) The increase in antibiotic resistance has encouraged drug companies to work on developing new antibiotics that are effective against the resistant strains. Unfortunately, the rate of development is slow, which means we're unlikely to be able to keep up with the demand for new drugs as more antibiotic-resistant strains develop and spread. It's also a very costly process.

Aaargh, a giant earwig! Run from the attack of the superbug...

The reality of 'superbugs' is even scarier than giant earwigs. Microorganisms that are resistant to all our drugs are a worrying thought. It'll be like going back in time to before antibiotics were invented.

Q1 Suggest a situation where antibiotics could be prescribed inappropriately. [1 mark]

Q2 Explain why it's important that people take the full course of antibiotics they are prescribed. [2 marks]

Classification

It seems to be a basic human urge to want to <u>classify</u> things — that's the case in <u>biology</u> anyway...

Classification is Organising Living Organisms into Groups

1) Traditionally, organisms have been <u>classified</u> according to a system first proposed in the 1700's by <u>Carl Linnaeus</u>, which <u>groups</u> living things according to their <u>characteristics</u> and the <u>structures</u> that make them up.

2) In this system (known as the <u>Linnaean system</u>), living things are first divided into <u>kingdoms</u> (e.g. the plant kingdom).

3) The kingdoms are then <u>subdivided</u> into smaller and smaller groups — <u>phylum</u>, <u>class</u>, <u>order</u>, <u>family</u>, <u>genus</u>, <u>species</u>.

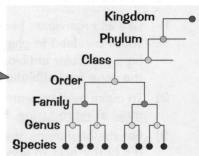

Classification Systems Change Over Time

1) As knowledge of the <u>biochemical processes</u> taking place inside organisms developed and <u>microscopes improved</u> (which allowed us to find out more about the <u>internal structures</u> of organisms), scientists put forward <u>new</u> models of classification.

2) In 1990, Carl Woese proposed the <u>three-domain system</u>. Using evidence gathered from <u>new chemical analysis techniques</u> such as RNA sequence analysis, he found that in some cases, species thought to be <u>closely related</u> in traditional classification systems are in fact <u>not</u> as closely related as first thought.

3) In the three-domain system, organisms are first of all split into <u>three large groups</u> called <u>domains</u>:

> 1) ARCHAEA — Organisms in this domain were once thought to be <u>primitive bacteria</u>, but they're actually a different type of <u>prokaryotic cell</u>. They were first found in <u>extreme places</u> such as hot springs and salt lakes.
>
> 2) BACTERIA — This domain contains <u>true bacteria</u> like *E. coli* and *Staphylococcus*. Although they often look similar to Archaea, there are lots of <u>biochemical differences</u> between them.
>
> 3) EUKARYOTA — This domain includes a <u>broad range</u> of organisms including <u>fungi</u> (page 46), <u>plants</u>, <u>animals</u> and <u>protists</u> (page 46).

4) These are then <u>subdivided</u> into smaller groups — kingdom, phylum, class, order, family, genus, species.

Organisms Are Named According to the Binomial System

1) In the binomial system, every organism is given its own <u>two-part</u> Latin name.

2) The <u>first</u> part refers to the <u>genus</u> that the organism belongs to. This gives you information on the organism's <u>ancestry</u>. The <u>second</u> part refers to the <u>species</u>. E.g. humans are known as *Homo sapiens*. '*Homo*' is the genus and '*sapiens*' is the species.

3) The binomial system is used <u>worldwide</u> and means that scientists in <u>different countries</u> or who speak <u>different languages</u> all refer to a particular species by the <u>same name</u> — avoiding potential confusion.

Evolutionary Trees Show Evolutionary Relationships

1) Evolutionary trees show how scientists think <u>different species</u> are <u>related</u> to each other.

2) They show <u>common ancestors</u> and relationships between species. The more <u>recent</u> the common ancestor, the more <u>closely related</u> the two species — and the more <u>characteristics</u> they're likely to share.

3) Scientists analyse lots of different types of <u>data</u> to work out evolutionary relationships. For <u>living</u> organisms, they use the <u>current classification data</u> (e.g. DNA analysis and structural similarities). For <u>extinct</u> species, they use information from the <u>fossil record</u> (see page 96).

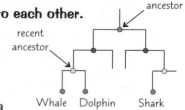

Whales and dolphins have a recent common ancestor so are closely related. They're both more distantly related to sharks.

Binomial system — uh oh, sounds like maths...

Sometimes, the genus in a binomial name is abbreviated to a capital letter with a full stop after it.

Q1   What genus does the Eurasian beaver, *Castor fiber*, belong to?   [1 mark]

Topic 6 — Inheritance, Variation and Evolution

Revision Questions for Topic 6

So you've finished <u>Topic 6</u> — Hoorah. Now here's a page full of questions to test your knowledge. Get in.

- Try these questions and <u>tick off each one</u> when you <u>get it right</u>.
- When you've done <u>all the questions</u> under a heading and are <u>completely happy</u> with it, tick it off.

<u>DNA, Genes and Mutations (p.84-86)</u> ☑

1) What do genes code for?
2) List the parts of a DNA nucleotide.
3) How many bases in a DNA sequence code for one amino acid?
4) Give a function of the non-coding parts of DNA.
5) Explain how mutations can lead to a change in the protein coded for by a gene.
6) True or False: "Most mutations have little or no effect on the protein coded for by a gene".

<u>Reproduction and Meiosis (p.87-89)</u> ☑

7) Name the male and female gametes of animals.
8) Which type of reproduction produces genetically identical cells?
9) State the type of cell division used to make gametes in humans.
10) How does variation in a population increase its chance of surviving environmental change?
11) Describe the methods of sexual and asexual reproduction used by strawberry plants.

<u>Sex Chromosomes, Genetic Diagrams and Inherited Disorders (p.90-93)</u> ☑

12) What is the probability that offspring will have the **XX** combination of sex chromosomes?
13) How many genes are responsible for controlling fur colour in mice?
14) What are alleles?
15) What does it mean if someone is heterozygous for a gene?
16) What is the chance of a child being born with polydactyly if one parent has a single dominant allele for the gene that controls it?
17) Give two arguments for and two arguments against screening embryos for genetic disorders.

<u>Mendel, Variation and Evolution (p.94-97)</u> ☐

18) What do we now know Mendel's "units" as?
19) What is variation?
20) Explain how beneficial characteristics can become more common in a population over time.
21) What was Jean-Baptiste Lamarck's theory about evolution?

<u>Selective Breeding, Genetic Engineering and Cloning (p.98-100)</u> ☑

22) What is selective breeding?
23) How might farmers use selective breeding?
24) What is genetic engineering?
25) How can embryo transplants be used to create animal clones?

<u>Fossils, Speciation and Antibiotic-Resistant Bacteria (p.101-103)</u> ☑

26) Give two ways that fossils can be formed.
27) What is speciation and when can it occur?
28) What leads to the formation of antibiotic-resistant strains of bacteria?

<u>Classification (p.104)</u> ☐

29) Name the groups that organisms are classified into in the Linnaean system.
30) Who proposed the 'three-domain system' of classification in 1990?

Competition

Ecology is all about organisms and the environment they live in, and how the two interact. Simples.

First Learn Some Words to Help You Understand Ecology...

This topic will make a lot more sense if you become familiar with these terms first:

1) Habitat — the place where an organism lives.
2) Population — all the organisms of one species living in a habitat.
3) Community — the populations of different species living in a habitat.
4) Abiotic factors — non-living factors of the environment, e.g. temperature.
5) Biotic factors — living factors of the environment, e.g. food.
6) Ecosystem — the interaction of a community of living organisms (biotic) with the non-living (abiotic) parts of their environment.

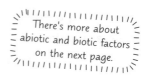
There's more about abiotic and biotic factors on the next page.

Organisms Compete for Resources to Survive

Organisms need things from their environment and from other organisms in order to survive and reproduce:

1) Plants need light and space, as well as water and mineral ions (nutrients) from the soil.
2) Animals need space (territory), food, water and mates.

Organisms compete with other species (and members of their own species) for the same resources.

Any Change in Any Environment can Have Knock-on Effects

In a community, each species depends on other species for things such as food, shelter, pollination and seed dispersal — this is called interdependence.

The interdependence of all the living things in an ecosystem means that any major change in the ecosystem (such as one species being removed) can have far-reaching effects.

The diagram on the right shows part of a food web (a diagram of what eats what) from a stream.

Stonefly larvae are particularly sensitive to pollution. Suppose pollution killed them in this stream. The table below shows some of the effects this might have on some of the other organisms in the food web.

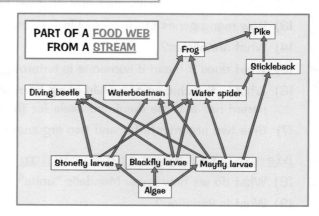
PART OF A FOOD WEB FROM A STREAM

Organism	Effect of loss of stonefly larvae	Effect on population
Blackfly larvae	Less competition for algae	Increase
	More likely to be eaten by predators	Decrease
Water spider	Less food	Decrease
Stickleback	Less food (if water spider or mayfly larvae numbers decrease)	Decrease

Remember that food webs are very complex and that these effects are difficult to predict accurately.

In some communities, all the species and environmental factors are in balance so that the population sizes are roughly constant (they may go up and down in cycles — see p.109). These are called stable communities. Stable communities include tropical rainforests and ancient oak woodlands.

I'm dependent on the cocoa tree...

If my source of chocolate was removed, it would have far-reaching effects on my revision and exam grades. Seriously though, make sure you know what organisms need and compete for in an ecosystem. Then try these...

Q1　　What is an ecosystem?　　　　　　　　　　　　　　　　　　　　　　　　　　[1 mark]

Q2　　Give three things plants compete for in an ecosystem.　　　　　　　　　　　[3 marks]

Q3　　What is meant by a 'stable community'?　　　　　　　　　　　　　　　　　[1 mark]

Abiotic and Biotic Factors

The environment in which organisms live changes all the time. The things that change are either abiotic (non-living) or biotic (living) factors. These can have a big effect on a community...

Abiotic Factors Can Vary in an Ecosystem...

Abiotic factors are non-living factors. For example:

1) Moisture level
2) Light intensity
3) Temperature
4) Carbon dioxide level (for plants)

5) Wind intensity and direction
6) Oxygen level (for aquatic animals)
7) Soil pH and mineral content

A change in the environment could be an increase or decrease in an abiotic factor, e.g. an increase in temperature. These changes can affect the size of populations in a community. This means they can also affect the population sizes of other organisms that depend on them (see previous page).

> For example, a decrease in light intensity, temperature or level of carbon dioxide could decrease the rate of photosynthesis in a plant species (see p.57). This could affect plant growth and cause a decrease in the population size.

> For example, a decrease in the mineral content of the soil (e.g. a lack of nitrates) could cause nutrient deficiencies (see p.55). This could also affect plant growth and cause a decrease in the population size.

Animals depend on plants for food, so a decrease in a plant population could affect the animal species in a community.

...and So Can Biotic Factors

Biotic factors are living factors. Here are some examples:

1) New predators arriving
2) Competition — one species may outcompete another so that numbers are too low to breed

3) New pathogens
4) Availability of food

A change in the environment could be the introduction of a new biotic factor, e.g. a new predator or pathogen. These changes can also affect the size of populations in a community, which can have knock-on effects because of interdependence (see previous page).

> For example, a new predator could cause a decrease in the prey population. There's more about predator-prey populations on p.109.

> For example, red and grey squirrels live in the same habitat and eat the same food. Grey squirrels outcompete the red squirrels — so the population of red squirrels is decreasing.

> The following graph shows the effect of a new pathogen on Species A. The population size of species A was increasing up until 1985, when it decreased rapidly until 1990 — suggesting that 1985 was the year that the new pathogen arrived. The population started to rise again after 1990.

Exams — a type of abiotic factor affecting my environment...

So, two lists of factors that would be a good idea to learn. I reckon this is a prime time for shutting the book, scribbling them all down and then checking how you did. Also, have a gander at that squirrel example.

Q1 Give four examples of abiotic factors that could affect a plant species.   [4 marks]

Q2 Cutthroat trout are present in lakes in Yellowstone National Park. In the last few decades, lake trout have been introduced to the lakes. However, lake trout have emerged as predators of the cutthroat trout. Give two other biotic factors that could affect the size of the cutthroat trout population.   [2 marks]

Adaptations

Life exists in so many different environments because the organisms that live in them have adapted to them.

Adaptations Allow Organisms to Survive

Organisms, including microorganisms, are adapted to live in different environmental conditions. The features or characteristics that allow them to do this are called adaptations. Adaptations can be:

1) Structural

These are features of an organism's body structure — such as shape or colour. For example:

Arctic animals like the Arctic fox have white fur so they're camouflaged against the snow. This helps them avoid predators and sneak up on prey.

Animals that live in cold places (like whales) have a thick layer of blubber (fat) and a low surface area to volume ratio to help them retain heat.

Animals that live in hot places (like camels) have a thin layer of fat and a large surface area to volume ratio to help them lose heat.

2) Behavioural

These are ways that organisms behave. Many species (e.g. swallows) migrate to warmer climates during the winter to avoid the problems of living in cold conditions.

3) Functional

These are things that go on inside an organism's body that can be related to processes like reproduction and metabolism (all the chemical reactions happening in the body). For example:

Desert animals conserve water by producing very little sweat and small amounts of concentrated urine.

Brown bears hibernate over winter. They lower their metabolism which conserves energy, so they don't have to hunt when there's not much food about.

Microorganisms Have a Huge Variety of Adaptations...

...so that they can live in a wide range of environments:

Some microorganisms (e.g. bacteria) are known as extremophiles — they're adapted to live in very extreme conditions. For example, some can live at high temperatures (e.g. in super hot volcanic vents), and others can live in places with a high salt concentration (e.g. very salty lakes) or at high pressure (e.g. deep sea vents).

In a nutshell, it's horses for courses...

In the exam, you might have to say how an organism is adapted to its environment. Look at its characteristics (e.g. colour/shape) as well as the conditions it has to cope with (e.g. predation/temperature) and you'll be sorted.

Q1 The diagram on the right shows a penguin. Penguins live in the cold, icy environment of the Antarctic. They swim in the sea to hunt for fish to eat. Some penguins also huddle together in large groups to keep warm.

   a) What type of adaptation is being described when penguins 'huddle together'? [1 mark]

   b) Explain one structural adaptation a penguin has to its environment. [2 marks]

Food Chains

If you like <u>food</u>, and you like <u>chains</u>, then <u>food chains</u> might just blow your mind. Strap yourself in and prepare for some 'edge of your seat' learning, because the show is about to begin...

Food Chains Show What's Eaten by What in an Ecosystem

1) <u>Food chains</u> always start with a <u>producer</u>.
   Producers <u>make</u> (produce) <u>their own food</u> using energy from the Sun.

2) Producers are usually <u>green plants</u> or <u>algae</u> — they make <u>glucose</u> by <u>photosynthesis</u> (see page 57).

3) When a green plant produces glucose, some of it is used to make <u>other biological molecules</u> in the plant.

4) These biological molecules are the plant's <u>biomass</u> — the <u>mass</u> of <u>living material</u>.

5) Biomass can be thought of as <u>energy stored</u> in a plant.

6) <u>Energy</u> is <u>transferred</u> through living organisms in an ecosystem when organisms <u>eat</u> other organisms.

7) Producers are eaten by <u>primary consumers</u>. Primary consumers are then eaten by <u>secondary consumers</u> and secondary consumers are eaten by <u>tertiary consumers</u>. Here's an example of a food chain:

> Consumers are organisms that eat other organisms. 'Primary' means 'first', so primary consumers are the first consumers in a food chain. Secondary consumers are second and tertiary consumers are third.

Producers   Primary consumers   Secondary consumer

<u>5000</u> dandelions... feed... <u>100</u> rabbits... which feed... <u>1</u> fox.

Populations of Prey and Predators Go in Cycles

Consumers that <u>hunt and kill</u> other animals are called <u>predators</u>, and their <u>prey</u> are what they eat.
In a <u>stable community</u> containing <u>prey</u> and <u>predators</u> (as most of them do of course):

> For more about a stable community see page 106.

1) The <u>population</u> of any species is usually <u>limited</u> by the amount of <u>food</u> available.

2) If the population of the <u>prey</u> increases, then so will the population of the <u>predators</u>.

3) However as the population of predators <u>increases</u>, the number of prey will <u>decrease</u>.

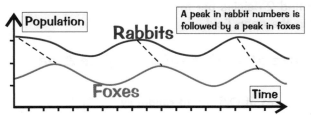

A peak in rabbit numbers is followed by a peak in foxes

E.g. <u>More grass</u> means <u>more rabbits</u>.
More rabbits means <u>more foxes</u>.
But more foxes means <u>fewer rabbits</u>.
Eventually fewer rabbits will mean <u>fewer foxes again</u>.
This <u>up and down pattern</u> continues...

4) Predator-prey cycles are always <u>out of phase</u> with each other. This is because it <u>takes a while</u> for one population to <u>respond</u> to changes in the other population. E.g. when the number of rabbits goes up, the number of foxes doesn't increase immediately because it takes time for them to reproduce.

When the TV volume goes up... my revision goes down...

You might think that the start of a food chain always has to be a plant. In most cases it is, but sometimes organisms like algae can be too because they photosynthesise. No wonder those algae I saw were looking smug...

Q1   Look at the following food chain for a particular area: grass → grasshopper → rat → snake
   a) Name the producer in the food chain.   [1 mark]
   b) How many consumers are there in the food chain?   [1 mark]
   c) Name the primary consumer in the food chain.   [1 mark]
   d) All the rats in the area are killed. Explain two effects that this could have on the food chain. [4 marks]

PRACTICAL | Using Quadrats

This is where the <u>fun</u> starts. Studying <u>ecology</u> gives you the chance to <u>rummage around</u> in bushes, get your hands <u>dirty</u> and look at some <u>real organisms</u>, living in the <u>wild</u>. Hold on to your hats folks...

Organisms Live in Different Places Because The Environment Varies

1) As you know from page 106, a <u>habitat</u> is the place where an organism <u>lives</u>, e.g. a playing field.

2) The <u>distribution</u> of an organism is <u>where</u> an organism is <u>found</u>, e.g. in a part of the playing field.

3) Where an organism is found is affected by <u>environmental factors</u> (see page 107). An organism might be <u>more common</u> in <u>one area</u> than another due to <u>differences</u> in environmental factors between the two areas. For example, in the playing field, you might find that daisies are <u>more common</u> in the open than under trees, because there's <u>more light</u> available in the open.

4) There are a couple of ways to <u>study</u> the distribution of an organism. You can:
   - <u>measure</u> how common an organism is in <u>two sample areas</u> (e.g. using <u>quadrats</u>) and compare them.
   - study how the distribution <u>changes</u> across an area, e.g. by placing quadrats along a <u>transect</u> (p.111).
   Both of these methods give <u>quantitative</u> data (numbers) about the distribution.

Use Quadrats to Study The Distribution of Small Organisms

A <u>quadrat</u> is a <u>square</u> frame enclosing a <u>known area</u>, e.g. 1 m². To compare <u>how common</u> an organism is in <u>two sample areas</u> (e.g. shady and sunny spots in that playing field) just follow these simple steps:

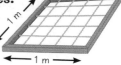
A quadrat

1) Place a <u>1 m² quadrat</u> on the ground at a <u>random point</u> within the <u>first</u> sample area. E.g. divide the area into a grid and use a random number generator to pick coordinates.

2) <u>Count</u> all the organisms <u>within</u> the quadrat.

3) <u>Repeat</u> steps 1 and 2 as many times as you can.

4) <u>Work out</u> the <u>mean</u> number of organisms per quadrat within the first sample area.

 **EXAMPLE:** Anna counted the number of daisies in 7 quadrats within her first sample area and recorded the following results: 18, 20, 22, 23, 23, 23, 25

Here the MEAN is: $\dfrac{\text{TOTAL number of organisms}}{\text{NUMBER of quadrats}} = \dfrac{154}{7} = 22$ daisies per quadrat

5) <u>Repeat</u> steps 1 to 4 in the <u>second</u> sample area.

6) Finally <u>compare</u> the two means. E.g. you might find 2 daisies per m² in the shade, and 22 daisies per m² (lots more) in the open field.

You Can Also Work Out the Population Size of an Organism in One Area

 **EXAMPLE:** Students used quadrats, each with an area of 0.5 m², to randomly sample daisies on an open field. The students found a mean of 10.5 daisies per quadrat. The field had an area of 800 m². Estimate the population of daisies on the field.

1) Work out the <u>mean number of organisms per m²</u>. $1 \div 0.5 = 2$
   $2 \times 10.5 = 21$ daisies per m²

2) Then multiply the <u>mean</u> by the <u>total area</u> (in m²) of the habitat. $800 \times 21 = 16\ 800$ daisies on the open field

The population size of an organism is sometimes called its abundance.

If your quadrat has an area of 1 m², the mean number of organisms per m² is just the same as the mean number per quadrat.

Drat, drat, and double drat — my favourite use of quadrats...

It's key that you make sure you put your quadrat down in a random place before you start counting.

Q1   A 1200 m² field was randomly sampled for buttercups using a quadrat with an area of 0.25 m². A mean of 0.75 buttercups were found per quadrat. Estimate the total population of buttercups.   [2 marks]

Using Transects

So, now you think you've learnt all about distribution. Well hold on — there's more ecology fun to be had.

Use Transects to Study The Distribution of Organisms Along a Line

You can use lines called transects to help find out how organisms (like plants) are distributed across an area — e.g. if an organism becomes more or less common as you move from a hedge towards the middle of a field. Here's what to do:

1) Mark out a line in the area you want to study using a tape measure.

2) Then collect data along the line.

3) You can do this by just counting all the organisms you're interested in that touch the line.

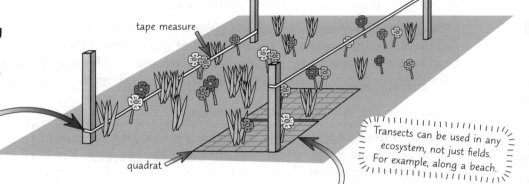

tape measure

quadrat

Transects can be used in any ecosystem, not just fields. For example, along a beach.

4) Or, you can collect data by using quadrats (see previous page). These can be placed next to each other along the line or at intervals, for example, every 2 m.

You Can Estimate the Percentage Cover of a Quadrat

If it's difficult to count all the individual organisms in the quadrat (e.g. if they're grass) you can calculate the percentage cover. This means estimating the percentage area of the quadrat covered by a particular type of organism, e.g. by counting the number of little squares covered by the organisms.

EXAMPLE:

Some students were measuring the distribution of organisms from one corner of a school playing field to another, using quadrats placed at regular intervals along a transect. Below is a picture of one of the quadrats. Calculate the percentage cover of each organism, A and B.

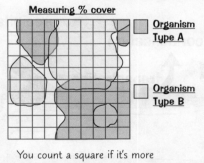

Measuring % cover

Organism Type A

Organism Type B

You count a square if it's more than half covered.

1) Count the number of squares covered by organism A.

2) Make this into a percentage — divide the number of squares covered by the organism by the total number of squares in the quadrat (100), then multiply the result by 100.

3) Do the same for organism B.

Type A = 42 squares

(42/100) × 100
= 0.42 × 100 = 42%

Type B = 47 squares

(47/100) × 100
= 0.47 × 100 = 47%

A slug that's been run over — definitely a widely-spread organism

So if you want to measure the distribution of a organism across an area, you could use a transect. You can either use them alone or along with quadrats. Now who's for a game of tennis... I've got my transect up.

Q1 What is a transect? [1 mark]

Q2 Some students want to measure how the distribution of dandelions changes across a field, from one corner to another. Describe a method they could use to do this. [2 marks]

Q3 How could you estimate the number of organisms in a quadrat, if they are difficult to count? [1 mark]

Environmental Change & The Water Cycle

Now you know how to measure the distribution of organisms (see pages 110-111), it's time to learn why their distribution may change over time. Then it's on to something completely different — the water cycle.

Environmental Changes Affect The Distribution of Organisms

Environmental changes can cause the distribution of organisms to change. A change in distribution means a change in where an organism lives. Environmental changes that can affect organisms in this way include:

1) A change in the AVAILABILITY of WATER. For example:

> The distribution of some animal and plant species in the tropics changes between the wet and the dry seasons — i.e. the times of year where there is more or less rainfall, and so more or less water available. E.g. each year in Africa, large numbers of giant wildebeest migrate, moving north and then back south as the rainfall patterns change.

2) A change in the TEMPERATURE. For example:

> The distribution of bird species in Germany is changing because of a rise in average temperature. E.g. the European bee-eater bird is a Mediterranean species but it's now present in parts of Germany.

3) A change in the composition of ATMOSPHERIC GASES. For example:

> The distribution of some species changes in areas where there is more air pollution. E.g. some species of lichen can't grow in areas where sulfur dioxide is given out by certain industrial processes.

These environmental changes can be caused by seasonal factors, geographic factors or human interaction. For example, the rise in average temperature (see point 2 above) is due to global warming, which has been caused by human activity (see pages 116-117).

The Water Cycle Means Water is Endlessly Recycled

The water here on planet Earth is constantly recycled. Strange but true...

1) Energy from the Sun makes water evaporate from the land and sea, turning it into water vapour. Water also evaporates from plants — this is known as transpiration (see p.43).

2) The warm water vapour is carried upwards (as warm air rises). When it gets higher up it cools and condenses to form clouds.

3) Water falls from the clouds as precipitation (usually rain, but sometimes snow or hail) onto land, where it provides fresh water for plants and animals.

4) It then drains into the sea, before the whole process starts again.

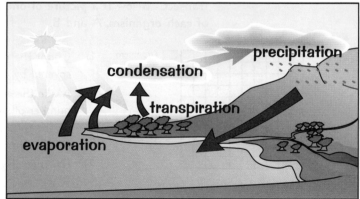

Come on out, it's only a little water cycle, it won't hurt you...

Because organisms rely on the biotic and abiotic factors affecting the environment (see page 107) it's no wonder that when the factors change, it affects where organisms live. Some of the non-living (abiotic) factors that affect us are in a constant cycle — read about the water cycle here and then the carbon cycle on the next page.

Q1   Give two environmental changes that can affect the distribution of living organisms.   [2 marks]

Q2   a) In the water cycle, how does water move from the land into the air?   [1 mark]
     b) How does the water cycle benefit plants and animals?   [1 mark]

The Carbon Cycle

Recycling may be a buzz word for us but it's old school for nature. All the nutrients in our environment are constantly being recycled — there's a nice balance between what goes in and what goes out again.

Elements are Cycled Back to the Start of the Food Chain by Decay

1) Living things are made of materials they take from the world around them. E.g. plants turn elements like carbon, oxygen, hydrogen and nitrogen from the soil and the air into the complex compounds (carbohydrates, proteins and fats) that make up living organisms. These get passed up the food chain.

2) These materials are returned to the environment in waste products, or when the organisms die and decay.

3) Materials decay because they're broken down (digested) by microorganisms. This happens faster in warm, moist, aerobic (oxygen rich) conditions because microorganisms are more active in these conditions.

4) Decay puts the stuff that plants need to grow (e.g. mineral ions — see point 1) back into the soil.

5) In a stable community, the materials that are taken out of the soil and used by plants etc. are balanced by those that are put back in. There's a constant cycle happening.

The Constant Cycling of Carbon is called the Carbon Cycle

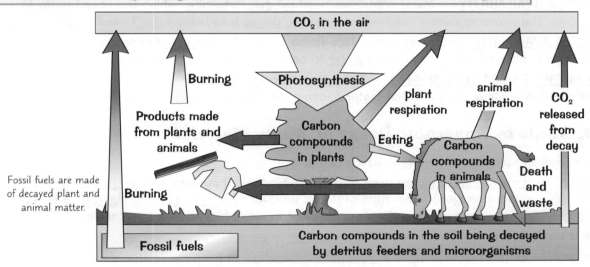

Fossil fuels are made of decayed plant and animal matter.

That can look a bit complicated at first, but it's actually pretty simple:

The energy that green plants and algae get from photosynthesis is transferred up the food chain.

1) CO_2 is removed from the atmosphere by green plants and algae during photosynthesis. The carbon is used to make glucose, which can be turned into carbohydrates, fats and proteins that make up the bodies of the plants and algae.

2) When the plants and algae respire, some carbon is returned to the atmosphere as CO_2.

3) When the plants and algae are eaten by animals, some carbon becomes part of the fats and proteins in their bodies. The carbon then moves through the food chain.

4) When the animals respire, some carbon is returned to the atmosphere as CO_2.

5) When plants, algae and animals die, other animals (called detritus feeders) and microorganisms feed on their remains. When these organisms respire, CO_2 is returned to the atmosphere.

6) Animals also produce waste that is broken down by detritus feeders and microorganisms.

7) The combustion (burning) of wood and fossil fuels also releases CO_2 back into the air.

8) So the carbon (and energy) is constantly being cycled — from the air, through food chains (via plants, algae and animals, and detritus feeders and microorganisms) and eventually back out into the air again.

What goes around comes around...

Carbon is very important for living things — it's the basis for all the organic molecules in our bodies.

Q1   What causes materials to decay?   [1 mark]

Q2   Describe how carbon is removed from the atmosphere in the carbon cycle.   [1 mark]

Decay

Microorganisms <u>break down</u> plant and animal material and waste to get <u>energy</u>. Not my idea of a good meal, but to them it's positively gourmet. This process of <u>decay</u> can be really useful to us — read on...

Decomposition Can Produce Compost

Compost is <u>decomposed organic matter</u> (e.g. food waste) that is used as a <u>natural fertiliser</u> for crops and garden plants. Farmers and gardeners try to provide the <u>ideal conditions</u> for quick decay to make <u>compost</u>.

The Rate of Decay is Affected by Several Factors

<u>Microorganisms</u> such as <u>bacteria</u> and <u>fungi</u>, as well as <u>detritus feeders</u> (p.113) are the critters responsible for <u>decomposition</u> (decay). You'd think that organisms that feed on dead stuff wouldn't be that <u>picky</u>, but they're a bit like Goldilocks — everything has to be <u>just right</u> for them to work at their best.

1) <u>TEMPERATURE</u> — <u>Warmer</u> temperatures make things decompose <u>quicker</u> because they <u>increase</u> the <u>rate</u> that the <u>enzymes</u> (see p.28) involved in decomposition work at. If it's <u>too hot</u> though, decomposition <u>slows down</u> or <u>stops</u> because the enzymes are <u>destroyed</u> and the <u>organisms die</u>. Really <u>cold</u> temperatures slow the rate of decomposition too.

2) <u>OXYGEN AVAILABILITY</u> — Many organisms need <u>oxygen</u> to <u>respire</u>, which they need to do to <u>survive</u>. The microorganisms involved in <u>anaerobic decay</u> (see below) <u>don't</u> need oxygen though.

3) <u>WATER AVAILABILITY</u> — Decay takes place faster in <u>moist environments</u> because the organisms involved in decay need <u>water</u> to carry out biological processes.

4) <u>NUMBER OF DECAY ORGANISMS</u> — The <u>more</u> microorganisms and detritus feeders there are, the <u>faster</u> decomposition happens.

Biogas is Made by Anaerobic Decay of Waste Material

1) Biogas is mainly made up of <u>methane</u>, which can be <u>burned</u> as a <u>fuel</u>.

2) Lots of <u>different microorganisms</u> are used to produce biogas. They decay <u>plant and animal waste</u> <u>anaerobically</u> (without oxygen). This type of decay produces <u>methane gas</u>. <u>Sludge waste</u> from, for example, <u>sewage works</u> or <u>sugar factories</u>, is used to make biogas on a large scale.

3) Biogas is made in a simple fermenter called a <u>digester</u> or <u>generator</u>.

4) Biogas generators need to be kept at a <u>constant temperature</u> to keep the microorganisms <u>respiring</u> away.

5) Biogas <u>can't be stored as a liquid</u> (it needs too high a pressure), so it has to be <u>used straight away</u> — for <u>heating</u>, <u>cooking</u>, <u>lighting</u>, or to <u>power a turbine</u> to <u>generate electricity</u>.

Not All Biogas Generators Are the Same

There are two main types of biogas generator — <u>batch generators</u> and <u>continuous generators</u>.

<u>Batch generators</u> make biogas in <u>small batches</u>. They're <u>manually loaded up with waste</u>, which is left to digest, and the by-products are cleared away at the end of each session.

<u>Continuous generators</u> make biogas <u>all the time</u>. Waste is <u>continuously fed in</u>, and biogas is produced at a <u>steady rate</u>. Continuous generators are more suited to <u>large-scale</u> biogas projects.

The diagram on the right shows a <u>simple biogas generator</u>. Whether it's a continuous or batch generator, it needs to have the following:

1) an inlet for <u>waste material</u> to be put in,

2) an outlet for the <u>digested material</u> to be removed through,

3) an outlet so that the <u>biogas</u> can be piped to where it is needed.

Inlet for waste material · Biogas outlet ·

Gas

Waste material

Outlet for digested material (to be used as fertiliser)

What a rotten subject...

Wow... So we can use poo (and other waste) to make a fuel. It's pretty gross, but I reckon it could come in handy.

Q1   Other than temperature, give three factors that affect the rate of decay.   [3 marks]

Investigating Decay

It's time for a <u>practical</u>. I hope you're not looking forward to a <u>milky brew</u>, because this might just put you off.

You Can Investigate the Effect of Temperature on the Rate of Decay

You can investigate <u>decay</u> by observing the action of the enzyme <u>lipase</u> on a sample of <u>milk</u> that has been made <u>alkaline</u>. When the lipase breaks the milk down, the <u>pH</u> of the milk <u>decreases</u>.

This practical looks at how <u>temperature</u> affects the rate of decay. In it, an indicator dye called <u>phenolphthalein</u> is used — it has a <u>pink</u> colour when the <u>pH</u> is around <u>10</u>, but becomes <u>colourless</u> when the pH falls <u>below 8.3</u>. Here's what you need to do:

1) Measure out <u>5 cm³</u> of <u>lipase solution</u> and add it to a <u>test tube</u>. <u>Label</u> this tube with an 'L' for lipase.

2) Measure out <u>5 cm³</u> of <u>milk</u> and add it to a <u>different test tube</u>.

3) Add <u>5 drops</u> of <u>phenolphthalein indicator</u> to the tube containing <u>milk</u>.

4) Then measure out <u>7 cm³</u> of <u>sodium carbonate solution</u> and add it to the tube containing <u>milk</u> and <u>phenolphthalein</u>. This makes the solution in the tube <u>alkaline</u>, so it should turn <u>pink</u>.

5) Put <u>both</u> tubes into a <u>water bath</u> set to <u>30 °C</u> and <u>leave them</u> to reach the <u>temperature</u> of the water bath. You could stick a <u>thermometer</u> into the <u>milk tube</u> to check this.

6) Once the tubes have <u>reached 30 °C</u>, use a <u>calibrated dropping pipette</u> (a dropping pipette with a scale) to put <u>1 cm³</u> of the <u>lipase solution</u> into the milk tube and start a <u>stopwatch</u> straight away.

7) <u>Stir</u> the contents of the tube with a glass rod. The enzyme will start to <u>decompose</u> the milk.

8) As soon as the solution loses its pink colour, <u>stop</u> the <u>stopwatch</u> and record <u>how long</u> the <u>colour change</u> took in a table.

9) <u>Repeat</u> the experiment at a range of <u>different temperatures</u> (e.g. 10 °C, 20 °C, 40 °C, 50 °C). Make sure you carry out the experiment <u>three times</u> at <u>each temperature</u>, then calculate the <u>mean time</u> taken for the colour change to occur at each temperature. (You can make a water bath capable of temperatures below room temperature by adding ice cubes to a beaker of water and measuring the temperature with a thermometer.)

10) You can use your results to <u>calculate</u> the <u>rate of decay</u> using this formula. The <u>units</u> will be s⁻¹ since rate is given per unit of time.

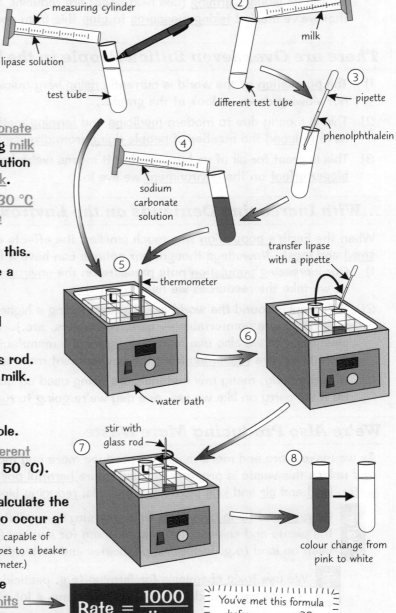

$$\text{Rate} = \frac{1000}{\text{time}}$$

You've met this formula before, on page 29.

You could also investigate decomposition in your gym bag...

I found that leaving my wet PE kit in my gym bag sure made for some interesting moulds... and smells.

Q1   Ted was investigating decay using the above method. It took 280 seconds for the solution to lose its pink colour. Calculate the rate of decay. Give your answer in s⁻¹.   [1 mark]

Biodiversity and Waste Management

Unfortunately, human activity can <u>negatively affect</u> the <u>planet</u> and its <u>variety of life</u>. Read on for bad news...

Earth's Biodiversity is Important

Biodiversity is the variety of different species of organisms on Earth, or within an ecosystem.

1) <u>High</u> biodiversity is important. It makes sure that <u>ecosystems</u> (see p.106) are <u>stable</u> because different species depend on each other for things like <u>shelter</u> and <u>food</u>. Different species can also help to maintain the right <u>physical environment</u> for each other (e.g. the acidity of the soil).

2) For the human species to <u>survive</u>, it's important that a good level of biodiversity is maintained.

3) Lots of human actions, including <u>waste production</u> (see below) and <u>deforestation</u> (see p.118), as well as <u>global warming</u> (see next page) are reducing biodiversity. However, it's only <u>recently</u> that we've started <u>taking measures</u> to <u>stop</u> this from continuing.

There are Over Seven Billion People in the World...

1) The <u>population</u> of the world is currently <u>rising</u> very quickly, and it's not slowing down — look at the graph...

2) This is mostly due to modern <u>medicine</u> and <u>farming</u> methods, which have <u>reduced</u> the number of <u>people dying</u> from <u>disease</u> and <u>hunger</u>.

3) This is great for all of us <u>humans</u>, but it means we're having a <u>bigger effect</u> on the <u>environment</u> we live in.

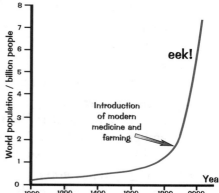

...With Increasing Demands on the Environment

When the <u>Earth's population</u> was much smaller, the effects of <u>human activity</u> were usually <u>small</u> and <u>local</u>. Nowadays though, our actions can have a far more <u>widespread</u> effect.

1) Our increasing <u>population</u> puts pressure on the <u>environment</u>, as we take the resources we need to <u>survive</u>.

2) But people around the world are also demanding a higher <u>standard of living</u> (and so demand luxuries to make life more comfortable — cars, computers, etc.). So we use more <u>raw materials</u> (e.g. oil to make plastics), but we also use more <u>energy</u> for the manufacturing processes. This all means we're taking more and more <u>resources</u> from the environment more and more <u>quickly</u>.

3) Unfortunately, many raw materials are being used up quicker than they're being replaced. So if we carry on like we are, one day we're going to <u>run out</u>.

We're Also Producing More Waste

As we make more and more things we produce more and more <u>waste</u>, including <u>waste chemicals</u>. And unless this waste is properly handled, more <u>harmful pollution</u> will be caused. Pollution affects <u>water</u>, <u>land</u> and <u>air</u> and <u>kills</u> plants and animals, <u>reducing biodiversity</u>.

Water — <u>Sewage</u> and <u>toxic chemicals</u> from industry can pollute lakes, rivers and oceans, affecting the plants and animals that rely on them for survival (including humans). And the <u>chemicals</u> used on land (e.g. fertilisers, pesticides and herbicides) can be washed into water.

Land — We use <u>toxic chemicals</u> for farming (e.g. pesticides and herbicides). We also bury <u>nuclear waste</u> underground, and we dump a lot of <u>household waste</u> in landfill sites.

Air — <u>Smoke</u> and <u>acidic gases</u> released into the atmosphere can pollute the air, e.g. <u>sulfur dioxide</u> can cause <u>acid rain</u>.

More people, more mess, less space, fewer resources...

Biodiversity's a useful thing, but the increasing rate of species extinction means that it's being reduced every day.

Q1   What is meant by the term 'biodiversity'?   [1 mark]

Global Warming

The Earth is getting <u>warmer</u>. Climate scientists are now trying to work out what the <u>effects</u> of global warming might be — sadly, it's not as simple as everyone having nicer summers.

Carbon Dioxide and Methane Trap Energy from the Sun

1) The <u>temperature</u> of the Earth is a <u>balance</u> between the energy it gets from the Sun and the energy it radiates back out into space.

2) Gases in the <u>atmosphere</u> naturally act like an <u>insulating layer</u>. They absorb most of the energy that would normally be radiated out into space, and re-radiate it in all directions (including back towards the Earth). This increases the <u>temperature</u> of the planet.

> This is what happens in a greenhouse. The Sun shines in, and the glass helps keeps some of the energy in.

3) If this didn't happen, then at night there'd be nothing to keep any energy <u>in</u>, and we'd quickly get <u>very cold</u> indeed. But recently we've started to worry that this effect is getting a bit out of hand...

4) There are several different gases in the atmosphere which help keep the <u>energy in</u>. They're called "<u>greenhouse gases</u>", and the <u>main ones</u> whose levels we worry about are <u>carbon dioxide</u> (CO_2) and <u>methane</u> — because the levels of these two gases are rising quite sharply.

5) The Earth is gradually heating up because of the increasing levels of greenhouse gases — this is <u>global warming</u>. Global warming is a type of <u>climate change</u> and causes other types of climate change, e.g. changing rainfall patterns.

The Consequences of Global Warming Could be Pretty Serious

There are several reasons to be <u>worried</u> about global warming. Here are a few:

1) Higher temperatures cause <u>seawater</u> to <u>expand</u> and <u>ice</u> to <u>melt</u>, causing the sea level to <u>rise</u>. It has <u>risen</u> a little bit over the last 100 years. If it keeps rising it'll be <u>bad news</u> for people and animals living in <u>low-lying</u> places. It will lead to <u>flooding</u>, resulting in the loss of <u>habitats</u> (where organisms live).

2) The <u>distribution</u> of many <u>wild animal</u> and <u>plant species</u> may change as <u>temperatures increase</u> and the amount of <u>rainfall changes</u> in different areas. Some species may become <u>more</u> widely distributed, e.g. species that need <u>warmer temperatures</u> may spread <u>further</u> as the conditions they <u>thrive</u> in exist over a <u>wider</u> area. Other species may become <u>less</u> widely distributed, e.g. species that need <u>cooler temperatures</u> may have <u>smaller</u> ranges as the conditions they <u>thrive</u> in exist over a <u>smaller</u> area.

3) There could be <u>changes in migration patterns</u>, e.g. some birds may migrate <u>further north</u>, as more northern areas are getting warmer.

4) <u>Biodiversity</u> (see p.116) could be <u>reduced</u> if some species are <u>unable to survive</u> a change in the climate, so become <u>extinct</u>.

The greenhouse effect — when you start growing into a tomato...

Global warming is rarely out of the news. Most scientists accept that it's happening and that human activity has caused most of the recent warming. However, they don't know exactly what the effects will be.

Q1   Explain how global warming could lead to the loss of low-lying habitats.   [3 marks]

Deforestation and Land Use

Trees and peat bogs trap carbon dioxide and lock it up. The problems start when it escapes...

Humans Use Lots of Land for Lots of Purposes

1) We use land for things like building, quarrying, farming and dumping waste.
2) This means that there's less land available for other organisms.
3) Sometimes, the way we use land has a bad effect on the environment — for example, if it requires deforestation or the destruction of habitats like peat bogs and other areas of peat.

Deforestation Means Chopping Down Trees

Deforestation is the cutting down of forests. This causes big problems when it's done on a large-scale, such as cutting down rainforests in tropical areas. It's done for various reasons, including:

- To clear land for farming (e.g. cattle or rice crops) to provide more food.
- To grow crops from which biofuels based on ethanol can be produced.

Deforestation Can Cause Many Problems

> More CO$_2$ in the atmosphere causes global warming (see previous page), which leads to climate change.

LESS CARBON DIOXIDE TAKEN IN

1) Cutting down loads of trees means that the amount of carbon dioxide removed from the atmosphere during photosynthesis is reduced.
2) Trees 'lock up' some of the carbon that they absorb during photosynthesis in their wood, which can remove it from the atmosphere for hundreds of years. Removing trees means that less is locked up.

MORE CARBON DIOXIDE IN THE ATMOSPHERE

1) Carbon dioxide is released when trees are burnt to clear land. (Carbon in wood doesn't contribute to atmospheric pollution until it's released by burning.)
2) Microorganisms feeding on bits of dead wood release carbon dioxide as a waste product of respiration.

LESS BIODIVERSITY

1) Biodiversity (p.116) is the variety of different species — the more species, the greater the biodiversity.
2) Habitats like forests can contain a huge number of different species of plants and animals, so when they are destroyed there is a danger of many species becoming extinct — biodiversity is reduced.

Destroying Peat Bogs Adds More CO$_2$ to the Atmosphere

1) Bogs are areas of land that are acidic and waterlogged. Plants that live in bogs don't fully decay when they die, because there's not enough oxygen. The partly-rotted plants gradually build up to form peat.
2) So the carbon in the plants is stored in the peat instead of being released into the atmosphere.
3) However, peat bogs are often drained so that the area can be used as farmland, or the peat is cut up and dried to use as fuel. It's also sold to gardeners as compost. Peat is being used faster than it forms.
4) When peat is drained, it comes into more contact with air and some microorganisms start to decompose it. When these microorganisms respire, they use oxygen and release carbon dioxide, contributing to global warming (see the previous page).
5) Carbon dioxide is also released when peat is burned as a fuel.
6) Destroying the bogs also destroys (or reduces the area of) the habitats of some of the animals, plants and microorganisms that live there, so reduces biodiversity.

Pete Boggs Demolition Ltd — the name in habitat destruction...

So removing trees and peat results in more atmospheric CO$_2$, which contributes to global warming. Bad times.

Q1   Suggest why deforestation can result in a higher CO$_2$ concentration in the atmosphere.   [3 marks]

Maintaining Ecosystems and Biodiversity

It's really important that biodiversity is <u>maintained</u>, but <u>other factors</u> also have to be taken into account.

Programmes *Can be Set Up to Protect Ecosystems* and Biodiversity

It's important that <u>biodiversity</u> is maintained at a <u>high enough level</u> to make sure that <u>ecosystems</u> are <u>stable</u> (see page 106). In some areas, <u>programmes</u> have been set up by <u>concerned citizens</u> and <u>scientists</u> to <u>minimise damage</u> by <u>human activities</u> (see p.116) to <u>ecosystems</u> and <u>biodiversity</u>. Here are a few examples:

1) <u>Breeding programmes</u> have been set up to help prevent <u>endangered species</u> from becoming <u>extinct</u>. These are where animals are bred in <u>captivity</u> to make sure the species survives if it dies out in the wild. Individuals can sometimes be <u>released</u> into the <u>wild</u> to boost or re-establish a population.

2) Programmes to <u>protect</u> and <u>regenerate rare habitats</u> like <u>mangroves</u>, <u>heathland</u> and <u>coral reefs</u> have been started. Protecting these habitats helps to <u>protect</u> the species that live there — <u>preserving</u> the <u>ecosystem</u> and <u>biodiversity</u> in the area.

3) There are programmes to <u>reintroduce hedgerows</u> and <u>field margins</u> around fields on farms where only a <u>single type</u> of crop is grown. Field margins are areas of land around the <u>edges</u> of fields where <u>wild flowers</u> and <u>grasses</u> are left to <u>grow</u>. Hedgerows and field margins provide a <u>habitat</u> for a <u>wider variety</u> of organisms than could survive in a single crop habitat.

4) Some governments have introduced regulations and programmes to <u>reduce</u> the level of <u>deforestation</u> taking place and the amount of <u>carbon dioxide</u> being released into the atmosphere by businesses. This could reduce the increase of <u>global warming</u> (see page 117).

5) People are encouraged to recycle to <u>reduce</u> the amount of <u>waste</u> that gets dumped in <u>landfill</u> sites. This could <u>reduce</u> the amount of <u>land</u> taken over for landfill, leaving <u>ecosystems</u> in place.

Conflicting Pressures *Can Affect How Biodiversity is Maintained*

Sadly for noble biodiversity warriors, maintaining biodiversity <u>isn't</u> as simple as you would hope. There are lots of <u>conflicting pressures</u> that have to be taken into account. For example:

1) Protecting biodiversity <u>costs money</u>. For example, governments sometimes pay farmers a <u>subsidy</u> to reintroduce hedgerows and field margins to their land. It can also cost money to keep a <u>watch</u> on whether the programmes and regulations designed to maintain biodiversity are being <u>followed</u>. There can be <u>conflict</u> between <u>protecting biodiversity</u> and <u>saving money</u> — money may be <u>prioritised</u> for other things.

2) Protecting biodiversity may come at a <u>cost</u> to local people's <u>livelihood</u>. For example, reducing the amount of deforestation is <u>great</u> for <u>biodiversity</u>, but the people who were <u>previously employed</u> in the tree-felling industry could be left <u>unemployed</u>. This could affect the <u>local economy</u> if people move away with their family to find work.

3) There can be conflict between protecting biodiversity and protecting our <u>food security</u>. Sometimes certain organisms are seen as <u>pests</u> by farmers (e.g. locusts and foxes) and are killed to <u>protect crops</u> and <u>livestock</u> so that <u>more food</u> can be produced. As a result, however, the food chain and biodiversity can be affected.

4) <u>Development</u> is <u>important</u>, but it can affect the environment. Many people want to <u>protect</u> biodiversity in the face of development, but sometimes <u>land</u> is in such <u>high demand</u> that <u>previously untouched</u> land with <u>high biodiversity</u> has to be used for development, e.g. for housing developments on the edge of towns, or for new agricultural land in developing countries.

Revision or sleep — now that's a conflicting pressure...

Like many situations in ecology, maintaining biodiversity isn't black and white. There are lots of factors to take into account before decisions on the best way to go forward can be made.

Q1 Give an example of how biodiversity can be increased in areas that farm single crops. [2 marks]

Q2 How could wild populations of endangered species be preserved by breeding programmes? [2 marks]

Trophic Levels

And now for something slightly different... The word 'trophic' comes from the Greek word <u>trophe</u> meaning '<u>nourishment</u>'. This page must contain something about food then. Probably worth reading on I reckon...

Food Chains **Can be Divided into Trophic Levels**

1) You might recognise some of this stuff about food chains from page 109. Unfortunately, now you need to learn a bit <u>more</u> about it. Enter the exciting world of <u>trophic levels</u>.

2) <u>Trophic levels</u> are the different <u>stages</u> of a food chain. They consist of one or more organisms that perform a <u>specific role</u> in the food chain.

3) Trophic levels are named after their location in the food chain using <u>numbers</u>. The first level is called <u>trophic level 1</u>. Each level after that is <u>numbered in order</u> based on <u>how far</u> along the food chain the organisms in the trophic level are. For example, the organisms <u>second</u> in line in the food chain belong to <u>trophic level 2</u>, organisms <u>third</u> in line are in <u>trophic level 3</u>, and so on.

Trophic Level 1 **Contains Producers**

1) Producers are the organisms at the <u>starting point</u> of a food chain, e.g. plants and algae.

2) They're called <u>producers</u> because they <u>make their own food</u> by <u>photosynthesis</u> using energy from the Sun.

Trophic Level 2 **Contains Primary Consumers**

1) <u>Herbivores</u> that eat the <u>plants</u> and <u>algae</u> are <u>primary consumers</u>.

2) Herbivores eat <u>only</u> plants and algae.

Trophic Level 3 **Contains Secondary Consumers**

1) <u>Carnivores</u> that <u>eat</u> the <u>primary consumers</u> are <u>secondary consumers</u>.

2) Carnivores are <u>meat eaters</u>.

Trophic Level 4 **Contains Tertiary Consumers**

1) <u>Carnivores</u> that eat <u>other carnivores</u> (the <u>secondary consumers</u>) are <u>tertiary consumers</u>.

2) Carnivores that have <u>no predators</u> are at the <u>top</u> of the food chain, so they're always in the <u>highest</u> trophic level. They're known as <u>apex predators</u>.

There can be more than four trophic levels in a food chain, but there are only usually 4 or 5 because so much energy is lost from the food chain at each trophic level (see p.122).

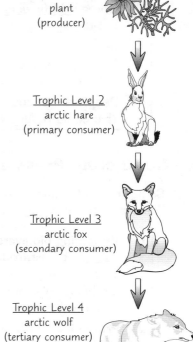

Trophic Level 1
plant
(producer)

Trophic Level 2
arctic hare
(primary consumer)

Trophic Level 3
arctic fox
(secondary consumer)

Trophic Level 4
arctic wolf
(tertiary consumer)

Decomposers **Break Down Uneaten Remains and Waste**

1) Decomposers such as <u>bacteria</u> and <u>fungi</u> play an <u>important role</u> in ecosystems.

2) They <u>decompose</u> any <u>dead plant</u> or <u>animal</u> material left in an environment.

3) They can do this by <u>secreting</u> (releasing) <u>enzymes</u> that <u>break</u> the dead stuff <u>down</u> into <u>small soluble food molecules</u>. These then <u>diffuse into</u> the microorganisms.

This process also releases nutrients into the environment, which the producers need in order to grow.

G, G, G, E♭, F, F, F, D — sorry, just decomposing Beethoven's 5th...

So, trophic level is just the fancy term for a stage in a food chain. Each trophic level always contains organisms that perform the same role. For example, the organisms in trophic level 3 are always the secondary consumers. And don't forget about those environmental champions, the decomposers. They clean up after everyone else.

Q1   Explain how decomposers break down dead material in an environment.   [1 mark]

Pyramids of Biomass

OK, I'll be straight with you. This isn't the most interesting page in the world, but hey — life's like that.

Pyramids of Biomass *Show the Relative Mass of Each Trophic Level*

There's less energy and less biomass every time you move up a stage (trophic level) in a food chain.
There are usually fewer organisms every time you move up a level too. Let's revisit our woodland
friends from p.109
as an example:

Biomass just means the mass of living material.

100 dandelions... feed... 10 rabbits... which feed... one fox.

This isn't always true though — for example, if 500 fleas are feeding on the fox, the number of organisms
has increased as you move up to that stage in the food chain. So a better way to look at the food chain is
often to think about biomass instead of number of organisms. You can use information about biomass to
construct a pyramid of biomass to represent the food chain:

1) Each bar on a pyramid of biomass shows the relative mass of living material at a trophic level
   — basically how much all the organisms at each level would "weigh" if you put them all together.

2) So the one fox above would have a big biomass and the hundreds of fleas would have
   a very small biomass. Biomass pyramids are practically always pyramid-shaped:

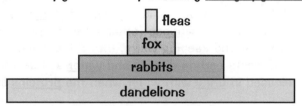

The big bar along the bottom of the pyramid shows trophic level 1. It always represents the producer
(e.g. plants or algae). The next bar will be the primary consumer (the animal that eats the producer), then
the secondary consumer (the animal that eats the primary consumer) and so on up the food chain. Easy.

Pyramids of Biomass *Give You Information About Food Chains*

1) It's easy to look at pyramids of
   biomass and explain what they
   show about the food chain —
   just remember, the biomass at
   each stage should be drawn to
   scale. For example:

2) If you're given actual numbers,
   you can use them to draw bars
   of the correct scale. Don't forget
   that the order of organisms in
   the pyramid must follow the
   order of the food chain, and
   each bar must be labelled.

E.g.

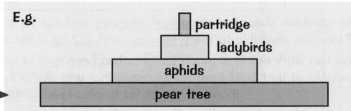

Even if you know nothing about the natural world, you're probably aware
that a tree is quite a bit bigger than an aphid. So what's going on here
is that lots (probably thousands) of aphids are feeding on a great big tree.
Quite a lot of ladybirds are then eating the aphids, and a few partridges
are eating the ladybirds. Biomass and energy are still decreasing as you go
up the levels — it's just that one tree can have a very big biomass, and can
fix a lot of the Sun's energy using all those leaves.

Constructing pyramids is a breeze — just ask the Egyptians...

There are actually a couple of exceptions where pyramids of biomass aren't quite pyramid-shaped. It happens
when the producer has a very short life but reproduces loads, like with plankton at certain times of year. But it's
very rare, so forget I ever mentioned it. Sorry. When you're done here, do something fun like sing to a squirrel.

Q1   What does each bar on a pyramid of biomass represent?   [1 mark]

Biomass Transfer

Great, steak for dinner — some <u>biomass</u> from a cow to help you <u>grow</u>. But you'll need some of that biomass for <u>respiration</u>, so you can <u>move about</u> and <u>revise</u>. And some will be <u>indigestible</u>. This is how biomass is <u>lost</u>...

Biomass is Lost Between Each Trophic Level

1) Energy from the <u>Sun</u> is the source of energy for <u>nearly all</u> life on Earth.

2) <u>Producers</u>, such as <u>green plants</u> and <u>algae</u>, use <u>energy</u> transferred by <u>light</u> from the Sun to make <u>food</u> (<u>glucose</u>) during <u>photosynthesis</u>. Of the energy that hits these producers, <u>only about 1%</u> is transferred for photosynthesis.

3) Some of the glucose is used by the plants and algae to make <u>biological molecules</u>. These biological molecules make up the plant's <u>biomass</u> — the <u>mass</u> of <u>living material</u>. Biomass <u>stores energy</u>.

4) <u>Biomass</u> is <u>transferred</u> through a <u>food chain</u> in an ecosystem when organisms <u>eat</u> other organisms. However, <u>not much biomass</u> gets transferred from one <u>trophic level</u> to the <u>next</u>. In fact, only about <u>10%</u> of the biomass is passed on to the next level.

5) Biomass is <u>lost</u> between the levels for a few different reasons:

- Organisms don't always eat <u>every single part</u> of the organism they're <u>consuming</u>. For example, some material that makes up plants and animals is <u>inedible</u> (e.g. bone). This means that <u>not all</u> the biomass can be <u>passed</u> to the next stage of the food chain.

- Organisms <u>don't absorb</u> all of the stuff in the food they <u>ingest</u> (take in). The stuff that they <u>don't</u> absorb is <u>egested</u> (released) as <u>faeces</u> (ahem... pooped out, to you and me).

- Some of the biomass taken in is converted into <u>other substances</u> that are lost as <u>waste</u>. For example, organisms use a lot of <u>glucose</u> (obtained from the biomass) in respiration to provide energy for movement and keeping warm, etc. rather than to make more biomass. This process produces lots of waste <u>carbon dioxide</u> and <u>water</u> as by-products. <u>Urea</u> is another waste substance, which is released in <u>urine</u> with <u>water</u> when the <u>proteins</u> in the biomass are <u>broken down</u>.

You Can Calculate the Efficiency of Biomass Transfer

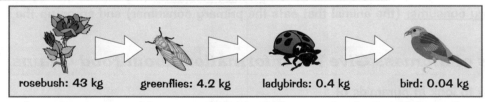

rosebush: 43 kg   greenflies: 4.2 kg   ladybirds: 0.4 kg   bird: 0.04 kg

1) The numbers show the <u>amount of biomass</u> available to the <u>next level</u>. So <u>43 kg</u> is the amount of biomass available to the <u>greenflies</u>, and <u>4.2 kg</u> is the amount available to the <u>ladybirds</u>.

2) You can work out how much biomass has been <u>lost</u> at each level by taking away the biomass that is available <u>at that</u> level from the biomass that was available at the <u>previous</u> level. For example:
Biomass <u>lost</u> at 1st trophic level = 43 kg – 4.2 kg = <u>38.8 kg</u>.

3) You can also calculate the <u>efficiency of biomass transfer</u> between trophic levels:

$$\text{efficiency} = \frac{\text{biomass transferred to the next level}}{\text{biomass available at the previous level}} \times 100$$

So at the 1st trophic level, <u>efficiency</u> of biomass transfer = 4.2 kg ÷ 43 kg × 100 = <u>9.8% efficient</u>.

Ah ah ah ah stayin' alive, stayin' alive...

The Bee Gees were definitely on to something — staying alive is important, but it does require a lot of energy. Remember though that hardly any of this energy makes it to the next level in the food chain — most is lost.

Q1   Give two ways that biomass is lost between trophic levels.   [2 marks]

Q2   Calculate the percentage efficiency of biomass transfer between some large fish with 995 kg of available biomass and a shark with 110 kg of available biomass.   [1 mark]

Food Security and Farming

There are more than 7 billion people on our planet and they all need feeding, so maintaining our food supply is important. We need to make sure that we use sustainable methods of food production wherever we can.

Lots of Factors Affect Food Security

Food security is having enough food to feed a population.
There's a wide range of things that can threaten food security. For example:

1) The world population keeps increasing, with the birth rate of many developing countries rising quickly.

2) As diets in developed countries change, the demand for certain foods to be imported from developing countries can increase. This means that already scarce food resources can become more scarce.

3) Farming can be affected by new pests and pathogens (e.g. bacteria and viruses) or changes in the environmental conditions (e.g. a lack of rain). This can result in the loss of crops and livestock, and can lead to widespread famine.

4) The high input costs of farming (e.g. the price of seeds, machinery and livestock) can make it too expensive for people in some countries to start or maintain food production, meaning that there sometimes aren't enough people producing food in these areas to feed the people.

5) In some parts of the world, there are conflicts that affect the availability of food and water.

Sustainable methods of food production are needed so that enough food can be made to feed everyone now and in the future. Sustainable production means making enough food without using resources faster than they renew.

Overfishing is Decreasing Fish Stocks

1) Fish stocks are declining in the oceans because we're fishing so much.

2) This means there's less fish for us to eat, the ocean's food chains are affected and some species of fish may disappear altogether in some areas — for example, cod are at risk of disappearing from the north west Atlantic.

3) To tackle this problem, we need to maintain fish stocks at a level where the fish continue to breed. This is sustainable food production. Fish stocks can be maintained (conserved) in these ways:

FISHING QUOTAS — there are limits on the number and size of fish that can be caught in certain areas. This prevents certain species from being overfished.

NET SIZE — there are different limits of the mesh size of the fish net, depending on what's being fished. This is to reduce the number of 'unwanted' and discarded fish — the ones that are accidently caught, e.g. shrimp caught along with cod. Using a bigger mesh size will let the 'unwanted' species escape. It also means that younger fish will slip through the net, allowing them to reach breeding age.

Food Production Can be Made More Efficient

Limiting the movement of livestock and keeping them in a temperature-controlled environment reduces the transfer of energy from livestock to the environment. This makes farming more efficient as the animals use less energy moving around and controlling their own body temperature. This means that more energy is available for growth, so more food can be produced from the same input of resources.

1) Livestock like calves and chickens can be factory farmed. This involves raising them in small pens.

2) Fish can also be factory farmed in cages where their movement is restricted.

3) Some animals are also fed high-protein food to further increase their growth.

Factory farmed chickens are also called battery chickens.

Some factory farming methods are controversial. Because the animals are kept so close together, disease can spread between them easily. There are also ethical objections, as some people think that making animals live in unnatural and uncomfortable conditions is cruel.

Fishermen are just too effishent...

Food security is seriously important, but there are lots of issues that threaten it. There are ways to reduce the threats though. Make sure you're familiar with the stuff on this page and your exam mark security may be vastly improved.

Q1 Explain how food production from livestock farming can be made more efficient. [4 marks]

Biotechnology

Biotechnology is where <u>living things</u> and <u>biological processes</u> are used and manipulated to produce a <u>useful product</u>. It's a wide and rapidly expanding field that could be really handy if used to its <u>full potential</u>.

Mycoprotein — Food from Fungi

1) Using <u>modern biotechnology</u> techniques, large amounts of <u>microorganisms</u> can be <u>cultured</u> (grown) industrially under <u>controlled conditions</u> in <u>large vats</u> for use as a <u>food source</u>.

2) <u>Mycoprotein</u> is used to make <u>high-protein meat substitutes</u> for <u>vegetarian</u> meals, e.g. Quorn™.

3) It's made from the fungus *Fusarium*, which is grown in <u>aerobic conditions</u> on <u>glucose syrup</u>, which it uses as food.

4) The fungal biomass is <u>harvested</u> and <u>purified</u> to produce the <u>mycoprotein</u>.

> Aerobic conditions are where oxygen is present.

Bacteria can be Engineered to Produce Human Insulin

Genetic engineering is <u>transferring</u> a <u>useful gene</u> from one organism to another (see page 99). Bacteria can be genetically engineered to <u>make human insulin</u>:

1) A <u>plasmid</u> (a loop of DNA) is <u>removed</u> from a bacterium.

2) The <u>insulin gene</u> is cut out of a human chromosome using a <u>restriction enzyme</u>. <u>Restriction enzymes</u> recognise <u>specific sequences</u> of DNA and <u>cut the DNA</u> at these points. The cut leaves <u>one</u> of the DNA strands with <u>unpaired bases</u> — this is called a '<u>sticky end</u>'.

3) The <u>plasmid</u> is cut open using the <u>same</u> restriction enzyme — leaving the <u>same sticky ends</u>.

4) The plasmid and the human insulin gene are <u>mixed together</u>.

5) <u>Ligase</u> (an <u>enzyme</u>) is added. This <u>joins</u> the sticky ends together to produce <u>recombinant DNA</u> (<u>two different bits</u> of DNA stuck together).

6) The recombinant DNA is <u>inserted</u> into a bacterium.

7) The <u>modified bacterium</u> is grown in a <u>vat</u> under <u>controlled conditions</u>. You end up with millions of bacteria that produce <u>insulin</u>. The insulin can be <u>harvested</u> and <u>purified</u> to treat people with <u>diabetes</u>.

human insulin gene
sticky ends
Restriction enzymes cut the gene out and cut open the plasmid...
plasmid
sticky ends
...ligase joins the two bits of DNA together...
... and the recombinant DNA is inserted into the bacteria.
The bacteria are grown like mad in a vat.
insulin

Crops Can be Genetically Modified

Many people in the world today don't have <u>enough</u> food to eat (or the diet they have isn't <u>varied</u>). This mostly happens in <u>developing countries</u> — like those in <u>Africa</u> and parts of <u>Asia</u>.

Biotechnology could help...

1) <u>Genetically modified</u> (<u>GM</u>) <u>crops</u> can be produced that are <u>resistant to pests</u> — improving crop yields.

2) They can be genetically modified to <u>grow better</u> in <u>drought conditions</u> — again improving crop yields.

3) And some crops can be modified to provide <u>more nutritional value</u>, e.g. '<u>Golden Rice</u>' has been <u>genetically engineered</u> to produce a chemical that's converted in the body to <u>vitamin A</u>.

...But not everyone agrees

1) Many people argue that people go hungry because they <u>can't afford</u> to buy food, not because there <u>isn't</u> any food about. So they argue that you need to <u>tackle poverty first</u>.

2) There are fears that countries may become <u>dependent</u> on <u>companies</u> who <u>sell</u> GM seeds.

3) Sometimes <u>poor soil</u> is the main reason why <u>crops fail</u>, and even GM crops <u>won't survive</u>.

I'll have a fungus sandwich with a side of GM rice please...

Genetic modification is a powerful biotechnological tool. It could hold the solution to a wide range of problems.

Q1　　What is 'Golden Rice'?　　　　　　　　　　　　　　　　　　　　　　[2 marks]

Revision Questions for Topic 7

That's <u>Topic 7</u> done with. I bet you're right in the mood for a long list of revision question now. You're in luck.

- Try these questions and <u>tick off each one</u> when you <u>get it right</u>.
- When you've done <u>all the questions</u> under a heading and are <u>completely happy</u> with it, tick it off.

Competition, Abiotic and Biotic Factors, and Adaptations (p.106-108) ☑

1) Define 'habitat'. ☑
2) What things do animals compete for in an ecosystem? ☑
3) What are biotic and abiotic factors? ☑
4) What are functional adaptations? ☑

Food Chains (p.109) ☑

5) What do food chains always start with? ☑
6) Explain what happens to the population size of a predator
   if its prey becomes more common in an ecosystem. ☑

Quadrats and Transects (p.110-111) ☑

7) Explain how a quadrat can be used to investigate the distribution of clover plants in two areas. ☑
8) Suggest why you might use a transect when investigating the distribution of organisms. ☑

Environmental Change, and The Water and Carbon Cycles (p.112-113) ☑

9) How might a change in the availability of water affect the distribution of species? ☑
10) When water vapour cools and condenses in the atmosphere, what does it change into? ☑
11) Explain how microorganisms return carbon to the atmosphere. ☑

Decay (p.114-115) ☑

12) Explain why temperature affects the rate of decay. ☑
13) Is biogas produced by aerobic or anaerobic decay? ☑

Human Impacts on the Planet (p.116-119) ☑

14) Suggest why it's important to have high biodiversity in an ecosystem. ☑
15) Name two gases linked to global warming. ☑
16) Give an example of how global warming could reduce biodiversity. ☑
17) Why might humans carry out deforestation? ☑
18) Explain why the destruction of peat bogs adds more carbon dioxide to the atmosphere. ☑
19) How can recycling programmes help to protect ecosystems? ☑

Trophic Levels and Biomass (p.120-122) ☑

20) What is a trophic level? ☑
21) In which trophic level are the tertiary consumers found? ☑
22) Does the bottom bar on a pyramid of biomass represent the tertiary consumer or the producer? ☑
23) Approximately what percentage of biomass is lost between trophic levels? ☑

Food Security and Biotechnology (p.123-124) ☑

24) Give an example of a factor that can affect food security. ☑
25) How can fish stocks be maintained at a sustainable level? ☑
26) What is mycoprotein? ☑
27) How can bacteria be used to produce human insulin? ☑

Measuring Substances

Get your lab coats on, it's time to find out about the skills you'll need in <u>experiments</u>...

Use the Right Apparatus to Take Readings

1) Mass

To weigh a solid, start by putting the <u>container</u> you are weighing your substance into on a <u>balance</u>. Set the balance to exactly <u>zero</u> and then weigh out the correct amount of your substance. Easy peasy.

2) Temperature

You can use a <u>thermometer</u> to measure the temperature of a solution. Make sure that the <u>bulb</u> of the thermometer is <u>completely submerged</u> in the solution and that you wait for the temperature to <u>stabilise</u> before you take your initial reading. Read off the <u>scale</u> on the thermometer at <u>eye level</u> to make sure it's correct.

When you're reading off a scale, write down the value of the graduation that the amount is closest to.

3) Volume of a Liquid

There's more than one way to measure the volume of a <u>liquid</u>. Whichever method you use, always read the volume from the <u>bottom of the meniscus</u> (the curved upper surface of the liquid) when it's at <u>eye level</u>.

Read volume from here — the bottom of the meniscus.

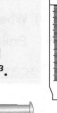

- <u>Using a pipette</u> — <u>Pipettes</u> are used to suck up and <u>transfer</u> volumes of liquid between containers. <u>Dropping pipettes</u> are used to transfer <u>drops</u> of liquid. <u>Graduated pipettes</u> are used to transfer <u>accurate</u> volumes. A <u>pipette filler</u> is attached to the end of a graduated pipette, to <u>control</u> the amount of liquid being drawn up.

- <u>Using a measuring cylinder</u> — <u>Measuring cylinders</u> come in all different <u>sizes</u>. Make sure you choose one that's the right size for the measurement you want to make. It's no good using a huge 1 dm³ cylinder to measure out 2 cm³ of a liquid — the graduations will be too big, and you'll end up with <u>massive errors</u>. It'd be much better to use one that measures up to 10 cm³.

4) Volume of a Gas

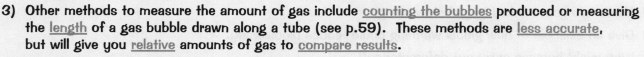

1) To accurately measure the <u>volume</u> of gas, you should use a <u>gas syringe</u>.
2) Alternatively, you can use an <u>upturned measuring cylinder</u> filled with <u>water</u>. The gas will <u>displace</u> the water so you can <u>read the volume</u> off the <u>scale</u>.
3) Other methods to measure the amount of gas include <u>counting the bubbles</u> produced or measuring the <u>length</u> of a gas bubble drawn along a tube (see p.59). These methods are <u>less accurate</u>, but will give you <u>relative</u> amounts of gas to <u>compare results</u>.
4) When you're measuring a gas, you need to make sure that the equipment is set up so that none of the gas can <u>escape</u>, otherwise your results won't be <u>accurate</u>.

5) pH

The method you should use to measure pH depends on what your experiment is.

1) <u>Indicators</u> are dyes that <u>change colour</u> depending on whether they're in an <u>acid</u> or an <u>alkali</u>. You use them by adding a couple of drops of the indicator to the solution you're interested in. <u>Universal indicator</u> is a <u>mixture</u> of indicators that changes colour <u>gradually</u> as pH changes. It's useful for <u>estimating</u> the pH of a solution based on its colour.

2) <u>Indicator paper</u> is useful if you don't want to colour the entire solution that you're testing. It <u>changes colour</u> depending on the pH of the solution it touches. You can also hold a piece of <u>damp indicator paper</u> in a <u>gas sample</u> to test its pH.

Blue litmus paper turns <u>red</u> in acidic conditions and red litmus paper turns <u>blue</u> in alkaline conditions.

3) <u>pH meters</u> have a <u>digital display</u> that gives an <u>accurate value</u> for the pH of a solution.

Experimentus apparatus...

Wizardry won't help you here, unfortunately. It's best you just get your head down and learn this stuff.

Heating, Safety and Ethics

More lab stuff coming up next — a bit about <u>heating things up</u> and then some important things to <u>think about</u>...

Bunsen Burners Have a Naked Flame

Bunsen burners are good for <u>heating things quickly</u>. But you need to make sure you're using them <u>safely</u>:

- You should always use a Bunsen burner on a <u>heat-proof mat</u>.
- If your Bunsen burner is alight but not heating anything, make sure you <u>close</u> the hole so that the flame becomes <u>yellow</u> and <u>clearly visible</u>.
- Use the <u>blue</u> flame to heat things. If you're heating a vessel <u>in</u> the flame, hold it at the <u>top</u> (e.g. with <u>tongs</u>) and point the opening <u>away from</u> yourself (and others).
- If you're heating something <u>over</u> the flame (e.g. a beaker of water), you should put a <u>tripod and gauze</u> over the Bunsen burner before you light it, and place the vessel on this.

Heat-proof mat
Hole is closed
to gas

The Temperature of Electric Water Baths & Electric Heaters Can Be Set

1) A <u>water bath</u> is a container filled with water that can be heated to a <u>specific temperature</u>. A <u>simple</u> water bath can be made by heating a <u>beaker of water</u> over a <u>Bunsen burner</u> and monitoring the temperature with a <u>thermometer</u>. However, it is difficult to keep the temperature of the water <u>constant</u>.

2) An <u>electric water bath</u> will monitor and adjust the temperature for you. Here's how you use one:

- <u>Set</u> the temperature on the water bath, and allow the water to <u>heat up</u>.
- To make sure it's reached the right temperature, use a <u>thermometer</u>.
- Place the vessel containing your substance in the water bath using test tube holders or tongs. The level of water outside the vessel should be <u>just above</u> the level of the substance in the vessel.
- The substance will then be warmed to the <u>same temperature</u> as the water. As the substance in the vessel is surrounded by water, the heating is very <u>even</u>.

3) <u>Electric heaters</u> are often made up of a metal plate that can be heated to a specified temperature. The vessel containing the substance you want to heat is placed on top of the hot plate. The vessel is only heated from below, so you'll usually have to <u>stir</u> the substance inside to make sure it's <u>heated evenly</u>.

Make Sure You're Working Safely in the Lab

1) <u>Before</u> you start any experiment, make sure you know about any <u>safety precautions</u> to do with your <u>method</u> or the <u>chemicals</u> you're using. You need to <u>follow</u> any instructions that your teacher gives you <u>carefully</u>. The chemicals you're using may be <u>hazardous</u> — for example, they might be <u>flammable</u> (<u>catch fire easily</u>), or they might <u>irritate</u> or <u>burn</u> your <u>skin</u> if it comes into contact with them.

2) Make sure that you're wearing <u>sensible clothing</u> when you're in the lab (e.g. open shoes won't protect your feet from spillages). When you're doing an experiment, you should wear a <u>lab coat</u> to protect your skin and clothing. Depending on the experiment, you may need to also wear <u>safety goggles</u> and <u>gloves</u>.

3) You also need to be aware of <u>general safety</u> in the lab, e.g. keep anything <u>flammable</u> away from lit Bunsen burners, don't directly touch any <u>hot equipment</u>, handle <u>glassware</u> carefully so it doesn't <u>break</u>, etc.

You Need to Think About Ethical Issues In Your Experiments

1) Any <u>organisms</u> involved in your investigations need to be treated <u>safely</u> and <u>ethically</u>.

2) <u>Animals</u> need to be treated <u>humanely</u> — they should be <u>handled carefully</u> and any wild animals captured for studying (e.g. during an investigation of the distribution of an organism) should be <u>returned to their original habitat</u>.

3) Any animals kept in the lab should also be <u>cared for</u> in a humane way, e.g. they should not be kept in <u>overcrowded conditions</u>.

4) If you are carrying out an experiment involving other <u>students</u> (e.g. investigating the effect of caffeine on reaction time), they should not be forced to participate <u>against their will</u> or feel <u>pressured</u> to take part.

Potometers and Microscopes

We're on to <u>potometers</u> and <u>microscopes</u> now, oh my...

Potometers Should Be Set Up Underwater

A <u>potometer</u> is a special piece of apparatus used to measure the <u>water uptake</u> by a plant.
Here's how to set one up:

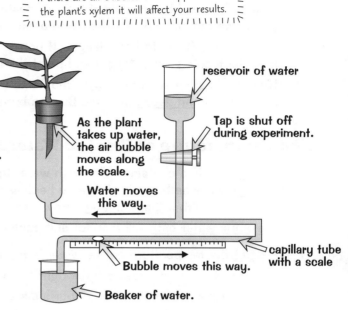

If there are air bubbles in the apparatus or the plant's xylem it will affect your results.

1) <u>Cut</u> a shoot <u>underwater</u> to prevent air from entering the xylem. Cut it at a <u>slant</u> to increase the surface area available for water uptake.

2) <u>Assemble</u> the potometer <u>in water</u> and insert the shoot <u>under water</u>, so no <u>air</u> can enter.

3) Remove the apparatus from the water but keep the end of the capillary tube <u>submerged</u> in a beaker of water.

4) Check that the apparatus is <u>watertight</u> and <u>airtight</u>.

5) <u>Dry</u> the leaves, allow time for the shoot to <u>acclimatise</u> and then <u>shut</u> the tap.

6) Remove the end of the capillary tube from the beaker of water until <u>one air bubble</u> has formed, then put the end of the tube <u>back into the water</u>.

7) A potometer can be used to estimate the <u>transpiration rate</u> of a plant. There's more about this on page 44.

Image labels: reservoir of water · Tap is shut off during experiment. · As the plant takes up water, the air bubble moves along the scale. · Water moves this way. · Bubble moves this way. · capillary tube with a scale · Beaker of water.

You Can Measure the Size of a Single Cell

When viewing <u>cells</u> under a <u>microscope</u>, you might need to work out their <u>size</u>.

To work out the size of a <u>single cell</u>:

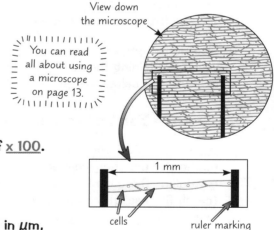

You can read all about using a microscope on page 13.

View down the microscope

1) Place a <u>clear, plastic ruler</u> on <u>top</u> of your microscope <u>slide</u>. <u>Clip</u> the <u>ruler</u> and <u>slide</u> onto the <u>stage</u>.

2) Select the <u>objective lens</u> that gives an overall magnification of <u>x 100</u>.

3) Adjust the <u>focus</u> to get a <u>clear image</u> of the cells.

4) <u>Move</u> the ruler so that the cells are <u>lined up</u> along <u>1 mm</u>. Then <u>count</u> the <u>number of cells</u> along this <u>1 mm sample</u>.

5) 1 mm = 1000 μm. So to <u>calculate</u> the <u>length</u> of a <u>single cell</u> in μm, you just need to <u>divide</u> 1000 μm by the <u>number of cells</u> in the sample.
    E.g. if you counted 4 cells in 1 mm, the length of a single cell would be: 1000 ÷ 4 = <u>250 μm</u>

Image labels: 1 mm · cells · ruler marking

Use the Cell Size to Work out the Length of a Scale Bar

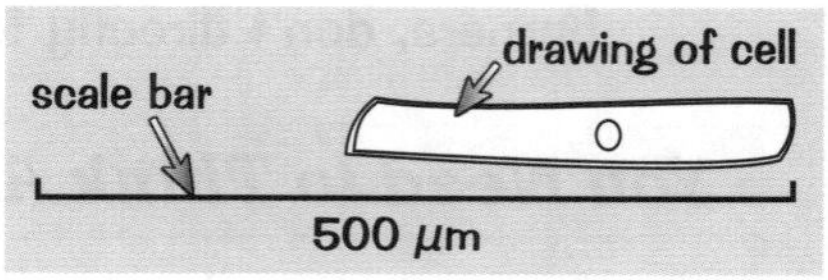

1) If you draw a <u>diagram</u> of a cell you've observed under a microscope, you might want to include a <u>scale bar</u>.

2) Once you know the <u>size of one cell</u>, you can use it to calculate how <u>long</u> your scale bar should be.

3) To draw a <u>500 μm scale bar</u>, just use this formula:

scale bar · drawing of cell · 500 μm

$$\text{scale bar length } (\mu m) = \frac{\text{drawn length of cell } (\mu m) \times 500}{\text{actual length of cell } (\mu m)}$$

Single cell, looking for love...

These techniques might seem a bit tricky at first, but if you practice them they'll become second nature. Honest.

Sampling

I love <u>samples</u>... especially when I'm a bit <u>peckish</u> in the supermarket and they're handing out <u>free cheese</u>. Unfortunately, this page isn't about those samples. It's a lot more useful than that...

Sampling Should be Random

1) When you're investigating a population, it's generally <u>not possible</u> to study <u>every single organism</u> in the population. This means that you need to take <u>samples</u> of the population you're interested in.

2) The sample data will be used to <u>draw conclusions</u> about the <u>whole</u> population, so it's important that it <u>accurately</u> represents the <u>whole population</u>.

3) To make sure a sample represents the population, it should be <u>random</u>.

If a sample doesn't represent the population as a whole, it's said to be biased.

Organisms Should Be Sampled At Random Sites in an Area

1) If you're interested in the <u>distribution</u> of an organism in an area, or its <u>population size</u>, you can take population samples in the area you're interested in using <u>quadrats</u> or <u>transects</u> (see pages 110-111).

2) If you only take samples from <u>one part</u> of the area, your results will be <u>biased</u> — they may not give an <u>accurate representation</u> of the <u>whole area</u>.

3) To make sure that your sampling isn't biased, you need to use a method of <u>choosing sampling sites</u> in which every site has an <u>equal chance</u> of being chosen. For example:

If you're looking at plant species in a field...

1) <u>Divide</u> the field into a <u>grid</u>.

2) <u>Label the grid</u> along the bottom and up the side with numbers.

3) Use a <u>random number generator</u> (on a computer or calculator) to select coordinates, e.g. (2,6).

4) Take your samples at these coordinates.

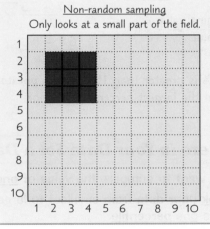

Non-random sampling
Only looks at a small part of the field.

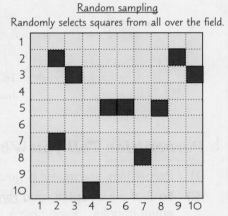

Random sampling
Randomly selects squares from all over the field.

Health Data Should be Taken from Randomly Selected People

1) As mentioned above, it's not practical (or even possible) to study an <u>entire human population</u>.

2) You need to use <u>random sampling</u> to choose members of the population you're interested in. For example:

A <u>health professional</u> is investigating <u>how many</u> people diagnosed with <u>Type 2 diabetes</u> in a particular country <u>also</u> have <u>heart disease</u>:

1) All the people who have been diagnosed with Type 2 diabetes in the country of interest are identified by <u>hospital records</u>. In total, there are <u>270 196</u> people.

2) These people are assigned a <u>number</u> between 1 and 270 196.

3) A <u>random number generator</u> is used to choose the sample group (e.g. it selects the individuals #72 063, #11 822, #193 123, etc.)

4) The <u>proportion</u> of people in the <u>sample</u> that have heart disease can be used to <u>estimate</u> the <u>total number</u> of people with Type 2 diabetes that also have heart disease.

'Eeny, meeny, miny, moe' just doesn't cut it any more...

Sampling is an important part of an investigation. It needs to be done randomly, or the data won't be worth much.

Comparing Results

Being able to <u>compare</u> your results is really important. Here are some ways you might do it. I spoil you.

Percentage Change Allows you to Compare Results

1) When investigating the <u>change</u> in a variable, you may want to <u>compare</u> results that didn't have the <u>same initial value</u>. For example, you may want to compare the <u>change in mass</u> of potato cylinders left in different concentrations of sugar solution that had <u>different initial masses</u> (see page 21).

2) One way to do this is to calculate the <u>percentage change</u>. You work it out like this:

$$\text{percentage (\%) change} = \frac{\text{final value} - \text{original value}}{\text{original value}} \times 100$$

EXAMPLE: A student is investigating the effect of the concentration of sugar solution on potato cells. She records the mass of potato cylinders before and after placing them in sugar solutions of different concentrations. The table on the right shows some of her results.

Which potato cylinder had the largest percentage change?

Potato cylinder	Concentration (mol/dm³)	Mass at start (g)	Mass at end (g)
1	0.0	7.5	8.7
2	1.0	8.0	6.8

1) Stick each set of results into the <u>equation</u>:

$$\% \text{ change} = \frac{\text{final value} - \text{original value}}{\text{original value}} \times 100$$

1. $\dfrac{8.7 - 7.5}{7.5} \times 100 = 16\%$ — The mass at the <u>start</u> is the <u>original value</u>. The mass at the <u>end</u> is the <u>final value</u>.

2. $\dfrac{6.8 - 8.0}{8.0} \times 100 = -15\%$ — Here, the mass has <u>decreased</u> so the percentage change is <u>negative</u>.

2) <u>Compare</u> the results. 16% is greater than 15%, so the potato cylinder in the 0.0 mol/dm³ sugar solution had the largest percentage change.

Percentiles Tell you Where in Your Data Set a Data Point Lies

1) Percentiles are useful if you want to compare the value of <u>one data point</u> to the <u>rest</u> of your data.

2) To find a percentile, you <u>rank</u> your data from smallest to largest, then <u>divide</u> it into <u>one hundred equal chunks</u>. Each chunk is <u>one percentile</u>.

3) This means that each percentile represents <u>one percent</u> of the data, and so the <u>value of a percentile</u> tells you what <u>percentage</u> of the data has a value <u>lower than</u> the data points in that percentile.

> E.g. Mike the Meerkat is in the <u>90th percentile</u> for <u>height</u> in his gang. This means that <u>90%</u> of the gang are <u>shorter</u> than Mike.

4) Percentiles can be used to give a more realistic idea of the <u>spread</u> of data than the <u>range</u> (see p.6) — by finding the range between the <u>10th</u> and <u>90th percentiles</u> in a data set (the middle 80% of the data), you can look at the spread of the data while ignoring any <u>outlying</u> results.

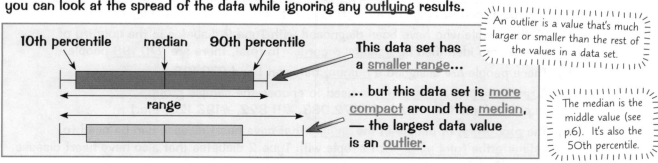

10th percentile   median   90th percentile

range

This data set has a <u>smaller range</u>...

... but this data set is <u>more compact</u> around the <u>median</u>, — the largest data value is an <u>outlier</u>.

An outlier is a value that's much larger or smaller than the rest of the values in a data set.

The median is the middle value (see p.6). It's also the 50th percentile.

Percentage change in how much I love maths after this page — 0%

Aaaand that's the end of Practical Skills, folks. Go forth, and science like you've never scienced before...

Answers

p.11 — Cells
Q1 Any two from: e.g. prokaryotic cells are smaller than eukaryotic cells *[1 mark]*. / Prokaryotic cells don't have mitochondria but eukaryotic cells do *[1 mark]*. / Prokaryotic cells don't have a true nucleus but eukaryotic cells do *[1 mark]*. / Prokaryotic cells have circular DNA but eukaryotic cells don't *[1 mark]*.

p.12 — Microscopy
Q1 real size = image size ÷ magnification
= 7.5 mm ÷ 100
= 0.075 mm *[1 mark]*
0.075 × 1000 = 75 µm *[1 mark]*

p.13 — More on Microscopy
Q1 To highlight objects within the sample by adding colour to them *[1 mark]*.

p.14 — Cell Differentiation and Specialisation
Q1 E.g. they have few subcellular structures. / They're joined end to end. / They're long. *[1 mark]*
Q2 The cell has a hair-like shape, which gives it a large surface area *[1 mark]* to absorb water and minerals from the soil *[1 mark]*.

p.15 — Chromosomes and Mitosis
Q1 The cell has to increase the amount of its subcellular structures *[1 mark]* and duplicate its DNA *[1 mark]*.

p.16 — Binary Fission
Q1 Lots of nutrients *[1 mark]* and a warm environment *[1 mark]*.
Q2 3 hours = 60 × 3 = 180 minutes
180 ÷ 30 = 6 divisions *[1 mark]*
$2^6 = 2 × 2 × 2 × 2 × 2 × 2$
= 64 cells *[1 mark]*

p.18 — Culturing Microorganisms
Q1 a) A *[1 mark]*
b) diameter = 13 mm
radius = 13 ÷ 2 = 6.5 mm *[1 mark]*
$\pi r^2 = \pi × 6.5^2 = 132.7...$
= 133 mm² *[1 mark]*
c) E.g. a disc soaked in sterile water *[1 mark]*.
d) To show that any difference in the growth of the bacteria is only due to the effect of the antiseptic *[1 mark]*.

p.19 — Stem Cells
Q1 Copies of the plant can be made by taking stem cells from the meristem of the plant *[1 mark]* and growing them into new, genetically identical plants (clones) *[1 mark]*.

p.20 — Diffusion
Q1 a) The ink will diffuse / spread out through the water *[1 mark]*. This is because the ink particles will move from where is a higher concentration of them (the drop of ink) to where there is a lower concentration of them (the surrounding water) *[1 mark]*.
b) The ink particles will diffuse / spread out faster *[1 mark]*.

p.21 — Osmosis
Q1 Water will move out of the piece of potato by osmosis *[1 mark]*, so its mass will decrease *[1 mark]*.

p.22 — Active Transport
Q1 Active transport allows nutrients such as glucose to move from a lower concentration in the gut to a higher concentration in the blood (against the concentration gradient) *[1 mark]*.

p.23 — Exchange Surfaces
Q1 Surface area:
(2 × 2) × 2 = 8
(2 × 1) × 4 = 8
8 + 8 = 16 µm² *[1 mark]*
Volume:
2 × 2 × 1 = 4 µm³ *[1 mark]*
So the surface area to volume ratio is 16 : 4, or 4 : 1 *[1 mark]*.

p.24 — Exchanging Substances
Q1 E.g. they have a large surface area. / They have a moist lining for dissolving gases. / They have very thin walls. / They have a good blood supply. *[1 mark]*
Q2 The surface of the small intestine is covered with small projections/villi *[1 mark]*.

p.25 — More on Exchanging Substances
Q1 Any two from: e.g. it is made up of gill filaments which give a large surface area. / Each gill filament is covered in lamellae, which further increases the surface area. / The lamellae have a thin surface layer of cells. / The lamellae have lots of capillaries. / A large concentration gradient is maintained between the water and the blood. *[2 marks]*

p.27 — Cell Organisation
Q1 That it is made up of different tissues *[1 mark]* that work together to perform a particular function *[1 mark]*.

p.28 — Enzymes
Q1 If the pH is too high or too low, it can interfere with the bonds holding the enzyme together. This changes the shape of the active site *[1 mark]* and denatures the enzyme *[1 mark]*.

p.29 — Investigating Enzymatic Reactions
Q1 33 ÷ 60 = 0.55 cm³/s *[1 mark]*

p.30 — Enzymes and Digestion
Q1 Bile is alkaline, so it neutralises the stomach acid and makes conditions in the small intestine alkaline *[1 mark]*. The enzymes of the small intestine work best in these alkaline conditions *[1 mark]*. It also emulsifies fats/breaks down fats into tiny droplets *[1 mark]*. This gives a bigger surface area of fat for the enzyme lipase to work on, making digestion faster *[1 mark]*.

p.31 — More on Enzymes and Digestion
Q1 Stomach *[1 mark]*, pancreas *[1 mark]* and small intestine *[1 mark]*.

p.32 — Food Tests
Q1 iodine solution *[1 mark]*

p.33 — The Lungs
Q1 495 ÷ 12
= 41 breaths per minute. *[1 mark]*

p.34 — Circulatory System — The Heart
Q1 The right ventricle *[1 mark]*.
Q2 They supply oxygenated blood to the heart itself *[1 mark]*.

p.35 — Circulatory System — Blood Vessels
Q1 They have a big lumen to help the blood flow despite the low pressure *[1 mark]* and they have valves to keep the blood flowing in the right direction *[1 mark]*.

p.36 — Circulatory System — Blood
Q1 They help the blood to clot at a wound *[1 mark]*.
Q2 They have a large surface area for absorbing oxygen *[1 mark]*. They don't have a nucleus, which allows more room for carrying oxygen *[1 mark]*. They contain haemoglobin, which can combine with oxygen in the lungs and release it in body tissues *[1 mark]*.

p.37 — Cardiovascular Disease
Q1 a) Stents can be inserted into the coronary arteries to keep them open *[1 mark]*. This ensures that the supply of oxygenated blood to the heart isn't interrupted *[1 mark]*.
b) Any two from: e.g. there is a risk of complications such as a heart attack during the operation. / There's a risk of infection from surgery. / There's a risk of the patient developing a blood clot/thrombosis near the stent *[2 marks]*.

p.38 — More on Cardiovascular Disease
Q1 a) The heart valves might not be able to open fully, meaning that less blood can flow through them *[1 mark]*. They can also become leaky, meaning that blood is able to flow in both directions *[1 mark]*.
b) By replacing the valve with a biological or mechanical valve *[1 mark]*.
Q2 Any one from: e.g. surgery to fit an artificial heart can lead to bleeding and infection. / Parts of the artificial heart could wear out. / The electric motor could fail. / Blood doesn't flow through the heart as smoothly, which could cause clots and lead to strokes. / The patient has to take blood thinning drugs to prevent blood clots, which could cause problems with bleeding if they're hurt in an accident *[1 mark]*.

p.39 — Health and Disease
Q1 The state of physical and mental wellbeing *[1 mark]*.
Q2 It can be spread from person to person *[1 mark]*.

p.40 — Risk Factors for Non-communicable Diseases
Q1 The presence of certain substances in the body. / The presence of certain substances in the environment *[1 mark]*.

p.41 — Cancer
Q1 Body cells dividing out of control *[1 mark]*.
Q2 Any three from: e.g. smoking / obesity / UV exposure / viral infection *[1 mark for each correct answer, up to 3 marks]*.

p.42 — Plant Cell Organisation
Q1 Meristem tissue is found at the growing tips of roots and shoots *[1 mark]* and is able to differentiate into lots of different types of plant cell *[1 mark]*.

p.43 — Transpiration and Translocation
Q1 Xylem is made up of dead cells joined together end to end *[1 mark]* with no end walls between them and a hole down the middle *[1 mark]*. It is strengthened by lignin *[1 mark]*.

Answers

p.44 — Transpiration and Stomata

Q1 As it gets darker, the stomata begin to close *[1 mark]*. This means that very little water can escape *[1 mark]* and the rate of transpiration decreases *[1 mark]*.

p.46 — Communicable Disease

Q1 Viruses replicate themselves by using the machinery of the cell they live in to produce many copies of themselves *[1 mark]*. The cell will usually then burst, releasing all the new viruses *[1 mark]*.

p.47 — Viral, Fungal and Protist Diseases

Q1 a red skin rash *[1 mark]*

Q2 Using a fungicide *[1 mark]* and by stripping the plants of the affected leaves and destroying them *[1 mark]*.

p.48 — Bacterial Diseases and Preventing Disease

Q1 Strains of the bacteria becoming resistant to antibiotics/penicillin *[1 mark]*.

Q2 To prevent the contamination of food by disease-causing pathogens *[1 mark]*.

p.49 — Fighting Disease

Q1 It is when white blood cells engulf foreign cells and digest them *[1 mark]*.

Q2 They secrete mucus to trap pathogens *[1 mark]*. They have cilia *[1 mark]*, which waft the mucus up to the back of the throat where it can be swallowed *[1 mark]*.

p.50 — Fighting Disease — Vaccination

Q1 antibodies *[1 mark]*

p.51 — Fighting Disease — Drugs

Q1 bacteria *[1 mark]*

p.52 — Developing Drugs

Q1 Whether the drug works and produces the effect you're looking for *[1 mark]*.

Q2 To make sure that the drug doesn't have any harmful side effects when the body is working normally *[1 mark]*.

Q3 To help to prevent false claims about the results *[1 mark]*.

p.53 — Monoclonal Antibodies

Q1 A B-lymphocyte *[1 mark]* and a tumour cell *[1 mark]*.

p.54 — More on Monoclonal Antibodies

Q1 A radioactive substance *[1 mark]*, a toxic drug *[1 mark]*, a chemical which stops cells growing and dividing *[1 mark]*.

p.55 — Plant Diseases and Defences

Q1 It will have stunted growth *[1 mark]*.

p.57 — Photosynthesis and Limiting Factors

Q1 Glucose *[1 mark]* and oxygen *[1 mark]*.

Q2 Light intensity *[1 mark]*, volume of CO_2 *[1 mark]* and amount of chlorophyll *[1 mark]*.

p.60 — The Rate of Photosynthesis

Q1 E.g. light intensity *[1 mark]*, CO_2 *[1 mark]*.

Q2 light intensity $\propto \dfrac{1}{\text{distance}^2}$ *[1 mark]*

p.61 — Respiration and Metabolism

Q1 Any two from: e.g. to build up larger molecules from smaller ones. / To contract muscles. / To keep body temperature steady. *[1 mark]*

Q2 The sum of all of the reactions that happen in a cell or the body *[1 mark]*.

p.62 — Aerobic and Anaerobic Respiration

Q1 Glucose *[1 mark]* and oxygen *[1 mark]*.

Q2 fermentation *[1 mark]*

p.63 — Exercise

Q1 Long periods of exercise *[1 mark]*.

Q2 An oxygen debt is the amount of extra oxygen your body needs to react with the build up of lactic acid and remove it from the cells *[1 mark]*.

p.65 — Homeostasis

Q1 To maintain the right conditions for cells to function properly and for enzyme action *[1 mark]*.

Q2 receptor (cell) *[1 mark]*

p.66 — The Nervous System

Q1 Muscles *[1 mark]*, glands *[1 mark]*.

p.67 — Synapses and Reflexes

Q1 A rapid, automatic response to a stimulus that doesn't involve the conscious part of the brain *[1 mark]*.

Q2 a) muscle *[1 mark]*

b) The stimulus is detected by receptors *[1 mark]*, which send impulses along a sensory neurone to the CNS *[1 mark]*. The impulse is transferred to a relay neurone *[1 mark]*. It is then transferred to a motor neurone and travels along it to the effector *[1 mark]*.

p.68 — Investigating Reaction Time

Q1 242 + 256 + 253 + 249 + 235 = 1235 *[1 mark]*
1235 ÷ 5 = 247 ms *[1 mark]*

p.69 — The Brain

Q1 cerebellum *[1 mark]*

p.70 — The Eye

Q1 cornea *[1 mark]*

Q2 The ciliary muscles contract *[1 mark]*, which slackens the suspensory ligaments *[1 mark]*. The lens becomes fat/more curved *[1 mark]*. This increases the amount by which it refracts light, so the image is focused on the retina *[1 mark]*.

p.71 — Correcting Vision Defects

Q1 The lens is the wrong shape / refracts the light too much, or the eyeball is too long *[1 mark]*. So images of distant objects are brought into focus in front of the retina *[1 mark]*.

Q2 The lenses refract the light rays so they focus on the retina *[1 mark]*.

p.72 — Controlling Body Temperature

Q1 thermoregulatory centre/hypothalamus *[1 mark]*

p.73 — The Endocrine System

Q1 Because it produces many hormones that act on other glands to regulate body conditions *[1 mark]*.

p.74 — Controlling Blood Glucose

Q1 The pancreas secretes insulin *[1 mark]*. Insulin causes glucose to move from the blood into liver and muscle cells *[1 mark]*. In the cells, glucose is turned into glycogen for storage *[1 mark]*.

p.75 — The Kidneys

Q1 The kidneys will reabsorb less water *[1 mark]*, so too much water may be lost from the body in urine *[1 mark]*.

p.76 — Kidney Failure

Q1 It allows ions and waste substances to diffuse out of the blood into the dialysis fluid *[1 mark]*, but not large molecules like proteins (so they won't be lost from the blood) *[1 mark]*.

p.77 — Puberty and the Menstrual Cycle

Q1 FSH/follicle-stimulating hormone *[1 mark]*

Q2 testes *[1 mark]*

p.78 — Controlling Fertility

Q1 The pill/oral contraceptives *[1 mark]*. The contraceptive patch *[1 mark]*.

p.79 — More on Controlling Fertility

Q1 They stimulate several eggs to mature *[1 mark]*.

Q2 E.g. it doesn't always work. / It can be expensive. / Too many eggs can be stimulated, resulting in unexpected multiple pregnancies. *[1 mark]*

p.80 — Adrenaline and Thyroxine

Q1 thyroid gland *[1 mark]*

Q2 When the high level of thyroxine is detected, the secretion of TSH from the pituitary gland is inhibited *[1 mark]*. This reduces the amount of thyroxine released from the thyroid gland *[1 mark]*, so the level in the blood falls back towards normal *[1 mark]*.

p.81 — Plant Hormones

Q1 More auxin accumulates on the side of the shoot that's in the shade *[1 mark]*. This causes the shaded side of the shoot to elongate faster *[1 mark]* so the shoot bends towards the light.

p.82 — Commercial Uses of Plant Hormones

Q1 E.g. to stimulate seed germination / to control dormancy / to stimulate flowering / to grow larger fruit *[1 mark]*.

p.84 — DNA

Q1 A small section of DNA found on a chromosome *[1 mark]* that codes for a particular sequence of amino acids *[1 mark]* that are put together to make a specific protein *[1 mark]*.

Q2 The entire set of genetic material in an organism *[1 mark]*.

p.85 — The Structure of DNA and Protein Synthesis

Q1 A and T *[1 mark]*.
C and G *[1 mark]*.

p.86 — Mutations

Q1 A mutation is a random change in an organism's DNA *[1 mark]*.

Q2 Mutations change the DNA base sequence *[1 mark]*. This can alter the amino acids that the bases code for *[1 mark]*. This can change the shape of the protein the amino acids make up, which can affect its function *[1 mark]*.

Answers

p.87 — Reproduction
Q1 mitosis *[1 mark]*

Q2 Because there are two parents, the offspring contain a mixture of their parents' genes *[1 mark]*. This mixture of genetic information produces variation *[1 mark]*.

p.88 — Meiosis
Q1 two *[1 mark]*

p.89 — More on Reproduction
Q1 Any three from: e.g. there only needs to be one parent unlike sexual reproduction, which requires two. / It takes less energy than sexual reproduction because organisms don't need to find a mate. / It is faster than sexual reproduction. / Many identical offspring can be produced in favourable conditions. *[1 mark for each correct answer, up to 3 marks]*

p.90 — X and Y Chromosomes
Q1 XX *[1 mark]*

p.91 — Genetic Diagrams
Q1 Your genotype is the combination of alleles you have *[1 mark]*. Your phenotype is the characteristics you have *[1 mark]*.

p.92 — More Genetic Diagrams
Q1

	T	t
t	Tt	tt
t	Tt	tt

long tailed : short tailed
1 : 1
[1 mark for correct gametes, 1 mark for correct offspring genotypes and 1 mark for correct ratio.]

p.93 — Inherited Disorders
Q1 Because the allele which causes cystic fibrosis is recessive *[1 mark]*, so you have to have two recessive alleles to have the disorder *[1 mark]*. Heterozygous people have one dominant and one recessive allele *[1 mark]*.

p.94 — The Work of Mendel
Q1 Scientists of the time didn't have the background knowledge to properly understand Mendel's findings because they didn't know about genes, DNA and chromosomes *[1 mark]*.

p.95 — Variation
Q1 Differences between members of the same species *[1 mark]* that have been caused by the environment/conditions something lives in *[1 mark]*.

p.96 — Evolution
Q1 Any three from: The environment changes too quickly. / A new predator kills all the individuals. / A new disease kills all the individuals. / They can't compete with another species for food. / A catastrophic event (e.g. a volcanic eruption or collision with an astroid) kills all the individuals. *[1 mark for each correct answer, up to 3 marks]*

p.97 — More About Evolution
Q1 It contradicted the common religious beliefs of the time that all life on earth was created by God *[1 mark]*. Darwin lacked the evidence that he needed to convince many other scientists *[1 mark]*. He also didn't have any explanation for why new beneficial characteristics appeared, or how they were passed on to offspring *[1 mark]*.

p.98 — Selective Breeding
Q1 E.g. to produce plants with large or unusual flowers *[1 mark]*.

Q2 Selective breeding reduces the gene pool *[1 mark]*. This causes an increased chance of organisms inheriting harmful genetic defects *[1 mark]*. There is also an increased chance that a population could be wiped out by a new disease *[1 mark]*.

p.99 — Genetic Engineering
Q1 Benefit — E.g. the characteristics chosen for GM crops can mean that they have an increased yield. / GM crops can be engineered to contain certain nutrients, which some people in developing nations may lack from their diets *[1 mark]*.
Concern — E.g. some people are not convinced that GM crops are safe and are concerned that we might not fully understand the effects of eating them on human health. / Some people say that growing GM crops will affect the number of wild flowers and insects that live in and around the crops. / There is concern that the transplanted genes could get out into the natural environment, which could lead to the creation of 'superweeds' *[1 mark]*.

p.100 — Cloning
Q1 The nucleus is removed from an unfertilised egg *[1 mark]* and a complete set of chromosomes from an adult body cell is inserted into the egg *[1 mark]*. The egg cell is then stimulated to divide to form an embryo by being given an electric shock *[1 mark]*. The embryo is then implanted into an adult female *[1 mark]*, where it develops into a clone of the original adult body cell *[1 mark]*.

p.101 — Fossils
Q1 The microbes that cause decay can't survive in low oxygen conditions *[1 mark]*, so the dead organisms are preserved rather than decayed *[1 mark]*.

p.102 — Speciation
Q1 The two populations may be in different environments *[1 mark]* and so different characteristics will be beneficial *[1 mark]*. Natural selection will work differently in each population so that individuals with the beneficial characteristics are more likely to survive and reproduce *[1 mark]*.

p.103 — Antibiotic-Resistant Bacteria
Q1 Any one from: e.g. when the illness is only minor. / When the infection is being caused by a virus *[1 mark]*.

Q2 Taking the complete course makes sure that all the bacteria are destroyed *[1 mark]*. This means that there are none left to mutate and develop into antibiotic-resistant strains *[1 mark]*.

p.104 — Classification
Q1 *Castor [1 mark]*

p.106 — Competition
Q1 The interaction of a community of organisms with the abiotic parts of their environment *[1 mark]*.

Q2 Any three from: light / space / water / mineral ions *[1 mark for each correct answer, up to 3 marks]*.

Q3 A community where all the species and environmental factors are in balance so that the population sizes are roughly constant *[1 mark]*.

p.107 — Abiotic and Biotic Factors
Q1 Any four from: moisture level / light intensity / temperature / carbon dioxide level / wind intensity / wind direction / soil pH / mineral content of soil *[1 mark for each correct answer, up to 4 marks]*.

Q2 Any two from: availability of food / competition for resources / new pathogens *[1 mark for each correct answer, up to 2 marks]*.

p.108 — Adaptations
Q1 a) A behavioural adaptation *[1 mark]*.

b) E.g. it has flippers *[1 mark]* so it can swim for food *[1 mark]*. / A thick layer of fat *[1 mark]* so it retains heat *[1 mark]*. / A low surface area to volume ratio *[1 mark]* so it retains heat *[1 mark]*.

p.109 — Food Chains
Q1 a) grass *[1 mark]*

b) three *[1 mark]*

c) grasshopper *[1 mark]*

d) The population of grasshoppers could increase *[1 mark]* as there's nothing to eat them *[1 mark]*. The population of snakes could decrease *[1 mark]* as there's nothing for them to eat *[1 mark]*.

p.110 — Using Quadrats
Q1 0.75 × 4 = 3 buttercups per m² *[1 mark]*.
3 × 1200 = 3600 buttercups in total *[1 mark]*.

p.111 — Using Transects
Q1 A line used to help find out how organisms are distributed across an area *[1 mark]*.

Q2 They could mark out a line across the field, from one corner to the other *[1 mark]*. Then they could count all of the dandelions that touch the line *[1 mark]*.

Q3 You could estimate the percentage of the quadrat covered by the organisms *[1 mark]*.

p.112 — Environmental Change & The Water Cycle
Q1 Any two from: e.g. a change in the availability of water / a change in temperature / a change in atmospheric gases *[1 mark for each correct answer, up to 2 marks]*.

Q2 a) By evaporation / transpiration *[1 mark]*.

b) By providing them with fresh water *[1 mark]*.

p.113 — The Carbon Cycle
Q1 Microorganisms/detritus feeders break them down/digest them *[1 mark]*.

Q2 By green plants and algae in photosynthesis *[1 mark]*.

p.114 — Decay
Q1 Oxygen availability *[1 mark]*, water availability *[1 mark]* and the number of microorganisms present *[1 mark]*.

Answers

p.115 — Investigating Decay
Q1 Rate = $\dfrac{1000}{time}$

Rate = $\dfrac{1000}{280}$ = 3.57 s^{-1} *[1 mark]*

p.116 — Biodiversity and Waste Management
Q1 The variety of different species of organisms on Earth, or within an ecosystem *[1 mark]*.

p.117 — Global Warming
Q1 Global warming causes higher temperatures, which cause ice to melt and seawater to expand *[1 mark]*. This causes the sea level to rise *[1 mark]*, which could lead to flooding of low-lying land and therefore the loss of habitats *[1 mark]*.

p.118 — Deforestation and Land Use
Q1 Trees 'lock up' some of the carbon that they absorb during photosynthesis, so if lots of trees are removed, less carbon will be locked up from the atmosphere *[1 mark]*. If the land is cleared by burning the trees, this means that lots of carbon dioxide is released *[1 mark]*. Microorganisms feeding on leftover dead wood release carbon dioxide as a waste product of respiration *[1 mark]*.

p.119 — Maintaining Ecosystems and Biodiversity
Q1 Hedgerows and field margins can be reintroduced around single-crop fields *[1 mark]*. These provide a habitat for organisms that would otherwise be unable to live in the area *[1 mark]*.

Q2 Breeding programmes breed endangered animals in captivity to make sure the species survives if they die out in the wild *[1 mark]*. Individuals can sometimes be released into the wild to boost or re-establish a population *[1 mark]*.

p.120 — Trophic Levels
Q1 They secrete enzymes that break down the dead material into small soluble food molecules *[1 mark]*.

p.121 — Pyramids of Biomass
Q1 The relative mass of living material at each trophic level in a food chain *[1 mark]*.

p.122 — Biomass Transfer
Q1 Any two from: e.g. organisms don't always eat every single part of the organism they're consuming. / Organisms don't absorb all of the material in the food they ingest. / Some of the biomass is converted into other substances and released as waste.
[1 mark for each correct answer, up to 2 marks]

Q2 110 ÷ 995 × 100 = 11.1% *[1 mark]*

p.123 — Food Security and Farming
Q1 The movement of livestock can be restricted *[1 mark]* and they can be kept in a temperature-controlled environment *[1 mark]*. This means that they use less energy moving around and controlling their own body temperature *[1 mark]*, so more energy is available for growth *[1 mark]*.

p.124 — Biotechnology
Q1 A genetically modified rice crop *[1 mark]* that has been genetically engineered to have a higher nutritional value/produce a chemical that's converted to vitamin A in the body *[1 mark]*.

Index

A
abiotic factors 107
abstinence 78
accommodation 70
accuracy (of results) 5
active sites 28
active transport 22
adaptations 108
adrenal glands 73, 80
adrenaline 80
adult cell cloning 100
aerobic respiration 62
alleles 91
alveoli 24, 33
ammonia 75
amylase 29-31
anaerobic respiration 62
ancestors 104
animal cells 11
anomalous results 5
antibiotic resistance 51, 103
antibiotics 51, 103
   investigating the effects of 17
antibodies 36, 49
anti-diuretic hormone (ADH) 75
antimicrobials 49
antiretroviral drugs 47
antitoxins 36, 49
aorta 34
apparatus 126
Archaea 104
arteries 35
artificial blood 38
artificial hearts 38

B
asexual reproduction 87, 89
aspirin 51
atria 34
auxins 81, 82

bacteria 11, 16, 17, 46, 48, 104
balances 126
bar charts 6
barrier methods (of contraception) 78
basal metabolic rate 80
behavioural adaptations 108
Benedict's reagent 32
benign tumours 41
bias 2
bile 30
binary fission 16
binomial system 104
biodiversity 116-119
  maintenance of 119
biogas 114
biological heart valves 38
biomass 122
biomass transfer 122
biotechnology 124
biotic factors 107
Biuret test 32
blind studies 52
body temperature 72
brain 69
breathing rate 33

C
bronchi 33
bronchioles 33
Bunsen burners 127

caffeine (effect on reaction time) 68
cancer 54
capillaries 35
carbohydrases 30
carbon cycle 113
catalysts 28
categoric data 6
cell
  cycle 15
  division 15, 16
  elongation 81
  membranes 11, 20
  walls 11
cells 11
  drawing 13
  specialised 14
central nervous system (CNS) 66, 67
cerebellum 69
cerebral cortex 69
chlorophyll 11, 57
chloroplasts 11, 57
cholesterol 37
chromosomes 15, 84
  X and Y 90
cilia 49
ciliary muscles 70
class (classification) 104

D
classification 104
climate change 117
clinical trials 52
cloning 100
communicable diseases 39, 46
communities 106
complementary base pairing 85
computational models 1
concave lenses 71
concentration gradients 20
conclusions 9
condensation 112
condoms 48, 78
contact lenses 71
contraception 78
control variables 4
convex lenses 71
corneas 70
coronary arteries 34
coronary heart disease 37
correlation 7, 9
cover slip (slides) 13
cuttings 82, 100
cystic fibrosis 93
cytoplasm 11

Darwin, Charles 96, 97
decay 113-115
  investigating 115
  rate of 114
decomposers 120
defences (of plants) 55
deforestation 118

Index

deletions (mutations) 86
dependent variables 4
detritus feeders 113
diabetes 74
dialysis 76
diaphragm (thorax) 33
diaphragms (contraceptive) 78
differentiation 14, 27
diffusion 20, 21, 23-25
digestive enzymes 30
digestive system 27, 31
digitalis 51
discrete data 6
distribution of organisms
    110-112
DNA 15, 84, 85
   nucleotides 85
dormancy (in seeds) 82
dosage 52
double-blind studies 52
double circulatory systems 33
drugs 51, 52
   development of 52

E
ecosystems 106
   maintenance of 119
effectors 65, 66
efficacy (of drugs) 52
electric heaters 127
electron microscopes 12
embryo screening 93
embryo transplants 100
endocrine system 73
endothermic reactions 57
environmental changes 112
environmental variation 95
enzymes 28-31
epidermal tissue 42
errors 5
ethene (in plants) 82
ethics (in investigations) 127
Eukaryota 104
eukaryotes 11, 46
evaluations 10
evaporation 112
evolutionary trees 104
evolution by natural selection 96,
    97, 102
exchange surfaces 23-25
exercise 63
exothermic reactions 61
extinction 96
eyes 70, 71

F
fair tests 4
family (classification) 104
family trees 92
farming 123
fatty acids 30
fermentation 62
fertility 78, 79

fertility treatments 79
fight or flight response 80
filtration (kidneys) 75
Fleming, Alexander 51
flowering 82
focusing 70
follicle-stimulating hormone
    (FSH) 77, 79
food chains 109, 120, 121
food poisoning 48
food production 123
food security 123
fossils 101
functional adaptations 108
fungi 46, 47

G
gall bladder 31
gamete fusion 88
gametes 87, 88
gas exchange 24, 25
gas syringes 126
gene pools 98, 100
genes 15, 84
genetically modified crops 99
genetic
   diagrams 90-93
   disorders 93
   engineering 99, 124
   variants 86
   variation 95
genomes 84
genotypes 91
genus 104
geotropism 81
germination 82
gibberellin 82
gills 25
glands 73
global warming 117
glucagon 74
glucose
   in the blood 74
   test for 32
   uses in plants 57
glycerol 30
glycogen 74
gonorrhoea 48
gradients 7
graphs 7
gravitropism 81
greenhouse gases 117
greenhouses 60
guard cells 44
gullet 31

H
habitats 106
haemoglobin 36
hazards 3
heart 34
heart valves 38
hereditary units 94

heterozygous organisms 91
HIV 47
homeostasis 65
homozygous organisms 91
hormones 73
hybridoma cells 53
hyperopia 71
hypotheses 1, 4

I
immune system 49
independent variables 4
indicators 126
'induced fit' model 28
infertility 79
inhibition zones 17, 18
insertions (mutations) 86
insulin 74
intercepts (on a graph) 7
interdependence 106
intrauterine devices (IUDs) 78
inverse
   correlations 7
   proportion 60
   square law 60
in vitro fertilisation (IVF) 79
iodine test (for starch) 29
irises 70
iris reflex 70
IVF 79

K
kidney failure 76
kidneys 75, 76
kingdom (classification) 104

L
lactic acid 62, 63
Lamarck, Jean-Baptiste 97
lamellae 25
large intestine 31
laser eye surgery 71
leaves
   gas exchange 25
   tissues in 25
lenses 70, 71
light microscopes 12, 13
limiting factors (of
    photosynthesis) 57-59
line graphs 7
lines of best fit 7
Linnaean system 104
Linnaeus, Carl 104
lipases 30
lipids (test for) 32
liver 31, 74
'lock and key' model 28
long-sightedness 71
lungs 33
luteinising hormone (LH) 77, 79
lymphocytes 53

M
magnetic resonance imaging
    (MRI) 69
magnification 12
malaria 47
malignant tumours 41
mean (average) 6
mean division time 16
measles 47
measuring cylinders 126
mechanical heart valves 38
median 6
medulla (brain) 69
meiosis 88
Mendel, Gregor 94
menstrual cycle 77
meristem tissue 42
merpeople 92
metabolism 61
microorganisms 46
   culturing 17, 18
microscopes 12, 13
migration patterns 117
   human 84
mitochondria 11
mitosis 15, 88
mode 6
models (scientific) 1
monoclonal antibodies 53, 54
motor neurones 66, 67
MRI scanning 69
mRNA 85
MRSA 51, 103
mucus 49
muscle cells 14
muscle fatigue 63
mutations 86, 95
mycoprotein 124
myopia 71

N
natural selection 96, 102
negative correlations 7
negative feedback systems 65
   blood glucose 74
   body temperature 72
   thyroxine 80
   water content 75
nerve cells 14
nervous system 66, 67
neurones 66, 67
neuroscientists 69
non-coding DNA 85, 86
non-communicable diseases 39
nucleotides 85
nucleus 11

O
oestrogen 77, 78
optic nerve 70
order (classification) 104
organ donors 76
organs 27

Index

organ systems 27
osmosis 21
ovaries 73, 77
overfishing 123
ovulation 77
oxygen debt 63

P

pacemakers 34
painkillers 51
palisade mesophyll tissue 42
pancreas 31, 73, 74
parasites 46
partially permeable membranes 21
pathogens 46
pea plants 94
peat bogs 118
peer review 1, 52
pepsin 30, 31
percentage
   change 130
   cover 111
percentiles 130
Petri dishes 17
phagocytosis 36, 49
phenolphthalein 115
phenotypes 91
phenotype variation 96
phloem cells 14
phloem tubes 42, 43
pH meters 126
photosynthesis 57-59
   rate of 58, 59
phototropism 81
phylum (classification) 104
pipettes 126
pituitary gland 73, 77, 80
placebo effect 52
plant
   cells 11
   diseases 55
   growth 81, 82
   hormones 81, 82
plasma 36
plasmids 11, 99
platelets 36
pleural membranes 33
pollution 116
polydactyly 93
population (human) 116
positive correlations 7
potatoes 21
potometers 44, 128
preclinical testing 52
precipitation 112
precision (of results) 5
predator-prey cycles 109
predators 109
pregnancy tests 53
prey 109
primary consumers 109
producers 109
progesterone 77, 78
prokaryotes 11, 16

proteases 30
proteins 85
   function of 85
   test for 32
protists 46, 47
puberty 77
pulmonary artery 34
pulmonary vein 34
Punnett squares 90, 91
pupils 70
pyramids of biomass 121

Q

quadrats 110, 111

R

random
   errors 5
   sampling 129
range (of data) 6
rates of reaction 29
reaction times 68
receptors 65, 66
rectum 31
red blood cells 36
reflex arcs 67
relay neurones 67
repeatability (of data) 4, 5
replacement lens surgery 71
representational models 1

reproducibility (of data) 4, 5
resolution (microscopes) 12
respiration 61, 62
retinas 70
ribcage 33
ribosomes 11, 85
ripening (of fruit) 82
risk 3
risk factors 40
root hair cells 14, 22
rooting powder 82
roots 81
rose black spot 47
rounding numbers 6

S

safety 3, 127
salivary glands 31
Salmonella 48
sample size 4
sampling 129
sclera 70
secondary consumers 109
secondary sexual characteristics 77
selective breeding 98
selective reabsorption 75
sensory neurones 66, 67
sex hormones 77-79
sexually transmitted diseases 48
sexual reproduction 87, 89

shivering 72
shoots 81
short-sightedness 71
SI units 8
significant figures 6
slides 13
small intestine 31
specialised cells 14
speciation 96, 102
species 102, 104
   in classification 102
sperm cells 14, 77
spermicide 78
spinal cord 69
spongy mesophyll tissue 42
stains (microscope) 13
standard form 12
starch 29
   test for 32
statins 37
stem cells 19
stents 37
sterilisation (contraception) 78
stomach 31
stomata 25, 44
structural adaptations 108
subcellular structures 11, 14
substitutions (mutations) 86
Sudan III 32
sugars (test for) 32
superbugs 103
surface area to volume ratios 23
survival of the fittest 96
suspensory ligaments 70
sweat 72, 75
synapses 67
systematic errors 5

T

tables (of data) 6
target organs 73
temperature receptors 72
tertiary consumers 109
testes 73, 77
testosterone 77
theories 1
thermometers 126
thermoregulatory centre 72
thorax 33
three-domain system
      of classification 104
thyroid gland 73, 80
thyroid stimulating hormone
      (TSH) 80
thyroxine 80
tissue culture 82, 100
tissues 27
tobacco mosaic virus 47
toxicity (of drugs) 52
trachea 33
transects 111
transpiration 43, 44, 112
   rate 44
transplants (organ) 76
trophic levels 120-122

tumour markers 54
tumours 41
Type 1 diabetes 74
Type 2 diabetes 74

U

uncertainty 10
units 8
urea 75
urine 75

V

vaccination 48, 50
vacuoles 11
valid results 4
valves (heart) 34, 38
variables 4
variation 95
vasoconstriction 72
vasodilation 72
vectors 46, 48, 99
veins 35
vena cava 34
ventricles 34
villi 24
viruses 46, 47
vision defects 71
volumes (measuring) 126

W

Wallace, Alfred Russel 102
waste management 116
water baths 127
water cycle 112
weed killers 82
white blood cells 36, 49
wizardry 126
Woese, Carl 104

X

X and Y chromosomes 90
xylem cells 14
xylem tubes 42, 43

Y

yeast cells 62

Z

zero errors 5